PROGRAMED REVIEWS OF CHEMICAL PRINCIPLES

JEAN D. LASSILA • GORDON M. BARROW • MALCOLM E. KENNEY

ROBERT L. LITLE • WARREN E. THOMPSON

PROGRAMED REVIEWS OF CHEMICAL PRINCIPLES

W. A. Benjamin, Inc.   New York   1970

PROGRAMED REVIEWS OF CHEMICAL PRINCIPLES

The authors and publisher
are pleased to acknowledge
the assistance of
Wladislaw Finne, who
designed the text and
the cover.

W. A. BENJAMIN, INC.

New York, New York 10016

PREFACE

To learn chemistry, students should master the basic building blocks: stoichiometry, nomenclature, introductory atomic and molecular structure, general properties of solutions, and equilibrium calculations. An understanding of these subjects requires the ability to apply the basic principles to solving problems. This book reviews these principles and provides sound techniques for applying to specific problems the general concepts of chemistry.

The reviews are intended to be supplementary; that is, the topics discussed are those we considered most essential, and their treatment is intended to give the student a firm basis for further study. Some knowledge of the concepts and terminology pertinent to each section is assumed, but the unifying material necessary for the complete development of the subject must be provided by lectures or reading assignments.

The book has been written to follow the order of topics in *Chemical Principles*, by Richard E. Dickerson, Harry B. Gray, and Gilbert P. Haight, Jr. Cross referencing between this book and *Chemical Principles* occurs when appropriate. (You should refer also to *A Study Guide to Chemical Principles*, by Wilbert Hutton, for more detailed discussion of difficult topics in the text.)

Nevertheless, an understanding of a section is not dependent on the material in *Chemical Principles:* These reviews (adapted from *Understanding Chemistry* by Barrow *et al.*) can be used with any general chemistry text or lecture course.

Programed Reviews of Chemical Principles is a programed instruction book, not a textbook or problem manual. The material is divided into chapters (called "reviews") and, when appropriate, into sections. The objective and relevance of each review and section is stated in the opening paragraphs, which also tell how a student can determine whether he has already mastered the material. Then there is a logical sequence of short, numbered items that provide information and require the student to answer a question. By participating in the development of each topic, the student learns, through independent study, topics that otherwise might cause him difficulty.

Individual items taken out of context may seem trivial, but to evaluate programed material, you should read through a complete sequence of items and note how a topic is developed. Use of programed instruction in chemistry is rather recent, but there is clear indication that, when properly used, this type of instruction is an effective teaching aid.

JEAN D. LASSILA
GORDON M. BARROW
MALCOLM E. KENNEY
ROBERT L. LITLE
WARREN E. THOMPSON

Edgartown, Massachusetts
September 1969

NOTE TO THE STUDENT

As you have probably noticed, the layout for this book is rather unusual; hence, the procedure for using the book may be new to you. The material presented here is programed; that is, it consists of a logical sequence of short numbered items (one or two sentences) that provide information and also require you to answer a question, carry out a calculation, or insert a word or number.

The instructions are simple. Read and complete the items in numerical order. On the third page after a given item is the correct answer (or answers). To derive the most benefit from the book, you should write your answers in the blanks and then turn the page to see whether you are on the right track. (In some items the blank is too small for the answer, but there is space beneath the item or at the right for large answers and computations.)

An understanding of each item depends on your comprehension of the preceding items; therefore, when you make an error, you should not go on to the next item until you know the reason for your mistake and have corrected it. Answers to problems can be calculated with a slide rule, and all answers have been rounded off to the correct number of significant figures. You will find that units are sometimes given with reciprocal numbers.

For example, moles liter^{-1} means moles per liter.

Each review leads to questions that are, in effect, summary problems that should indicate whether you have mastered the material. Then, if you want to try your skill, you can work the problems in the book by Ian S. Butler and Arthur E. Grosser, *Relevant Problems for Chemical Principles.* The average completion time for each review or section is between one and two hours.

CONTENTS

REVIEW 1   GRAM-ATOMS, MOLES, AND EMPIRICAL FORMULAS

Early in your study of chemistry—and probably as long as you continue it—you will find it necessary to measure amounts of chemicals. You will need to know how much of one substance will react with a measured amount of another substance. For that elementary and practical information, you must know what chemical symbols mean and how they are related both to measured weights of elements and compounds and to numbers of atoms and molecules.

This review will examine in detail the concepts of the gram-atom (Section 1–1) and the mole (Section 1–2), the quantities which relate weights to number of atoms or molecules. Section 1–3 will show how gram-atoms and moles relate the percentage by weight composition of a compound to its empirical formula.

To use this book effectively, you should read Item 1 on page 4 and write the answer in the blank. (In some items there will be too little room to write the answer in the blank, but there will be space underneath or beside the item for it. This space can be used also for calculation.) When you turn the page, you will find the correct answer to Item 1 at the top, right-hand side (page 7). Item 2 is across from it, on the left-hand side (page 6). Right away you will understand how this works. It allows you to check your answer easily, yet not be able to see answers to later items. At Item 9 you should return to page 4 to work through the second row of items.

1-1 GRAM-ATOMS

In Chapter 1 of *Chemical Principles* you learned about chemical symbols and about gram-atoms and moles, the quantities which relate weights of elements and compounds to numbers of atoms and molecules. This section will review in detail the meaning and use of the gram-atom. This term is no longer used by everyone (some chemists use the word "mole" for this quantity when discussing elements as well as compounds). However, an understanding of the concept is necessary and fundamental.

The items in the section will seem trivial at first, but work through each one in the numbered order. Write down the answer before you check it. Although some atomic weights are given to four significant figures, as is usually done in atomic weight tables, values for all quantities needed in the problems can be used with three significant figures so slide rule calculation is possible.

When you have finished the review you will be able to solve problems such as "Given that the atomic weight of sulfur is 32.1, calculate the number of atoms and gram-atoms in 5.21 g of sulfur." If you can do this calculation and the items beginning with number 50 easily and logically, you have an adequate mastery of the gram-atom concept and can proceed directly to Section 1-2.

ITEM 1

Symbols are used to represent the chemical elements. For example, Cu is the chemical symbol for _____.

ITEM 10

It is more convenient, however, to have the symbols imply different masses of the different elements but always the same number of _____ of the elements.

ITEM 19

A table of atomic weights can be regarded as giving either the relative masses of the atoms of different elements or the actual masses of the atoms of various elements expressed in _____.

ITEM 28

A gram atomic weight, often shortened to *gram-atom*, is the weight of the element in grams that is numerically equal to the mass of _____ atom of the element expressed in _____.

ITEM 37

When the symbols are used to imply *pound atomic weights*, as they sometimes are in engineering calculations, the symbol C implies _____ of carbon.

ITEM 46

A 3.70-g sample of copper contains _____ g-atoms of copper. Since each gram-atom of any element contains _____ atoms, this sample contains _____ atoms of copper.

ITEM 2 The smallest unit of an element that we are concerned with in chemical studies is the _____. The chemical symbol, therefore, is often used to represent one _____.

ITEM 11 When the chemical symbols imply one atom, the mass represented by the symbol O is different from the mass represented by H. In fact, O represents a mass that is _____ than that represented by H by a factor of about _____.

ITEM 20 Since one atom of hydrogen has a mass of about 1.67×10^{-24} g, or about _____ amu, we see that an atomic mass unit is very _____ compared to weights used in the laboratory.

ITEM 29 12.01 g of carbon is one _____ of carbon.

ITEM 38 Then 1 pound of hydrogen, 12 pounds of carbon, and 16 pounds of oxygen would each correspond to about 1 _____ of the element, and there would be approximately _____ number of atoms of each element in these amounts.

ITEM 47 A 1.34-g sample of hydrogen contains _____ g-atoms, or _____ atoms of hydrogen.

ANSWER 1   copper

ANSWER 10   atoms

ANSWER 19   amu (atomic mass units)

ANSWER 28   one
    amu

ANSWER 37   12.01 pounds (1 pound atomic weight)

ANSWER 46

$$\frac{3.70 \text{ g}}{63.5 \text{ g g-atom}^{-1}} = 0.0583 \text{ g-atom}$$

6.02×10^{23}
0.0583 g-atom $(6.02 \times 10^{23}$ atoms g-atom$^{-1})$
    $= 3.51 \times 10^{22}$ atoms

ITEM 3

For example, when symbols are used in a structural formula, as in the one at the right for the water molecule, each individual symbol represents one _____ of the element.

ITEM 12

The *relative* masses of atoms of different elements are listed in tables, or are presented in periodic charts (see inside front cover), and are generally referred to as _____ weights.

ITEM 21

Tables of atomic weights used by chemists can be interpreted as giving the mass, in _____, of one *average* atom of the element as it occurs in nature.

ITEM 30

Samples containing 12 g of carbon or 1.0 g of hydrogen or 63.5 g of copper will all have about the same _____.

ITEM 39

A *pound atomic weight,* then, is defined as the weight of an element, expressed in _____, that is numerically equal to the _____.

ITEM 48

In general, the number of gram-atoms in a sample is calculated by dividing the _____ of the sample by the _____ of the element.

H   H
 \   /
   O

ANSWER 2   atom
              atom

ANSWER 11   greater
              16

ANSWER 20   1
              small

ANSWER 29   gram-atom
              (or gram atomic weight)

ANSWER 38   pound atomic weight
              the same

ANSWER 47

$$\frac{1.34 \text{ g}}{1.01 \text{ g g-atom}^{-1}} = 1.33 \text{ g-atoms}$$

1.33 g-atoms (6.02 × 10²³ atoms g-atom⁻¹)
    = 8.01 × 10²³ atoms

9

ITEM 4

Since one hydrogen atom has a mass of about 1.67×10^{-24} g, the chemical symbol H, if it implies one atom, would correspond to a mass of _____ g.

ITEM 13

Atomic weights do not give us the actual masses of the atoms of the elements in grams; what they do give are the _____ masses of the atoms of different elements.

ITEM 22

The value given for copper in a table of atomic weights is 63.54. This means that the mass of _____.

ITEM 31

When dealing with laboratory amounts of chemicals, it is convenient to have the chemical symbol for an element imply one _____ of the element.

ITEM 40

A *gram atomic weight* of an element is defined as _____.

ITEM 49

To calculate the weight of an element that would be required to give x g-atoms of the element, we would _____ x by the _____ of the element.

H

ANSWER 3   atom

ANSWER 12   atomic

ANSWER 21   amu

ANSWER 30   number of atoms

ANSWER 39   pounds
            atomic weight

ANSWER 48   weight (or mass) in grams
            atomic weight

ITEM 5

The oxygen atom is about 16 times as heavy as the hydrogen atom, and if the chemical symbol O implies one atom of oxygen, it would correspond to a mass of _____ g.

ITEM 14

Although, historically, these relative atomic weights were based on the mass of an atom of the lightest element _____ being assigned the value 1, and later an atom of oxygen being assigned the value _____, they are now based on the carbon isotope of mass number 12 being assigned the value _____.

ITEM 23

The atomic weight given for carbon is 12.01115 (we shall use 12.01). This means that, in addition to the atoms that have a mass of exactly 12 amu, there must be at least one naturally occurring isotope with a mass _____ than 12 amu.

ITEM ??

With this understanding, we can say that C not only designates the element as _____, but also implies _____ g of carbon.

ITEM 41

Since the number of atoms in 1 gram atomic weight is 6.02×10^{23} (using three significant figures), the number of atoms implied by the chemical symbol could be one or, more conveniently for laboratory purposes, could be _____.

ITEM 50

What is the mass in grams of one atom of xenon (at. wt: 131)?

O

Avogadro's number:
6.0228 × 10²³

ANSWER 4 1.67×10^{-24}

ANSWER 13   relative

ANSWER 22   an average atom of naturally occurring copper is 63.54 amu

ANSWER 31   gram atomic weight (or gram-atom)

ANSWER 40   the weight of the element in grams that is numerically equal to its atomic weight

ANSWER 49   multiply
atomic weight

ITEM 6   When chemical symbols represent one atom of the element, each symbol represents a different mass because the average mass per atom of every element is _____ from that of every other element.

ITEM 15   A table of atomic weights gives the value for copper as 63.54. This implies that, if one atom of carbon, ^{12}C, weighs exactly 12 units, one atom of copper weighs _____ units.

ITEM 24   If it were possible to measure samples of carbon and copper weighing 1201 and 6354 amu, respectively, there would be _____ atoms in each of these samples.

ITEM 33   In the same manner, Cu implies _____ g of _____.

ITEM 42   In general, the symbol C, when not used in a structural formula to indicate one atom, implies _____ g and _____ atoms of carbon.

ITEM 51   Calculate the number of atoms contained in a sample of nickel (at. wt: 58.7) weighing 7.30×10^{-3} g.

ANSWER 5 $16(1.67 \times 10^{-24}) = 27 \times 10^{-24}$
or 2.7×10^{-23}

ANSWER 14   hydrogen
16
12 (exactly)

ANSWER 23   greater

ANSWER 32   carbon
12.01

ANSWER 41 6.02×10^{23}

ANSWER 50

$$\frac{131 \text{ g g-atom}^{-1}}{6.02 \times 10^{23} \text{ atoms g-atom}^{-1}}$$

$= 2.18 \times 10^{-22}$ g atom^{-1}

15

ITEM 7 The masses of individual atoms are of the order of (i.e., in terms of powers of 10) _____ g.

ITEM 16 Since most naturally occurring elements are made up of atoms with different masses, that is, most elements are composed of two or more _____, the atomic mass used by chemists is an average value.

ITEM 25 Since individual atoms of carbon and copper have average masses that are in the ratio C/Cu = _____/_____, larger samples of carbon and copper will have equal numbers of atoms so long as the weights of the samples are in the ratio _____/_____.

ITEM 34 Since each atom of carbon has a mass that is 12 times greater than that of each atom of hydrogen, the number of atoms of carbon in 12 g of carbon will be the same as the number of atoms of hydrogen in _____ of hydrogen.

ITEM 43 Similarly, the symbol O implies _____ g and _____ atoms of oxygen.

ITEM 52 Calculate the number of gram-atoms and atoms in a sample of cadmium (at. wt: 112) weighing 72.2 g.

Isotope	Natural abundance, %
^{64}Zn	48.9
^{66}Zn	27.6
^{67}Zn	4.1
^{68}Zn	18.7
^{70}Zn	0.7

ANSWER 6   different

ANSWER 15   63.54

ANSWER 24   100

ANSWER 33   63.54
                    copper

ANSWER 42   12.01
                    6.02×10^{23}

ANSWER 51

$$\frac{7.30 \times 10^{-3} \text{ g}}{58.7 \text{ g g-atom}^{-1}} = 1.24 \times 10^{-4} \text{ g-atoms}$$

number of atoms
$= 6.02 \times 10^{23}$ atoms g-atom^{-1} (1.24×10^{-4} g-atoms)
$= 7.46 \times 10^{19}$ atoms

ITEM 8

If the chemical symbol is used to refer to an amount of material that is convenient for laboratory work, it must imply a larger weight of the element and a _____ number of atoms of the element than is implied when the symbol represents one atom.

ITEM 17

A unit of mass, called the *atomic mass unit*, is defined so one atom of ^{12}C has a mass of 12 of these units. Therefore, the table of atomic weights expresses the actual mass of _____ atom of each of the elements as measured in _____ units.

ITEM 26

If 12.01 g of carbon contain x atoms, 63.54 g of copper will contain _____ atoms.

ITEM 35

A gram-atom of one element contains the same number of _____ as a gram-atom of any other element.

ITEM 44

The mass of one atom of oxygen can be calculated from the values of the previous item to be _____ g (to three significant figures).

ITEM 53

How many grams of sulfur (at. wt: 32.1) must be weighed to make up a sample containing 0.0250 g-atom?

ANSWER 7 10^{-23} $(10^{-24}$ to $10^{-22})$

ANSWER 16   isotopes

ANSWER 25   12.01/63.54
12.01/63.54

ANSWER 34   1 g

ANSWER 43   15.9994 (or about 16.00)
6.02×10^{23}

ANSWER 52

$$\frac{72.2 \text{ g}}{112 \text{ g g-atom}^{-1}} = 0.645 \text{ g-atom}$$

6.02×10^{-23} atoms g-atom^{-1} (0.645 g-atom)
$= 3.88 \times 10^{23}$ atoms

ITEM 9   One could require the chemical symbol to signify a convenient weight (1 g or 1 pound, for instance) of each element. Then, since the atoms of different elements have different masses, the chemical symbols for the different elements would all refer to _____ numbers of atoms.

ITEM 18   If the abbreviation amu is used for this unit that measures masses of atoms, we would say that one atom of ^{12}C weighs 12 _____, one atom of hydrogen weighs about _____, and one atom of copper weighs 63.54 _____.

ITEM 27   Weights of carbon of 12.01 g and of copper of 63.54 g are amounts known as *gram atomic weights.* This term is used because they correspond to weights in grams that are numerically equal to the masses of individual atoms expressed in _____.

ITEM 36   The chemical symbols for various elements imply the same _____ but different _____ of the elements.

ITEM 45   One gram-atom (g-atom) of copper contains _____ atoms.

ITEM 54   What weight of iron (at. wt: 55.9) must be measured in order to have a sample that contains 0.384×10^{23} atoms?

ANSWER 8   larger

ANSWER 17   one
             atomic mass

ANSWER 26 x

ANSWER 35   atoms

ANSWER 44 $$\frac{16.00 \text{ g g-atom}^{-1}}{6.02 \times 10^{23} \text{ atoms g-atom}^{-1}}$$

$$= 2.66 \times 10^{-23} \text{ g atom}^{-1}$$

ANSWER 53

0.0250 g-atom (32.1 g g-atom^{-1})
    = 0.803 g

ANSWER 9   different

(Item 10 is on page 4.)

ANSWER 18   amu
                        1 amu
                        amu

(Item 19 is on page 4.)

ANSWER 27   amu

(Item 28 is on page 4.)

ANSWER 36   number of atoms
                        weights (or masses)

(Item 37 is on page 4.)

ANSWER 45 6.02×10^{23}

(Item 46 is on page 4.)

ANSWER 54

number of gram-atoms

$$= \frac{0.384 \times 10^{23} \text{ atoms}}{6.02 \times 10^{23} \text{ atoms g-atom}^{-1}} = 0.0638 \text{ g-atom}$$

Therefore, the weight of sample should be
0.0638 g-atom (55.9 g g-atom^{-1}) = 3.57 g.

23

You have learned how symbols of elements and atomic weights are related to measured weights and numbers of atoms. You know what a gram-atom is and that the number of atoms in a gram-atom is Avogadro's number, 6.02×10^{23}. Now you are ready to broaden this concept and to learn about molecules and the ever-necessary mole.

1-2 MOLES

In calculations involving elements and atoms, as in Section 1–1, you need not be concerned about whether an element is made up of single atoms, pairs of atoms, or large crystals of atoms. However, some calculations involving polyatomic elements and most calculations involving compounds must be done on the basis of molecules, rather than atoms. These calculations, as you will see, are analogous to those that you have already done for weights, atoms, and gram-atoms in a sample of an element. Chemical formulas will be used to represent amounts of compounds in exactly the same way that chemical symbols are used to represent amounts (one atom or 1 g-atom) of elements.

Again, we often use four significant figures for atomic weights, as they are given in tables. Nevertheless, to facilitate computation, all problems can be done by using three significant figures.

ITEM 1

When the water molecule is represented by the structural formula at the right, the formula indicates that two hydrogen _____ and one oxygen _____ are arranged as shown.

ITEM 7

A gram molecular weight, or mole, of a chemical compound is defined, then, as the weight of the compound, expressed in grams, that is numerically equal to _____ expressed in _____.

ITEM 13

Because in one molecule of chlorine, Cl_2, there are _____ atoms of chlorine, there are _____ g-atoms of chlorine in 1 mole of chlorine.

ITEM 19

When you hear of moles of electrons, moles of photons, moles of positive charges, and so forth, you should realize that the word "mole" is being used to imply _____ electrons, photons, positive charges, and so on.

ITEM 25

A mole of oxygen atoms contains _____ atoms.

ITEM 31

A cylinder holding 0.13 g of ethane, C_2H_6, contains _____ mole(s) of C_2H_6, _____ molecules of C_2H_6, _____ atoms of C, and _____ atoms of H.

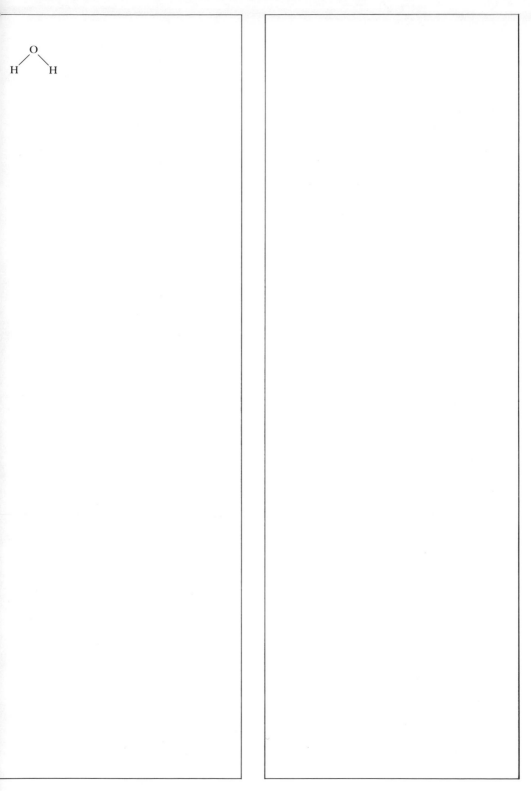

ITEM 2

More often we would simply write H_2O and could view this formula as indicating that one molecule of water contains _____ of hydrogen and _____ of oxygen.

ITEM 8

One molecule of H_2O contains _____ of hydrogen and _____.

ITEM 14

Since one molecule of sulfur in some forms of the element contains eight atoms, 1 mole of sulfur will be equivalent to _____ g-atom(s).

ITEM 20

An 18-g sample of water contains _____ mole(s) of water, or _____ g-atom(s) of hydrogen and _____ g-atom(s) of oxygen.

ITEM 26

When not specified otherwise, a mole of oxygen refers to a mole of oxygen molecules, so the number of atoms in a mole of oxygen is _____. But the terms "1 mole O" or "a mole of O atoms" indicate that the number of atoms referred to is _____.

ITEM 32

When the chemical formula of a compound is thought of as representing one molecule, it tells us the number of _____.

S_8

ANSWER 1   atoms
                atom

ANSWER 7   the mass of one molecule
                amu

ANSWER 13   two
                2

ANSWER 19 6.02×10^{23}

ANSWER 25 6.02×10^{23}

ANSWER 31

$$\frac{0.13 \text{ g}}{30 \text{ g mole}^{-1}} = 0.0043 \text{ mole}$$

0.0043 mole (6.02×10^{23} molecules mole^{-1})
  $= 2.6 \times 10^{21}$ molecules
2.6×10^{21} molecules (2 C atoms molecule^{-1})
  $= 5.2 \times 10^{21}$ C atoms
2.6×10^{21} molecules (6 H atoms molecule^{-1})
  $= 1.6 \times 10^{22}$ H atoms

29

The mass of one molecule of water, then, is the sum of the masses of _____. Expressed in amu, the mass of one molecule of H_2O is _____.

One mole of water contains _____ g-atom(s) of hydrogen and _____.

A mole of a chemical compound is defined as _____.

An 18-g sample of water contains _____ molecules of water, or _____ atoms of hydrogen and _____ atoms of oxygen.

Using the periodic table to obtain atomic weights, calculate the weight of a mole of each of the following compounds:
CH_4 _____
$BaCl_2$ _____
P_2O_5 _____

For the amounts of materials that are used in the laboratory, it is more convenient to have the chemical symbol for an element denote 1 g-atom of the element and the formula for a compound denote _____ of the compound.

ANSWER 2   two atoms
                     one atom

ANSWER 8   two atoms
                     one atom of oxygen

ANSWER 14   8

ANSWER 20   1
                     2
                     1

ANSWER 26 12.04×10^{23}
                     6.02×10^{23}

ANSWER 32   atoms of the various elements
that compose one molecule of
the compound

ITEM 4

The sum of the atomic masses, in amu, of all the atoms of a molecule gives the mass of _____ in _____ units.

ITEM 10

Since 2 g-atoms of hydrogen weigh _____ g and 1 g-atom of oxygen weighs _____ g, 1 mole of water weighs _____ g.

ITEM 16

Just as 1 g-atom of any element contains _____ atoms, 1 mole of any compound contains _____.

ITEM 22

Oxygen gas consists of diatomic molecules that are indicated by the formula _____. One molecule of oxygen contains _____ atom(s).

ITEM 28

3.70 moles of methane, CH_4, weigh _____ and contain _____ molecules.

ANSWER 3   two atoms of hydrogen and
           one atom of oxygen
           $16.00 + 2(1.01) = 18.02$

ANSWER 9   2
           1 g-atom of oxygen

ANSWER 15 the weight of the compound,
           expressed in grams, that is
           numerically equal to the mass
           of one molecule, expressed in
           amu

ANSWER 21 6.02×10^{23}
           12.04×10^{23}
           6.02×10^{23}

ANSWER 27

CH_4: $12.01 + 4(1.01) = 16.05$ g
$BaCl_2$: $137.34 + 2(35.45) = 208.24$ g
P_2O_5: $2(30.97) + 5(16.00) = 141.94$ g

ANSWER 33   1 mole

ITEM 5

Just as it was convenient to deal with a quantity designated by the term "one gram atomic weight," or "1 g-atom," rather than "one atom," it is also convenient to use one *gram molecular weight* rather than one _____.

ITEM 11

When the symbol H_2O stands for one molecule of water, it indicates that one molecule of water contains _____ and has a mass of _____ amu.

ITEM 17

In practice, the term "mole" is synonymous with the number 6.02×10^{23} to the extent that the current trend is to refer to a collection of Avogadro's number of *anything* as a _____.

ITEM 23

One mole of O_2 weighs _____ g and contains _____ molecules.

ITEM 29

One mole of sulfuric acid, H_2SO_4, weighs _____ g.

ANSWER 4   one molecule
              atomic mass

ANSWER 10   2.02
               16.00
               18.02

ANSWER 16 6.02×10^{23}
               6.02×10^{23} molecules

ANSWER 22 O_2
               two

ANSWER 28

3.70 moles (16.1 g mole^{-1}) = 59.6 g
3.70 moles (6.02×10^{23} molecules mole^{-1})
 $= 22.3 \times 10^{23}$

ITEM 6
The term "gram molecular weight" (usually abbreviated "mole") is used when we deal with molecules and compounds, just as the term _____ is used in dealing with atoms and elements.

ITEM 12
More conveniently for chemical calculations, the symbol H_2O can denote 1 mole of water. The symbol then represents a mass of _____.

ITEM 18
Thus, we speak of a mole of water (6.02×10^{23} molecules) or a mole of argon (6.02×10^{23} atoms). For a monatomic element, a mole is equivalent to a _____.

ITEM 24
One mole of oxygen molecules contains _____ g-atom(s) of oxygen, or _____ atoms of oxygen.

ITEM 30
A beaker containing 257 g of H_2SO_4 contains _____ mole(s) of H_2SO_4. The number of gram-atoms of hydrogen present is _____.

ANSWER 5   molecule

ANSWER 11   two atoms of hydrogen and
one atom of oxygen
18.02

ANSWER 17   mole

ANSWER 23 $16.0 \times 2 = 32.0$
6.02×10^{23}

ANSWER 29

H_2SO_4: $2(1.01) + 32.06 + 4(16.00) = 98.08$ g

ANSWER 6   gram atomic weight
(or gram-atom)

(Item 7 is on page 26.)

ANSWER 12   18.02 g

(Item 13 is on page 26.)

ANSWER 18   gram-atom
(or gram atomic weight)

(Item 19 is on page 26.)

ANSWER 24   2
$2(6.02 \times 10^{23}) = 12.04 \times 10^{23}$

(Item 25 is on page 26.)

ANSWER 30 $\dfrac{257 \text{ g}}{98.1 \text{ g mole}^{-1}} = 2.62$ moles

2.62 moles (2 g-atoms mole^{-1})
$= 5.24$ g-atoms

(Item 31 is on page 26.)

Just as you learned in Section 1–1 to relate the number of grams, the number of gram-atoms, and the number of atoms in a sample, now you have learned to do similar calculations involving grams, moles, and molecules. Furthermore, you know how to tie together these two aspects by calculating, for example, the number of atoms of the elements in a sample of a compound containing a certain number of moles or having a given weight.

1–3 EMPIRICAL FORMULAS

As you learned in *Chemical Principles* (Section 1–9), atomic weights and gram-atoms or moles are important in the determination of empirical formulas of compounds from data obtained from elemental analysis. In this section you can test your knowledge of gram-atoms and moles and prove to yourself that you can do empirical formula calculations.

Because in empirical formula problems the relative numbers of atoms must be determined, the gram-atom concept is used constantly. However, a common practice is to use the term "mole," instead of "gram-atom," and to specify that a mole of atoms is meant. The terms will be used interchangeably in this section, but always with the qualification that when a mole of atoms is meant, it will be designated as such. Remember that for some elements, such as oxygen, fluorine, and hydrogen, it is essential to indicate those instances when "mole" means "mole of atoms."

When you do empirical formula determinations in the laboratory, it will be necessary to use as many significant figures as possible. The use of four or five significant figures may help to minimize the number of possible formulas. However, for the purposes of this section, two or three significant figures and slide rule computation will be adequate.

ITEM 1

When you know the atomic weights of hydrogen (1.0) and oxygen (16.0), it is easy to calculate that 1 mole of water weighs _____ g, of which hydrogen atoms constitute _____ g and oxygen atoms constitute _____ g.

ITEM 6

When the ratio of the number of gram-atoms of hydrogen to gram-atoms of oxygen is translated from the calculated value of 11/5.6 to small whole numbers, it becomes H/O = _____.

ITEM 11

Since the number of gram-atoms of H is 5.9 and of O is 5.9, the ratio of hydrogen atoms to oxygen atoms in any size sample is _____.

ITEM 16

Since the compound contains 22.6% phosphorus, the number of grams of phosphorus in 100 g of compound is _____, and the number of moles of phosphorus atoms is _____. The number of grams of chlorine is _____, and the number of moles of chlorine atoms is _____.

ITEM 21

A sample of compound XB21 weighs 0.00530 g and contains C (0.00205 g), N (0.00239 g), and H. The number of gram-atoms of carbon is _____, of nitrogen is _____, and of hydrogen is _____.

ITEM 26

Compound YD25 was prepared by a method expected to give $CH_3C_6H_4COOH$. Calculate the percentage composition expected for $C_8H_8O_2$ and compare it with the one calculated in Item 25.

ITEM 2
The percentage by weight of hydrogen in an 18.0-g sample of water is _____, and the percentage by weight of oxygen is _____.

ITEM 7
The ratio of gram-atoms of hydrogen to gram-atoms of oxygen in any sample of pure water is _____; in a one-molecule sample, the ratio of the number of atoms of H to the number of atoms of O is

_____

ITEM 12
The empirical formula of a compound is the simplest kind of formula, giving only the relative numbers of atoms in a molecule in the smallest possible whole numbers. The empirical formula of the compound in Items 8, 9, 10, and 11 is _____.

ITEM 17
The ratio (in small whole numbers) of the number of moles P to the number of moles Cl is _____/ _____. (The ratios calculated from the numbers of gram-atoms or moles are not always easy to translate into small whole numbers, but a slide rule is invaluable in doing so. Check this one by slide rule.)

ITEM 22
The ratio of the number of gram-atoms of hydrogen to the number of gram-atoms of carbon is

_____

ITEM 27
Topaz has the following composition: 29.3% aluminum, 15.3% silicon, 34.8% oxygen, and 20.7% fluorine. The empirical formula of this mineral is

_____

ANSWER 1   18.0
2.0
16.0

ANSWER 6   2/1

ANSWER 11   1/1

ANSWER 16

22.6

$$\frac{22.6 \text{ g}}{31.0 \text{ g mole}^{-1} \text{ P}} = 0.73 \text{ mole P}$$

77.4

$$\frac{77.4 \text{ g}}{35.5 \text{ g mole}^{-1} \text{ Cl}} = 2.18 \text{ moles Cl}$$

ANSWER 21

$$\frac{0.00205 \text{ g}}{12.0 \text{ g g-atom}^{-1} \text{ C}} - 1.71 \times 10^{-4} \text{ g-atom C}$$

$$\frac{0.00239 \text{ g}}{14.0 \text{ g g-atom}^{-1} \text{ N}} = 1.71 \times 10^{-4} \text{ g-atom N}$$

$$\frac{0.00530 \text{ g} - 0.00444 \text{ g}}{1.0 \text{ g g-atom}^{-1} \text{ H}} = 8.6 \times 10^{-4} \text{ g-atom H}$$

ANSWER 26

$$\frac{8 \text{ g-atoms } (12.0 \text{ g g-atom}^{-1})(100)}{8(12.0) \text{ g} + 8(1.0) \text{ g} + 2(16.0) \text{ g}} = 70.6\% \text{ C}$$

$$\frac{2 \text{ g-atoms } (16.0 \text{ g g-atom}^{-1})(100)}{8(12.0) \text{ g} + 8(1.0) \text{ g} + 2(16.0) \text{ g}} = 23.5\% \text{ O}$$

$$\frac{8 \text{ g-atoms } (1.0 \text{ g g-atom}^{-1})(100)}{8(12.0) \text{ g} + 8(1.0) \text{ g} + 2(16.0) \text{ g}} = 5.9\% \text{ H}$$

Within the accuracy of the analysis, the percentages are the same.

ITEM 3   In any pure sample of natural water, the percentage
                                    by weight of hydrogen is _____, and the per-
                                    centage by weight of oxygen is _____.

ITEM 8   In another compound of hydrogen and oxygen, the
                                    percentage by weight of hydrogen is 5.9. In a 100-g
                                    sample of this compound the number of grams of
                                    hydrogen is _____. The number of gram-atoms
                                    of hydrogen is _____.

ITEM 13   The known molecular weight of this compound is
                                    34.0. Can the empirical formula be the actual for-
                                    mula of the molecule?

ITEM 18   The empirical formula of the compound in Item 17
                                    is _____.

ITEM 23   The empirical formula of compound XB21 is
                                    _____.

ANSWER 2 $\dfrac{2.0 \text{ g}}{18 \text{ g}} \times 100 = 11$

$\dfrac{16 \text{ g}}{18 \text{ g}} \times 100 = 89$

ANSWER 7 2/1
2/1

ANSWER 12 HO

ANSWER 17 1/3

ANSWER 22 $\dfrac{8.6 \times 10^{-4}}{1.7 \times 10^{-4}} = \dfrac{5}{1}$

ANSWER 27

$\dfrac{29.3 \text{ g}}{27.0 \text{ g mole}^{-1} \text{ Al}} = 1.09 \text{ moles Al}$

$\dfrac{15.3 \text{ g}}{28.1 \text{ g mole}^{-1} \text{ Si}} = 0.54 \text{ mole Si}$

$\dfrac{34.8 \text{ g}}{16.0 \text{ g mole}^{-1} \text{ O}} = 2.18 \text{ moles O}$

$\dfrac{20.7 \text{ g}}{19.0 \text{ g mole}^{-1} \text{ F}} = 1.09 \text{ moles F}$

empirical formula is $Al_2SiO_4F_2$

In 100 g of H_2O the number of grams of hydrogen is _____, and the number of gram-atoms of hydrogen is _____.

If the compound contains 5.9% hydrogen, the percentage by weight of oxygen is _____.

Since the molecular weight of the compound is 34.0, the actual formula of the molecule must be _____.

Aluminum oxide contains 47.0% oxygen. The number of moles of aluminum in 100 g of this oxide is _____, and the number of moles of oxygen atoms is _____.

Every problem involving the percentage by weight composition of a compound is basically a restatement of the familiar relationship: no. of moles of atoms of an element or no. of gram-atoms of an element = no. of grams of the element divided by the _____.

ANSWER 3   11
             89

ANSWER 8   5.9

$$\frac{5.9 \text{ g}}{1.0 \text{ g g-atom}^{-1}} = 5.9 \text{ g-atoms}$$

ANSWER 13   No, because the molecular
             weight of HO is 17.0.

ANSWER 18 PCl_3

ANSWER 23 CH_5N

In 100 g of H_2O the number of grams of oxygen is _____, so the number of gram-atoms is _____.

The number of grams of oxygen atoms in the compound is _____, and the number of gram-atoms is _____.

A compound contains 22.6% phosphorus and 77.4% chlorine. The ratio of P to Cl atoms is the same in any size sample, but it is most convenient to calculate the ratio in a sample weighing _____ g.

The ratio of moles Al to moles O is _____, and the empirical formula is _____.

A carefully purified sample of compound YD25 weighs 0.00840 g. Analysis shows that it contains 4.94×10^{-4} mole C and 1.25×10^{-4} mole O. The other element present is hydrogen. What is the percentage by weight of C, H, and O?

ANSWER 4   11

$$\frac{11 \text{ g}}{1.0 \text{ g g-atom}^{-1}} = 11$$

ANSWER 9   94.1

ANSWER 14 H_2O_2

ANSWER 19

$$\frac{53.0 \text{ g}}{27.0 \text{ g mole}^{-1} \text{ Al}} = 1.96 \text{ moles Al}$$

$$\frac{47.0 \text{ g}}{16.0 \text{ g mole}^{-1} \text{ O}} = 2.94 \text{ moles O}$$

ANSWER 24   atomic weight

ANSWER 5   89

$$\frac{89 \text{ g}}{16 \text{ g g-atom}^{-1}} = 5.6$$

(*Item 6 is on page 42.*)

ANSWER 10   94.1

$$\frac{94.1 \text{ g}}{16.0 \text{ g g-atom}^{-1}} = 5.9 \text{ g-atoms}$$

(*Item 11 is on page 42.*)

ANSWER 15   100

(*Item 16 is on page 42.*)

ANSWER 20   2/3
Al_2O_3

(*Item 21 is on page 42.*)

ANSWER 25

4.94×10^{-4} mole C(12.0 g mole^{-1} C)
  $= 0.00593$ g of C

$$\frac{0.00593 \text{ g}(100)}{0.00840 \text{ g}} = 70.6\% \text{ C}$$

1.25×10^{-4} mole O(16.0 g mole^{-1} O)
  $= 0.00200$ g of O

$$\frac{0.00200 \text{ g}(100)}{0.00840 \text{ g}} = 23.8\% \text{ O}$$

0.00840 g $- 0.00200$ g $- 0.00593$ g
  $= 0.00047$ g of H

$$\frac{0.00047 \text{ g}(100)}{0.0084 \text{ g}} = 5.6\% \text{ H}$$

53

(*Item 26 is on page 42.*)

REVIEW 2 THE IDEAL GAS LAWS

From Chapter 1 of *Chemical Principles* it is clear that the study of gases is of critical importance to the development of our knowledge of the number of atoms in molecules and of the concept of the mole. Of particular importance is Amadeo Avogadro's hypothesis that the volume occupied by a gas at a given temperature and pressure depends only on the number of molecules present and not on any other property of the gas

In Chapter 2 you read about the development of laws relating the volume, temperature, pressure, and number of moles of a gas. The first part of the chapter, concerning the ideal gas laws, is essential to your further study of chemistry; for that reason it is reviewed here. You realize, of course, that the statements and the equations apply only to what are called ideal gases. Although they describe exactly the behavior of no real gas (except at zero pressure), they constitute extremely useful approximations at the temperatures and pressures encountered in many experiments.

At the conclusion of this review you will be able to make calculations of the following type: "What is the molecular weight of a gas whose density at 0° and 0.1 atm is 0.390 g liter^{-1}?" If you can work correctly the items beginning with number 80 at the end of the review, it will not be necessary for you to do the others.

ITEM 1

When the pressure on a sample of gas is increased while the temperature is held constant, the gas is compressed; that is, the volume of the gas _____.

ITEM 16

If the temperature is raised and the pressure kept constant, the gas will expand. That is, the volume will _____.

ITEM 31

One (1.00) liter of a gas at 0°C will expand, when heated to 100°C, to a volume of _____ liter(s).

ITEM 46

At 1 atm and 0°C the volume of 1.81 g of nitrogen is 1.45 liters. The density of nitrogen under these is _____.

ITEM 61

One mole of chlorine, Cl_2, contains _____ molecules and weighs _____ g.

ITEM 76

The volume of 0.376 g of CO_2 at STP is _____ liter(s).

ITEM 2

Conversely, when the pressure is decreased the gas will expand; that is, the volume will _____.

ITEM 17

If the temperature of a gas sample is increased from 20°C to 40°C, the volume is found to increase by about 7%, not 100%. Hence, the volume of a gas is not directly proportional to the temperature expressed in _____.

ITEM 32

To cause a gas sample to contract from a volume of 3.8 liters to 1.4 liters, the absolute temperature can be lowered to _____ times its initial value or the pressure can be _____ to _____ times its initial value.

ITEM 47

At the same _____ and _____, the density of nitrogen is _____ times greater than the density of hydrogen.

ITEM 62

One mole of any substance contains the _____ number of molecules as 1 mole of any other substance.

ITEM 77

A gas sample occupies a volume of 546 ml at STP. It contains, therefore, _____ mole(s) of gas.

**Density (g liter⁻¹)
at 1 atm and 0°C**

H_2	$D = 0.090$
N_2	$D = 1.25$

ANSWER 1   decreases

ANSWER 16   increase

ANSWER 31   1.00 liter (373 deg/273 deg)
$\qquad$ = 1.37 liters

ANSWER 46   1.81 g/1.45 liters
$\qquad$ = 1.25 g liter⁻¹

ANSWER 61 6.023×10^{23}
$\qquad$ $2(35.45) = 70.90$

ANSWER 76

$V = nRT/P$

$$= \frac{\dfrac{0.376\ \text{g}}{44.0\ \text{g mole}^{-1}} \times 0.0821\ \dfrac{\text{liter atm}}{\text{deg mole}} \times 273\ \text{deg}}{1.00\ \text{atm}}$$

$= 0.191$ liter

(or $\dfrac{0.376\ \text{g}}{44.0\ \text{g mole}^{-1}} \times 22.4$ liters mole⁻¹

$= 0.191$ liter)

59

ITEM 3

The relation between the pressure and the volume of a constant number of moles of a gas at constant temperature is shown graphically at the right. If the pressure on a gas is doubled, the volume is reduced to half its original value. If the pressure is decreased to one fifth of its original value, the volume will _____ by a factor of _____.

ITEM 18

In fact, if the temperature is raised from 20°C to 40°C, the volume of a gas sample increases by an amount that is 20/273 of its volume at 0°C. In general, for every 1°C rise in temperature, the volume of a gas increases by _____ of its value at 0°C.

ITEM 33

Boyle's law states that: *The volume of a constant number of moles of a gas* _____. This can be written as _____ $=$ constant $(n, T$ constant$)$.

ITEM 48

The equation $V = kw$, where k is a constant, can be written for any individual gas at a fixed temperature and pressure. Since the density D is defined as w/V, the constant k is related to the density as $k =$ _____.

ITEM 63

One mole of any gas will occupy, at a given temperature and pressure, the same _____ as 1 mole of any other gas.

ITEM 78

A 0.264-g sample of H_2S gas contains _____ mole(s) and occupies, at 100°C and 743 torr pressure, a volume of _____ liter(s). (Recall that 1 atm $=$ 760 torr.)

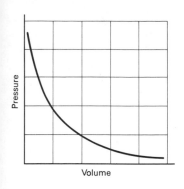

Pressure

Volume

ANSWER 2   increase

ANSWER 17   °C (degrees centigrade)

ANSWER 32   1.4 liters/3.8 liters = 0.37
increased
3.8 liters/1.4 liters = 2.7

ANSWER 47   temperature
pressure

$$\frac{1.25}{0.090} = 14$$

ANSWER 62   same

ANSWER 77

$n = PV/RT$

$$= \frac{(1.00 \text{ atm})(0.546 \text{ liter})}{\left(0.0821 \dfrac{\text{liter atm}}{\text{deg mole}}\right)(273 \text{ deg})}$$

$= 0.0244$ mole

(or $\dfrac{0.546 \text{ liter}}{22.4 \text{ liter mole}^{-1}} = 0.0244$ mole)

61

ITEM 4

This relationship is described by the generalization: The volume of an ideal gas is _____ proportional to the pressure if the number of moles remains constant and the _____ remains constant. This statement is known as *Boyle's law.*

ITEM 19

Thus, for a gas sample at fixed pressure, the plot of V versus $t°C$ has the form shown at the right. (The dashed line represents the extrapolation that is necessary because gases become liquids and solids at low temperature.) According to the extrapolation, the volume would be zero at a temperature of _____ °C.

ITEM 34

Charles' law states that: *The volume of a constant number of moles of a gas is* _____. This can be written as _____ = constant (n, P constant).

ITEM 49

The relation between the volume and mass of a given gas at a fixed pressure and temperature can then be written $V =$ _____ w.

ITEM 64

At a given T and P, the volume of any ideal gas sample will not be determined by the size, shape, mass, or chemical properties of the gas molecules but will be determined by the _____ in the sample.

ITEM 79

The volume of 22.4 liters is occupied at STP by 1 mole, or _____ molecule(s), of any gas.

Boyle's law

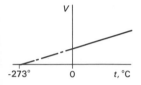

$V = kw$
$k = 1/D$

ANSWER 3   increase
            five

ANSWER 18   1/273

ANSWER 33   is inversely proportional to
            the pressure if the tempera-
            ture remains constant.
            PV

ANSWER 48 $1/D$

ANSWER 63   volume

ANSWER 78

$0.264g/34.1g\ mole^{-1} = 0.00774$
$V = nRT/P$

$$= \frac{0.00774\ mole(373\ deg)\left(0.0821\ \dfrac{liter\ atm}{deg\ mole}\right)}{(743/760)\ atm}$$

$= 0.242$ liter

ITEM 5

When the pressure on a sample of a gas (at a fixed temperature) is increased from 1.2 atm to 6.0 atm, the new volume will be what fraction of the original volume?

ITEM 20

A straight line as shown at the right represents the equation $y = m(x + b)$, where m is the slope of the line. A comparison of this graph and the graph of the preceding item shows that, for constant pressure and constant number of moles of gas, we can write the equation $V = m(\underline{\hspace{1.5cm}} + \underline{\hspace{1.5cm}})$.

ITEM 35

These laws can be combined to show the dependence of V on both P and T by the proportionality equation $V \propto T/P$ (n constant), or, with the proportionality constant α, by $V = \alpha \underline{\hspace{1.5cm}}$.

ITEM 50

Since, at the same T and P, the densities of different gases are $\underline{\hspace{1.5cm}}$, the proportionality constants between volume and mass for different gases are different.

ITEM 65

In relating gas volumes to numbers of moles or molecules, we should, for convenience, have a set of standard conditions. The standard temperature and pressure (STP) generally agreed upon are $T = 0°C$, or $\underline{\hspace{1.5cm}}$ °K, and $P = 1$ atm.

ITEM 80

If the size, shape, and weight of molecules do not affect ideal gas behavior, it follows that, even if there are different kinds of molecules making up the gas sample, the relation $PV = nRT$ will apply, where n is the total $\underline{\hspace{1.5cm}}$ of gas present.

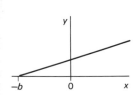

inversely
temperature

-273

directly proportional to the
absolute temperature if the
pressure remains constant.
V/T

$(1/D)$

number of molecules
(or number of moles)

6.023×10^{23}

ITEM 6

To increase the volume of a sample of gas, the pressure must be _____. For the volume to change from 1.56 liters to 4.28 liters, the pressure must be _____ from its original value to _____ times its original value.

ITEM 21

Thus, for a gas sample at fixed pressure, V is proportional not to $t°C$ but to _____.

ITEM 36

This equation can be rearranged to show that, for a given sample of gas, the function of P, V, and T that remains constant is _____.

ITEM 51

Therefore, when more than one gas is considered, we cannot expect to find a general formula for the volume in terms of only the temperature, pressure, and _____ of the gases.

ITEM 66

The density of N_2 at STP is 1.25 g per liter, and therefore 1 mole of N_2 (that is, _____ g) occupies _____ liter(s) at STP.

ITEM 81

A mixture of 3.00 moles of hydrogen and 1.00 mole of argon contains a total of _____ mole(s) and occupies _____ liter(s) at STP.

$V = \alpha(T/P)$

ANSWER 5   1.2 atm/6.0 atm = 0.20

ANSWER 20 $(t°C + 273)$

ANSWER 35 T/P (m constant)

ANSWER 50   different

ANSWER 65   273

ANSWER 80   number of moles

ITEM 7

To compress a gas sample that occupies 2.5 liters at a pressure of 1.8 atm to a volume of 1.5 liters (temperature remaining constant), the pressure must be _____ to a value of 1.8 atm × _____ = _____ atm.

ITEM 22

The absolute, or Kelvin (K), temperature scale is related to the centigrade (C) scale as follows: $T_{°K} = t_{°C} + 273$. Thus, $10°C = $ _____ $°K$.

ITEM 37

Thus, Boyle's and Charles' laws can be combined into the convenient mathematical expression _____ = constant (n constant).

ITEM 52

This goal can be achieved, to the extent that gases behave ideally, with the following added assumption, first proposed by Avogadro: *Equal volumes of different gases at the same temperature and pressure contain _____ number of molecules.*

ITEM 67

Similarly, once allowances are made for nonideal behavior of other gases, it is found that 1 mole of any gas at STP should occupy the volume of _____ liter(s).

ITEM 82

A mixture of 2.76 g of CH_4 and 9.34 g of NH_3 contains _____ mole(s) and, at 200°C and 3.00 atm, occupies _____ liter(s).

ANSWER 6 decreased
decreased
1.56 liters/4.28 liters = 0.364

ANSWER 21 $(t°C + 273)$ or $(t + 273)°C$

ANSWER 36 PV/T

ANSWER 51 mass (or density)

ANSWER 66 28.0

$$\frac{28.0 \text{ g mole}^{-1}}{1.25 \text{ g liter}^{-1}} = 22.4$$

ANSWER 81 4.00
22.4 liters mole^{-1} (4.00 moles)
$= 89.6$ liters

ITEM 8

Boyle's law states that: *The* _____ *of a gas sample (constant number of moles) is* _____ *to the* _____ *of the gas if the temperature remains constant.*

ITEM 23

Since V is directly proportional to ($t°C + 273$), V is also _____ to the Kelvin temperature.

ITEM 38

For initial values V_1, P_1, and T_1, and final values V_2, P_2, and T_2, this relation can be written _____ = _____ (n constant).

ITEM 53

At the same temperature and pressure, 1 liter of nitrogen and 1 liter of hydrogen have _____ masses but _____ number of molecules.

ITEM 68

The volume of 3.2 moles of cyanogen gas (C_2N_2) at STP is _____ liter(s).

ITEM 83

Air consists very nearly of 80 mole % N_2 and 20 mole % O_2; that is, in 100 moles of air, 80 will be N_2 and 20 will be O_2.

(a) One mole of air at 25°C and 1 atm has a volume of _____ liters. It contains _____ mole(s), or _____ g, of N_2 and _____ mole(s), or _____ g, of O_2.

(b) From (a), the total mass of N_2 and O_2 in 1 mole of air is calculated to be _____ g. Thus, the density of air at 25°C and 1 atm is _____.

ANSWER 7   increased
2.5 liters/1.5 liters
3.0

ANSWER 22   283

ANSWER 37 PV/T

ANSWER 52   the same

ANSWER 67   22.4

ANSWER 82

$$\text{no. of moles} = \frac{2.76 \text{ g}}{16.0 \text{ g mole}^{-1}} + \frac{9.34 \text{ g}}{17.0 \text{ g mole}^{-1}}$$

$$= 0.722 \text{ mole}$$

$$V = nRT/P$$

$$= \frac{0.722 \text{ mole}}{3.00 \text{ atm}} \left(0.0821 \frac{\text{liter atm}}{\text{deg mole}}\right) 473 \text{ deg}$$

$$= 9.35 \text{ liters}$$

ITEM 9

Boyle's law is written $V \propto 1/P$ (n, T constant), or, with the proportionality constant a, $V =$ _____, or $PV =$ _____.

ITEM 24

The volume of a gas sample at constant pressure varies with the temperature according to $V = m(t°C + 273) = m$ _____, where m is a proportionality constant.

ITEM 39

This equation can be rearranged as $V_2 = V_1 \times T_2/T_1 \times$ _____ (n constant) and in this form shows explicitly its relation to Charles' and Boyle's laws.

ITEM 54

At a given temperature and pressure, the volume occupied by N molecules of nitrogen gas is _____ the volume occupied by the same number of hydrogen molecules, or any kind of gas molecules.

ITEM 69

The volume of a sample of gas is directly proportional to the _____ and to the _____ and inversely proportional to the _____.

ITEM 84

The volume of gas in a meteorological balloon is 7.00 ft³ at ground level, where the pressure is 1 atm and the temperature is 25°C. At an altitude of 22 miles the pressure is about 4 torr and the temperature is −12°C. The volume of the gas in the balloon is then _____ ft³.

$$\frac{P_1V_1}{T_1} = \frac{P_2V_2}{T_2}$$

ANSWER 8   volume
inversely proportional
pressure

ANSWER 23   directly proportional

ANSWER 38 P_1V_1/T_1
P_2V_2/T_2

ANSWER 53   different
the same

ANSWER 68   (22.4 liters mole^{-1})(3.2 moles)
= 72 liters

ANSWER 83
(a)
V = 22.4 liters (298 deg/273 deg)
= 24.5 liters
[or $V = nRT/P$

$$= 1 \text{ mole} \left(0.0821 \frac{\text{liter atm}}{\text{deg mole}}\right) \frac{298 \text{ deg}}{1 \text{ atm.}}$$

= 24.5 liters]
0.80
0.80 mole (28 g mole^{-1}) = 22.4 g
0.20
0.20 mole (32 g mole^{-1}) = 6.4 g
(b)
22.4 g + 6.4 g = 28.8 g
$D = w/V = (28.8 \text{ g mole}^{-1})/(24.5 \text{ liters mole}^{-1})$
= 1.2 g liter^{-1}

ITEM 10

The relation $PV = a$ shows that, for a given sample of gas, the product of the pressure and volume is constant if the _____ remains constant.

ITEM 25

If the pressure on a sample of gas remains constant, the volume is _____ proportional to the _____ temperature. This statement is known as *Charles', or Gay-Lussac's, law.*

ITEM 40

When the pressure on a 7.63-liter sample of a gas is increased from 2.35 atm to 7.60 atm and the temperature is decreased from 400°K to 300°K, the volume will _____, and the new volume will be _____ liters.

ITEM 55

Avogadro's hypothesis states that: *At the same conditions of temperature and pressure equal volumes of different gases* _____.

ITEM 70

If the number of moles in a sample of gas is indicated by n, the dependence of V on n, P, and T can be written as $V \propto$ _____.

ITEM 85

One (1.00) liter of an unknown gas at 0.425 atm and 30°C has a mass of 0.548 g. The molecular weight (mol wt) of the gas is _____, and the gas might be _____.

Charles' law

$V_2 = V_1 \times \dfrac{T_2}{T_1} \times \dfrac{P_1}{P_2}$

ANSWER 9 a/P (n, T constant)
               a (n, T constant)

ANSWER 24 $T_{°K}$ (or T)

ANSWER 39 P_1/P_2

ANSWER 54   equal to

ANSWER 69   absolute temperature
               number of moles
               pressure

ANSWER 84

$P_1V_1/T_1 = P_2V_2/T_2$

$V_2 = \left(\dfrac{760 \text{ torr}}{4 \text{ torr}}\right)\left(\dfrac{261 \text{ deg}}{298 \text{ deg}}\right)(7.00 \text{ ft}^3)$

$= 1160$ (approximately 1200)

ITEM 11

For a sample of gas at pressure P_1 and volume V_1, $P_1V_1 = $ _____. For the same sample of gas under different conditions, P_2 and V_2, it is also true that $P_2V_2 = $ _____. Hence, $P_1V_1 = $ _____ (n, T constant).

ITEM 26

If the absolute temperature of a gas sample is tripled and the pressure is kept constant, the volume _____ to _____ times its original value.

ITEM 41

When the temperature of a gas sample is increased from 0°C to 250°C, that is, from _____ °K to _____ °K, and the pressure on the gas is doubled, the volume will be changed by a factor of _____.

ITEM 56

The volume of a gas sample, at given T and P, is proportional to the amount of gas, which can be measured by the mass of the gas or by the number of _____ in the sample.

ITEM 71

If the proportionality constant R is introduced, the relation can be written as $V = $ _____.

ITEM 86

An ideal gas with a volume of 20.0 liters at STP is compressed to 8.50 liters and, at the same time, is heated to 200°C. What is the final pressure exerted by the gas?

$$\frac{P_1 V_1}{T_1} = \frac{P_2 V_2}{T_2}$$

$$V \propto nT/P$$

ANSWER 10   temperature
(and number of moles)

ANSWER 25   directly
absolute (Kelvin)

ANSWER 40

decrease

$$7.63 \text{ liters} \frac{(300 \text{ deg})(2.35 \text{ atm})}{(400 \text{ deg})(7.60 \text{ atm})} = 1.77 \text{ liters}$$

ANSWER 55   *contain the same number of molecules*

ANSWER 70 nT/P

ANSWER 85

$$n = \frac{PV}{RT} = \frac{(0.425 \text{ atm})(1.00 \text{ liter})}{\left(0.0821 \dfrac{\text{liter atm}}{\text{deg mole}}\right)(303 \text{ deg})}$$

$$= 0.0171 \text{ mole}$$

mol wt $= 0.548 \text{ g}/0.0171 \text{ mole}$
$= 32.0 \text{ g mole}^{-1}$

O_2

77

ITEM 12

This result can be rearranged to $V_1/V_2 = $ _____ (n, T constant), which shows that the volume varies inversely as the pressure.

ITEM 27

To cause a gas to contract from a volume of 250 milliliters (ml) to 170 ml at a constant pressure of 1 atm, the initial absolute temperature must be multiplied by a factor of _____.

ITEM 42

At the same T and P, the volume occupied by 2 g of H_2 is twice the volume occupied by 1 g of H_2. The volume is proportional to the _____ of gas.

ITEM 57

For a given gas at fixed T and P, one can write $V \propto$ (number of molecules) or, using the proportionality constant k', $V = $ _____ (P, T constant).

ITEM 72

This equation, representing the *ideal gas law*, is usually written $PV = $ _____. The constant R, known as the gas constant, must be _____ for all ideal gases.

ITEM 87

What volume is occupied by 1.34 g of gaseous C_2H_6 at 25°C and 747 torr?

$P_1V_1 = P_2V_2$
(n, T constant)

ANSWER 11 a
a
P_2V_2

ANSWER 26   increases
three

ANSWER 41   273
$273 + 250 = 523$
$V_2/V_1 = (P_1/P_2)(T_2/T_1)$

$$= \frac{1}{2}\left(\frac{523 \text{ deg}}{273 \text{ deg}}\right)$$

$$= 0.958$$

ANSWER 56   molecules or moles

ANSWER 71 RnT/P (or nRT/P)

ANSWER 86 $P_1V_1/T_1 = P_2V_2/T_2$

$$P_2 = \frac{20.0 \text{ liters}}{8.50 \text{ liters}}\left(\frac{473°}{273°}\right)1.00 \text{ atm}$$

$$= 4.08 \text{ atm}$$

ITEM 13

The pressure on a gas sample is increased from 1.0 atm to 12 atm. If the original volume was 3.8 liters, the new volume could be calculated as $V_2 = V_1(P_1/P_2)$ or $V_2 = 3.8$ liters $\times$ _____ = _____ liter(s).

ITEM 28

The mathematical formulation of Charles' law is $V \propto$ _____ (n, P constant); or, using the proportionality constant c, $V =$ _____ or $V/T =$ _____.

ITEM 43

If the amount of gas is measured by its mass w, then at constant temperature and pressure $V \propto$ _____ or, if the proportionality constant k is introduced, $V = k$ _____.

ITEM 58

Since equal volumes of different gases at the same temperature and pressure contain _____, the constant k' must be _____ for different gases.

ITEM 73

The gas constant R can have various numerical values, depending on the units in which it is expressed. If $PV = nRT$ is to be used with P in atmospheres, V in liters, T in degrees Kelvin, and n in moles, the units of R will be _____.

ITEM 88

Calculate the density of uranium hexafluoride (UF_6) vapor at 56°C and 1.00 atm.

$$\frac{V_1}{V_2} = \frac{P_2}{P_1}$$

ANSWER 12 P_2/P_1

ANSWER 27   170 ml/250 ml $= 0.680$

ANSWER 42   mass
(amount or number of moles)

ANSWER 57 k' (number of molecules)

$PV = nRT$

ANSWER 72 nRT
the same

ANSWER 87

mol wt of $C_2H_6 = 2(12.0) + 6(1.01) = 30.1$

$V = nRT/P$

$$= \frac{\left(\dfrac{1.34 \text{ g}}{30.1 \text{ g mole}^{-1}}\right)\left(0.0821 \dfrac{\text{liter atm}}{\text{deg mole}}\right)(298 \text{ deg})}{(747/760) \text{ atm}}$$

$= 1.11$ liters

ITEM 14

To increase the volume of a gas sample from 2.84 liters to 7.56 liters at constant temperature, the pressure must be _____ from 4.20 atm to _____ atm.

ITEM 29

For initial conditions V_1 and T_1, $V_1/T_1 =$ _____; for final conditions V_2 and T_2, $V_2/T_2 =$ _____. Hence, $V_1/T_1 =$ _____ (n, P constant).

ITEM 44

By definition, the density D of a gas is the mass per unit volume; that is, $D =$ _____.

ITEM 59

The conventional unit for measuring numbers of molecules is Avogadro's number, $N = 6.023 \times 10^{23}$. This is the number of molecules in 1 _____ of any substance.

ITEM 74

Since 1 mole of any gas occupies 22.4 liters at STP, you can calculate the value of the gas constant R. $R =$ _____ liter atm deg^{-1} $mole^{-1}$.

ITEM 89

Calculate the molecular weight of an unknown gas, given that 1.51 g of the gas occupy a volume of 405 ml at 100°C and 735 torr.

ANSWER 13   1.0 atm/12 atm
0.32

ANSWER 28 T
cT (n, P constant)
c (n, P constant)

ANSWER 43 w
w

ANSWER 58   the same number of
molecules
the same

ANSWER 73   liter atm deg^{-1} mole^{-1}

For R values in other units, see *Chemical Principles*, Section 2–5.

ANSWER 88

volume of 1.00 mole $= 1.00\ RT/P$

$$= \frac{1.00\ \text{mole}\left(0.0821\ \dfrac{\text{liter atm}}{\text{deg mole}}\right)329\ \text{deg}}{1.00\ \text{atm}}$$

$= 27.0$ liters

[or $V_{\text{mole}} = 22.4$ liters $\left(\dfrac{329°}{273°}\right) = 27.0$ liters]

density $= \dfrac{352\ \text{g mole}^{-1}}{27.0\ \text{liters mole}^{-1}} = 13.0$ g liter^{-1}

ITEM 15

If the pressure on a gas sample is kept constant and no molecules of gas are added or subtracted, the volume can be changed by changing the _____ of the gas.

ITEM 30

When a gas with an initial volume of 14.7 liters is heated from 300°K to 450°K and the pressure is kept constant, the volume _____ to _____ liter(s).

ITEM 45

At 1 atm and 0°C, 0.26 g of hydrogen occupies 2.88 liters. The density under these conditions is

_____ .

ITEM 60

One mole of O_2 weighs 32.0 g and contains _____ molecule(s).

ITEM 75

Problems involving the *PVT* behavior of gases can be solved either by using Boyle's law, Charles' law, and the fact that 1 mole of any gas occupies _____ at STP or by using the equation _____, which summarizes these features.

ITEM 90

What volume of helium gas at STP is required to produce 1.00 liter of liquid helium? The density of liquid helium is 0.122 g ml^{-1}.

$$\frac{V_1}{T_1} = \frac{V_2}{T_2}$$

ANSWER 14

decreased
4.20 atm (2.84 liters/7.56 liters)
$\quad$ = 1.58 atm

ANSWER 29 $\quad c$
$\qquad\qquad\qquad c$
$\qquad\qquad\qquad V_2/T_2$

ANSWER 44 $\quad w/V$

ANSWER 59 $\quad$ mole

ANSWER 74

$R = PV/nT$

$\quad = \dfrac{(1.00 \text{ atm})(22.4 \text{ liters})}{(1.00 \text{ mole})(273 \text{ deg})}$

$\quad = 0.0821$

ANSWER 89

$n = \dfrac{PV}{RT} = \dfrac{(735/760) \text{ atm } (0.405 \text{ liter})}{\left(0.0821 \dfrac{\text{liter atm}}{\text{deg mole}}\right)(373 \text{ deg})}$

$\quad = 0.0128$ mole
mol wt = 1.51 g/0.0128 mole = 118 g mole^{-1}

ANSWER 15   temperature

(Item 16 is on page 56.)

ANSWER 30   increases
14.7 liters (450 deg/300 deg)
= 22.1 liters

(Item 31 is on page 56.)

ANSWER 45   0.26 g/2.88 liters
= 0.090 g liter^{-1}

(Item 46 is on page 56.)

ANSWER 60 6.023×10^{23}

(Item 61 is on page 56.)

ANSWER 75   22.4 liters
$PV = nRT$ [or $PV = n(0.0821)T$
if P is in atm, V is in liters,
and T is in degrees Kelvin]

(Item 76 is on page 56.)

ANSWER 90

wt of He $= (1.00 \text{ liter})(122 \text{ g liter}^{-1}) = 122$ g
moles of He $= (122 \text{ g})/4.00 \text{ g mole}^{-1}$
$= 30.5$ moles
thus, $V = (30.5 \text{ moles})(22.4 \text{ liters mole}^{-1})$
$= 683$ liters

REVIEW 3 IONS AND THE ELECTROLYSIS OF MOLTEN SALTS

The study of the electrolytic decomposition of molten salts is preparation for understanding concepts and words used in all branches of chemistry. The development here of ideas concerning the reduction and oxidation of ions in electrolysis reactions will serve as a review of Sections 3–1 and 3–2 of *Chemical Principles* and as an introduction to the study of ionic nomenclature and charge that will be continued in Review 5.

If you can correctly answer Items 50–60 at the end of the review, you are already familiar with this material and you need not work through the beginning items.

ITEM 1

Atoms are made up of protons, neutrons, and electrons. Although neutrons are electrically neutral, protons have a unit positive charge and electrons have a unit _____ charge.

ITEM 11

The conduction of electricity through any material requires the movement of charged particles. A metal conducts electricity because some of the electrons are not tightly held but are free to _____ through a metal crystal.

ITEM 21

Two chlorine atoms at the anode will form a molecule of chlorine gas and escape from the liquid. The reactions at the anode can be written

$$Cl^- \rightarrow Cl + e^-$$
$$2Cl \rightarrow Cl_2 \uparrow$$

The reaction at the cathode can be written _____.

ITEM 31

The electrolysis of molten cuprous oxide, Cu_2O, made up of Cu^+ ions and O^{2-} ions proceeds according to the equation $2Cu_2O \rightarrow 4Cu + O_2 \uparrow$. The reduction half-reaction is _____. The oxidation half-reaction is _____.

ITEM 41

To five significant figures, 1 $\mathscr{F}$ is 96,487 coulombs. One coulomb will produce _____ g of silver metal (at. wt: 107.868).

ITEM 51

The equation for the complete reaction (with the same number of electrons on both sides) is _____.

ITEM 2

Since an atom has equal numbers of protons and electrons, it is electrically neutral. If an electron is added to an atom, the atom becomes an *ion* and has a unit _____.

ITEM 12

Solid salts will not conduct electricity: All the electrons are tightly held to the ions, and the ions themselves are tightly held in the crystal. But when salts are melted, the liquid conducts electricity because the ions _____.

ITEM 22

Two electrons must be removed from Cl^- ions to form Cl_2, and at the same time two electrons must be added to _____ Na^+ ions to form _____.

ITEM 32

The salt silver bromide, AgBr, is made up of Ag^+ ions and Br^- ions. The _____ charged silver ion is called the _____ and the _____ charged bromide ion is called the _____.

ITEM 42

This quantity is important because the coulomb is now defined as the amount of electricity that will deposit 0.0011180 g of silver from a solution of silver nitrate. This is just the amount of electricity that will deposit 1/96,487 of a _____ of silver from a molten silver salt.

ITEM 52

Calculate the number of grams of iron (at. wt: 55.9) and chlorine gas (at. wt Cl: 35.5) produced by 0.500 A for 1.00 h.

$Fe^{3+} + 3e^- \rightarrow Fe$

$2Cl^- \rightarrow Cl_2 \uparrow + 2e^-$

ANSWER 1   negative

ANSWER 11   move

ANSWER 21 $Na^+ + e^- \rightarrow Na$

ANSWER 31 $Cu^+ + e^- \rightarrow Cu$
(or $4Cu^+ + 4e^- \rightarrow 4Cu$)
$2O^{2-} \rightarrow O_2 \uparrow + 4e^-$

ANSWER 41 $$\frac{107.868 \text{ g mole}^{-1}}{96,487 \text{ coulombs mole}^{-1}}$$

$$= 0.0011180$$

ANSWER 51

$$2Fe^{3+} + 6e^- \rightarrow 2Fe$$
$$\underline{6Cl^- \qquad \rightarrow 3Cl_2 + 6e^-}$$
$$2Fe^{3+} + 6Cl^- + 6e^- \rightarrow 2Fe + 3Cl_2 \uparrow + 6e^-$$

ITEM 3

Some atoms can add more than one electron. (You will study in Review 5, and in Chapter 5 and later chapters of *Chemical Principles*, how to predict which atoms can add electrons and how many.) The negative charge on any ion formed by addition of electrons to an atom is equal to _____.

ITEM 13

If two electrodes (rods of carbon or platinum) are immersed in molten sodium chloride and an electric potential is applied across the rods, one electrode will have excess electrons and a _____ charge. It will attract ions with a _____ charge.

ITEM 23

Thus, the total reaction for this process is written as the addition

$$2Na^+ + 2e^- \rightarrow 2Na$$
$$\underline{2Cl^- \qquad \rightarrow Cl_2 \uparrow + 2e^-}$$

ITEM 33

When silver bromide is electrolyzed, silver metal collects at the _____, and the gas Br_2 is given off at the _____.

ITEM 43

The charge of one mole of electrons constitutes the quantity of electricity known as the _____. It is equivalent to _____ coulombs.

ITEM 53

Although solid crystals of ionic salts will not conduct electricity, molten salts and water solutions of ionic salts are conductors of electricity. In both cases the liquid conducts a current because _____.

negative charge

are free to move through the liquid. They are no longer held in the crystal.

two
two Na atoms

positively
cation
negatively
anion

mole (or g-atom)

ANSWER 52

$$\frac{0.500 \text{ coulomb sec}^{-1} (3600 \text{ sec h}^{-1})}{96,500 \text{ coulombs } \mathscr{F}^{-1}} (1.00 \text{ h})$$

$$= 0.0187 \ \mathscr{F}$$

Fe: $\quad 0.0187 \ \mathscr{F} \ (0.333 \text{ mole Fe } \mathscr{F}^{-1})$
$\quad\quad = 0.00623 \text{ mole Fe}$
$\quad\quad 0.00623 \text{ mole } (55.9 \text{ g mole}^{-1} \text{ Fe})$
$\quad\quad = 0.348 \text{ g}$

Cl_2: $\quad 0.0187 \ \mathscr{F} \ (0.500 \text{ mole } Cl_2 \ \mathscr{F}^{-1})$

$\quad\quad 0.00935 \text{ mole } (71.0 \text{ g mole}^{-1}) = 0.664 \text{ g}$

95

ITEM 4

For example, if an electron is added to a fluorine atom, F, the fluoride ion has a charge of 1− and is written F⁻. If two electrons are added to an oxygen atom, O, the ion has a charge of _____ and is written _____ .

ITEM 14

The negative electrode is called the *cathode*. The ions of molten sodium chloride, Na^+Cl^-, that will be attracted to the cathode are the _____ ions.

ITEM 24

The overall reaction is the decomposition of the salt NaCl into its elements. This process is called *electrolytic decomposition* or *electrolysis*. Write equations similar to the ones in Item 23 for the electrolysis of calcium chloride, $CaCl_2$ or $Ca^{2+}(Cl^-)_2$.

ITEM 34

The reduction half-reaction for the electrolysis of AgBr is _____ , and the oxidation half-reaction is _____ .

ITEM 44

An electrical current of 1 ampere (A) is equivalent to a current of 1 coulomb sec⁻¹. The number of faradays equivalent to a current of 1.00 A for 1.00 hour (h) is _____ .

ITEM 54

What you have learned about the electrolysis of molten salts is valid for water solutions of salts, except that water itself may be oxidized or reduced. Therefore, it is more difficult to predict the reaction products. Nevertheless, there still must be a reduction reaction for every _____ reaction.

Cathode

Electrolysis

ANSWER 3   the number of electrons added

ANSWER 13   negative
positive

ANSWER 23

$$2Na^+ + 2Cl^- + 2e^- \rightarrow 2Na + Cl_2 \uparrow + 2e^-$$
(or $2Na^+ + 2Cl^- \rightarrow 2Na + Cl_2 \uparrow$)

ANSWER 33   cathode
anode

ANSWER 43   faraday
96,500

ANSWER 53   the *ions* are free to move to the electrodes

ITEM 5

Conversely, in some reactions electrons can be removed from an atom. If one electron is removed from an atom, the atom becomes an ion having a unit _____.

ITEM 15

Since positive ions are attracted to the _____ charged electrode, called the _____, positive ions are known as *cations*.

ITEM 25

When molten $CaCl_2$ is electrolyzed, the calcium metal collects at the _____ charged electrode, which is called the _____, and the chlorine is given off at the ·_____ electrode, which is called the _____.

ITEM 35

When the two reactions are added together so the $2e^-$ in each equation cancel, the equation for the total reaction is _____.

ITEM 45

The equation for the reduction of Ag^+ is _____.
The number of atoms of silver deposited by a current of 1.00 A for 1.00 h can be calculated as follows:
Number of $\mathscr{F}$ used is _____.
Number of Ag atoms deposited by 1 $\mathscr{F}$ is _____.
Number of Ag atoms deposited is _____.

ITEM 55

The electrolysis cell always consists of two electrodes immersed in the liquid. One has an excess of electrons pumped in by an electric generator and is called the _____. The other electrode is positively charged and is called the _____.

Cation

ANSWER 4 2−
O^{2-} or $O^=$

ANSWER 14 Na^+

ANSWER 24

$Ca^{2+} + 2e^- \rightarrow Ca$
$\underline{2Cl^- \qquad \rightarrow Cl_2 \uparrow + 2e^-}$
$Ca^{2+} + 2Cl^- + 2e^- \rightarrow Ca + Cl_2 \uparrow + 2e^-$
(or $Ca^{2+} + 2Cl^- \rightarrow Ca + Cl_2 \uparrow$)

ANSWER 34 $Ag^+ + e^- \rightarrow Ag$
$2Br^- \qquad \rightarrow Br_2 \uparrow + 2e^-$

ANSWER 44

$$\frac{1.00 \text{ coulomb sec}^{-1} (3600 \text{ sec h}^{-1})}{96{,}500 \text{ coulombs } \mathscr{F}^{-1}}$$

$= 0.0373 \, \mathscr{F} \, h^{-1}$

ANSWER 54 oxidation

ITEM 6   Removal of one electron from a sodium atom, Na, forms an ion with the symbol _____, and if three electrons are removed from an aluminum atom, Al, the symbol for the ion is written _____.

ITEM 16   The positive electrode is called the *anode*. The ions of molten sodium chloride that are attracted to the anode are the _____ ions.

ITEM 26   When electrons are added to an atom or ion, the process is known as *reduction*. In the reaction

$$Ca^{2+} + 2Cl^- \rightarrow Ca + Cl_2 \uparrow$$

the ion that is reduced is _____.

ITEM 36   The equation for the half reaction $Ag^+ + e^- \rightarrow Ag$ indicates that $1e^-$ is added to 1 Ag^+ ion to produce 1 Ag atom. And it also indicates that when 1 *mole* of electrons is added to 1 mole of _____, 1 _____ of _____ is produced. (See Review 1 if this concept is unfamiliar.)

ITEM 46   The equation for the reduction of Li^+ to Li metal is _____. Calculate the number of grams of Li (at. wt: 6.94) deposited by a current of 0.500 A for 1.50 h.

ITEM 56   The positive ions of a salt are attracted to the _____ charged electrode and are called _____. The negative ions of a salt are attracted to the _____ charged electrode and are called _____.

Anode

Reduction

ANSWER 5   positive charge

ANSWER 15   negatively
                 cathode

ANSWER 25   negatively
                 cathode
                 positively charged
                 anode

ANSWER 35 $2Ag^+ + 2Br^- \rightarrow 2Ag + Br_2 \uparrow$

ANSWER 45

$Ag^+ + 1e^- \rightarrow Ag$
from Item 44, 1.00 A for 1.00 h = 0.0373 $\mathscr{F}$
6.02×10^{23}
0.0373 $\mathscr{F}$ $(6.02 \times 10^{23}$ Ag atoms $\mathscr{F}^{-1})$
    $= 2.25 \times 10^{22}$ Ag atoms

ANSWER 55   cathode
                 anode

ITEM 7

Salts are compounds made up of ions. The negative ions can be any ions except hydroxide, OH^-, and the positive ions can be any except H^+. Since salts are electrically neutral, the total number of positive charges of the ions in a salt must be _____ the total number of negative charges.

ITEM 17

Negative ions are attracted to the _____ charged electrode, called the _____. Therefore, negative ions often are called *anions*.

ITEM 27

The equation for the reduction of a calcium ion is _____.

ITEM 37

The charge of 1 mole of electrons is given the name *faraday*, $\mathscr{F}$. Therefore, the number of electrons contained in the quantity of electricity known as the faraday is _____.

ITEM 47

The equation for the oxidation of chloride ion to chlorine gas is _____. The production of 1.00 mole of Cl_2 requires that 2.00 $\mathscr{F}$ of electrons be donated from Cl^- ions to the electric circuit. This is equivalent to _____ coulombs.

ITEM 57

Reduction is the process of _____, and oxidation is the process of _____.

Salt

Anion

The faraday

ANSWER 6   Na$^+$
            Al^{3+} (or Al^{+++})

ANSWER 16   Cl$^-$

ANSWER 26   Ca^{2+}

ANSWER 36   Ag$^+$ ions
             mole
             Ag atoms

ANSWER 46

Li$^+$ + e^- → Li

$$\frac{0.500 \text{ coulomb sec}^{-1} (3600 \text{ sec h}^{-1})(1.5 \text{ h})}{96,500 \text{ coulombs } \mathscr{F}^{-1}}$$

= 0.0280 $\mathscr{F}$

0.0280 $\mathscr{F}$ (1.00 mole Li $\mathscr{F}^{-1}$)(6.94 g mole^{-1} Li)
   = 0.194 g

ANSWER 56   negatively
             cations
             positively
             anions

ITEM 8

Compounds that contain the OH⁻ ion usually are called *bases*. (A more general concept of a base will be discussed in Review 4.) Although the compound sodium hydroxide is made up of Na^+ and OH^- ions, NaOH is called a _____. Sodium chloride, NaCl, is a well-known example of a _____.

ITEM 18

When these names are applied to the ions of sodium chloride, the Cl^- ion is called the _____, and the Na^+ ion is called the _____ because Cl^- is attracted to the _____ and Na^+ is attracted to the _____.

ITEM 28

The opposite process, removal of electrons from an atom or ion, is known as *oxidation*. In the reaction

$$2Na^+ + 2Cl^- \rightarrow 2Na + Cl_2 \uparrow$$

the _____ ions are oxidized to _____.

ITEM 38

Electrical charge is usually measured in *coulombs*. The charge of 1 $\mathscr{F}$ is 96,500 coulombs, so the electrical charge of 1 mole of electrons is known to be

_____.

ITEM 48

The equation for the reduction of Ca^{2+} to Ca is _____. The production of 3.00 moles of calcium metal requires _____ coulombs.

ITEM 58

The half-reaction for the oxidation of oxide ions, O^{2-}, to oxygen gas, O_2, is _____. The production of 1.00 mole of O_2 requires _____ $\mathscr{F}$ or _____ coulombs of electricity.

Oxidation

ANSWER 7   equal to

ANSWER 17   positively
anode

ANSWER 27 $Ca^{2+} + 2e^- \rightarrow Ca$

ANSWER 37 6.02×10^{23}

ANSWER 47

$2Cl^- \rightarrow Cl_2 \uparrow + 2e^-$
$2.00 \; \mathscr{F} \; (96,500 \text{ coulombs } \mathscr{F}^{-1}) = 193,000$

ANSWER 57   addition of electrons
to atoms or ions
donation of electrons
from atoms or ions

ITEM 9

No compounds contain a free hydrogen ion, H^+, but compounds that dissolve in water and donate H^+ ions to water molecules are known as *acids*. Thus, hydrogen chloride, HCl, is an acid because _____.

ITEM 19

When a sodium ion is adjacent to the cathode, an electron jumps from the rod onto the ion. The addition of an electron to Na^+ converts it to _____, which becomes attached to the rod.

ITEM 29

The equation for the oxidation of Cl^- to Cl_2 is written _____.

ITEM 39

The charge, in coulombs, of one electron can be calculated from these values to be _____.

ITEM 49

The equation for the reduction of Al^{3+} to aluminum metal is _____. $0.500 \ \mathscr{F}$ will produce _____ mole(s) of Al.

ITEM 59

The equation for the reduction half-reaction of a barium ion, Ba^{2+}, to barium metal is _____. Calculate the number of coulombs required to convert 0.357 g of $BaCl_2$ to Ba (at. wt: 137) and Cl_2.

ANSWER 8   base
            salt

ANSWER 18   anion
            cation
            anode
            cathode

ANSWER 28 Cl^-
            Cl_2 (or Cl atoms that combine
                to form Cl_2 molecules)

ANSWER 38   96,500 coulombs

ANSWER 48

$Ca^{2+} + 2e^- \rightarrow Ca$
3.00 moles of Ca require 6.00 $\mathscr{F}$ of electrons
   6.00 $\mathscr{F}$ (96,500 coulombs $\mathscr{F}^{-1}$)
   $= 579,000$ coulombs

ANSWER 58

$2O^{2-} \rightarrow O_2 \uparrow + 4e^-$
4.00
4.00 $\mathscr{F}$ (96,500 coulombs $\mathscr{F}^{-1}$)
   $= 386,000$ coulombs

ITEM 10

Acids and bases will be treated in Review 4. However, it is already necessary to know that when water solutions of acids and bases are mixed, the H^+ ions and the OH^- ions combine to form _____. The other ions in solution will form a _____ when the water is removed.

ITEM 20

When a chloride ion is adjacent to the anode, an electron from the ion is donated to the rod and conducted away. The removal of an electron from Cl^- converts it to _____.

ITEM 30

Each of these equations that include the number of electrons lost or gained by an atom is known as a *half-reaction* because each equation tells half the story. In a complete reaction there must be a reduction reaction for every _____ reaction.

ITEM 40

When 1 mole of AgBr is electrolyzed, _____ mole(s) of electrons is (are) required to reduce all Ag^+ to Ag. Given that the atomic weight of silver is 107.868, you know that the number of coulombs of electricity required to reduce 107.868 g of silver ions is _____.

ITEM 50

The electrolysis of ferric chloride, $FeCl_3$, produces iron metal and chlorine gas. The reduction reaction is $Fe^{3+} +$ _____. The oxidation reaction is _____.

ITEM 60

Calculate the number of hours needed to maintain a current of 0.500 A in order to convert 5.00 g of Al_2O_3 to pure aluminum (at. wt: 27.0).

$Al \rightarrow Al^{3+} + 3e^-$

ANSWER 9 it dissolves in water and donates H^+ ions to water molecules

ANSWER 19 an atom of Na

ANSWER 29 $2Cl^- \rightarrow Cl_2 \uparrow + 2e^-$

ANSWER 39 $\dfrac{96,500 \text{ coulombs } \mathscr{F}^{-1}}{6.02 \times 10^{23} \text{ electrons } \mathscr{F}^{-1}}$

$$= 1.60 \times 10^{-19} \text{ coulombs electron}^{-1}$$

ANSWER 49 $Al^{3+} + 3e^- \rightarrow Al$
1 $\mathscr{F}$ will produce $\frac{1}{3}$ mole Al,
so $\frac{1}{2}\mathscr{F}$ will produce $\frac{1}{6}$ mole Al

ANSWER 59

$Ba^{2+} + 2e^- \rightarrow Ba$
0.357 g/208 g mole^{-1} $BaCl_2$
  = 0.00172 mole $BaCl_2$
1 mole $BaCl_2$ gives 1 mole Ba
0.00172 mole (2 $\mathscr{F}$ mole^{-1} Ba)(96,500
  coulombs $\mathscr{F}^{-1}$) = 332 coulombs

ANSWER 10 H_2O
             salt

(Item 11 is on page 90.)

ANSWER 20   an atom of Cl

(Item 21 is on page 90.)

ANSWER 30   oxidation

(Item 31 is on page 90.)

ANSWER 40   1
             96,500

(Item 41 is on page 90.)

ANSWER 50 $3e^- \rightarrow Fe$
             $2Cl^- \rightarrow Cl_2 \uparrow + 2e^-$

(Item 51 is on page 90.)

ANSWER 60

$Al \rightarrow Al^{3+} + 3e^-$
5.00 g/102 g mole^{-1} Al_2O_3 = 0.0490 mole Al_2O_3
0.0490 mole Al_2O_3 gives 0.0980 mole Al
0.0980 mole (3 $\mathscr{F}$ mole^{-1} Al)(96,500
     coulombs $\mathscr{F}^{-1}$) = 28400 coulombs
28,400 coulombs/0.5 coulomb sec^{-1} = 56,800
     sec
56,800 sec/3600 sec h^{-1} = 15.8 h

REVIEW 4 STOICHIOMETRY

Perhaps the most practical of your chemical studies concerns stoichiometry. Whenever you synthesize a compound, measure the rate of a reaction, or carry out any one of dozens of kinds of chemical experiments, you will have to know how much of one reagent to mix with another and you will want to know how much product to expect. Stoichiometry is the application of the laws of chemical combination and is therefore an essential tool in determining the quantities of reactants used and products formed.

The first element of stoichiometry is the balanced chemical equation. Section 4–1 will show you how to interpret a chemical equation in terms of moles of reagents. Since most reactions are carried out in solution, Sections 4–2, 4–3, and 4–4 will describe solutions of ions and show you how to do calculations involving various kinds of concentrations of dissolved compounds. Sections 4–3 and 4–4 are specific for acids and bases: Section 4–3 will introduce the Brønsted theory of acid–base reactions and Section 4–4 will review the concentration terms used in stoichiometric calculations. You may be surprised to learn that heat is also a reagent in chemical reactions. Section 4–5 will demonstrate why and how this is so.

4–1 CHEMICAL EQUATIONS

Stoichiometry is based on chemical equations that are balanced with respect to mass, atoms, and charge. (Balancing of simple equations is discussed in Section 4–3 of *Chemical Principles*.) Once you have the equation for a reaction and understand what that equation means, the calculation of relative amounts of reactants and products is only a matter of using what you already know about gram-atoms, moles, and ideal gas laws. In this section, which reviews Sections 4–1 and 4–2 of *Chemical Principles*, you will see how these fit together in stoichiometric calculations.

If you can calculate easily and logically the answers to Items 25–29 you are already prepared for Section 4–2.

ITEM 1

If a sample contains 100 hydrogen molecules, the reaction of these according to the equation $2H_2 + O_2 \rightarrow 2H_2O$ requires _____ molecule(s) of oxygen and will form _____ molecule(s) of water.

ITEM 6

The coefficients in front of the formulas in a balanced chemical equation give the relative number of _____ or of _____ of each compound involved in the reaction.

ITEM 11

To produce 7 moles of CO_2 in the reaction $CH_4 + 2O_2 \rightarrow CO_2 + 2H_2O$, we would start with _____ moles of methane and _____ moles of O_2.

ITEM 16

To form 0.164 mole of ammonia by the reaction $N_2 + 3H_2 \rightarrow 2NH_3$ requires _____ of nitrogen and _____ of hydrogen.

ITEM 21

In the following items look up atomic weights in the periodic table in the inside front cover.

What weight of Na_2CO_3 would be needed to react with 0.124 mole of HCl according to the equation $Na_2CO_3 + 2HCl \rightarrow 2NaCl + H_2O + CO_2$.

Moles of Na_2CO_3 needed = _____.

Weight, in grams, of Na_2CO_3 needed = _____.

ITEM 26

Calculate the number of moles of HCl produced by the reaction of 1.5×10^{23} molecules of H_2 with 5.00 liters at STP of Cl_2.

Moles of H_2 present   = _____.

Moles of Cl_2 present   = _____.

Moles of HCl produced = _____.

$H_2 + Cl_2 \rightarrow 2HCl$

ITEM 2

Although the equation for a chemical reaction shows how many individual molecules react to form product molecules, it is more convenient in doing chemical calculations to let each chemical symbol in the equation represent 1 _____ of the element and each formula represent 1 _____ of the compound.

ITEM 7

The combustion of methane, CH_4, leads to the formation of water and carbon dioxide. The balanced equation for this reaction is $CH_4 +$ _____ $O_2 \rightarrow$ _____ $CO_2 +$ _____.

ITEM 12

An air sample containing 0.240 mole of oxygen is capable of oxidizing _____ mole(s) of methane to CO_2 and H_2O.

ITEM 17

To use a balanced equation for deducing how much product can be formed in a given reaction, we must first know the number of _____ of the reactants. Then the equation will show how many _____ of the products are formed.

ITEM 22

Using the same type of steps as in the previous items, calculate the weights of Zn and HCl needed to produce 0.763 mole of hydrogen, according to the reaction $Zn + 2HCl \rightarrow ZnCl_2 + H_2$.

ITEM 27

How many grams of $AgNO_3$ are required to react completely with 0.624 mole of $BaCl_2$ by the reaction $2AgNO_3 + BaCl_2 \rightarrow 2AgCl + Ba(NO_3)_2$?

$$CH_4 + 2O_2 \rightarrow CO_2 + 2H_2O$$

ANSWER 1   50
100

ANSWER 6   molecules
moles
(On the molecular level, the qualifications discussed in Section 4–2 of *Chemical Principles* must be observed.)

ANSWER 11   7
14

ANSWER 16 $\frac{1}{2}(0.164 \text{ mole}) = 0.082 \text{ mole}$
$\frac{3}{2}(0.164 \text{ mole}) = 0.246 \text{ mole}$

ANSWER 21 $\frac{1}{2}(0.124 \text{ mole}) = 0.0620 \text{ mole}$
$0.0620 \text{ mole } (106 \text{ g mole}^{-1})$
$= 6.57 \text{ g}$

ANSWER 26 $\dfrac{1.5 \times 10^{23} \text{ molecules}}{6.0 \times 10^{23} \text{ molecules mole}^{-1}}$
$= 0.25 \text{ mole}$

$\dfrac{5.00 \text{ liters}}{22.4 \text{ liters mole}^{-1}}$
$= 0.223 \text{ mole}$

$2(0.223 \text{ mole}) = 0.446 \text{ mole}$

ITEM 3

Thus, the equation $2H_2 + O_2 \rightarrow 2H_2O$ states that 2 moles of hydrogen react with _____ and form _____.

ITEM 8

This equation (Answer 7) shows that the oxidation of one molecule of methane requires _____ of oxygen and that this reaction produces _____ and _____.

ITEM 13

To form 0.7 mole of H_2S by the laboratory preparation method represented by the equation $FeS + H_2SO_4 \rightarrow FeSO_4 + H_2S$, we would start with _____ mole(s) of FeS and _____ mole(s) of H_2SO_4.

ITEM 18

In the reaction represented by the equation $3Fe + 4H_2O \rightarrow Fe_3O_4 + 4H_2$, how many moles, and what weight, of hydrogen will be produced by the reaction of 4.76 moles of iron? Moles of H_2 formed = _____. Weight, in grams, of H_2 formed (at. wt H: 1.01) = _____.

ITEM 23

If 1.00 g, or _____ mole(s), of Zn is to react according to the equation $Zn + 2HCl \rightarrow ZnCl_2 + H_2$, at least _____ mole(s) or _____ g of HCl must be present.

ITEM 28

Oxygen reacts with ammonia according to the equation $4NH_3 + 7O_2 \rightarrow 4NO_2 + 6H_2O$. If 0.10 ml (i.e., 1.0×10^{-4} liter) of O_2 at STP is allowed to react in 1.04 g of NH_3 how many *molecules* of NO_2 are produced?

ANSWER 2   g-atom
mole

ANSWER 7   2
1
$2H_2O$
$(CH_4 + 2O_2 \rightarrow CO_2 + 2H_2O)$

ANSWER 12   0.120

ANSWER 17   moles
moles

ANSWER 22   Moles of Zn needed $= 0.763$
Weight of Zn needed $=$
0.763 mole $(65.4 \text{ g mole}^{-1}) =$
49.9 g
Moles of HCl needed $=$
$2 \times 0.763 = 1.526$
Weight of HCl needed $=$
1.526 moles (36.5 g
$\text{mole}^{-1}) = 55.7$ g

ANSWER 27   1.248 moles of $AgNO_3$ required
1.248 moles (170 g mole^{-1})
$= 212$ g

ITEM 4

The balanced equation for the reaction of hydrogen with acetylene to give ethane is $2H_2 + C_2H_2 \rightarrow C_2H_6$. In terms of molecules, this equation indicates that _____.

ITEM 9

To deal with samples more nearly the size used in the laboratory, we would say that for every mole of methane oxidized _____ mole(s) of oxygen are required and there are produced _____ and _____.

ITEM 14

The coefficients of the formulas of the compounds in a balanced equation indicate _____.

ITEM 19

The weight and volume at STP of chlorine needed for complete reaction with 10 g of H_2, according to the equation $H_2 + Cl_2 \rightarrow 2HCl$, can be calculated as follows:

Moles of $H_2 = \dfrac{10 \text{ g}}{2.0 \text{ g mole}^{-1}} = $ _____.

Moles of Cl_2 needed = _____.
Weight of Cl_2 needed (at. wt Cl: 35.5) = _____.
Volume, in liters at STP, of Cl_2 needed = _____.

ITEM 24

Suppose that 2 moles of Zn are added to a solution containing 6 moles of HCl. Then _____ mole(s) of $ZnCl_2$ are produced and _____ mole(s) of _____ remain unreacted.

ITEM 29

How many grams of water and carbon dioxide are produced by the combustion of 1.00 liter at STP of methane, CH_4, in excess oxygen?

$Zn + 2HCl \rightarrow ZnCl_2 + H_2$

ANSWER 3   1 mole of oxygen
2 moles of water

ANSWER 8   two molecules
one molecule of CO_2
two molecules of H_2O

ANSWER 13   0.7
0.7

ANSWER 18 $\frac{4}{3}$(4.76 moles) $= 6.35$ moles
6.35 moles (2.02 g mole^{-1})
$= 12.8$ g

ANSWER 23   1.00 g/(65.4 g mole^{-1})
$= 0.0153$ mole
2(0.0153 mole)
$= 0.0306$ mole
0.0306 mole (36.5 g mole^{-1})
$= 1.12$ g

ANSWER 28

$$\text{moles NH}_3 = \frac{1.04 \text{ g}}{17.0 \text{ g mole}^{-1}} = 0.0612$$

$$\text{moles O}_2 = \frac{1.0 \times 10^{-4} \text{ liter}}{22.4 \text{ liters mole}^{-1}} = 4.5 \times 10^{-6}$$

Moles NH_3 needed to react with $O_2 = \frac{4}{7}(4.5 \times 10^{-6}$ mole$) = 2.6 \times 10^{-6}$. Thus, NH_3 is in excess. All O_2 will be used, and molecules of NO_2 produced $= \frac{4}{7}$ (4.5 $\times$ 10^{-6} mole)(6.02 $\times$ 10^{23} molecules mole^{-1}) $= 1.5 \times 10^{18}$ molecules.

ITEM 5

In terms of moles, the equation $2H_2 + C_2H_2 \rightarrow C_2H_6$ suggests that _____.

ITEM 10

If a sample containing 10 moles of methane were burned, _____ moles of oxygen would be required; _____ of CO_2 and _____ of H_2O would be produced.

ITEM 15

The formation of x moles of ammonia according to the reaction $N_2 + 3H_2 \rightarrow 2NH_3$ requires the use of _____ moles of nitrogen and _____ moles of hydrogen.

ITEM 20

The weight and volume at STP of N_2 needed to produce 150 g of NH_3 according to the equation $N_2 + 3H_2 \rightarrow 2NH_3$ is calculated as follows:

Moles of NH_3 to be produced $= 150$ g$/17.0$ g mole^{-1}
$= 8.82$ moles.

Moles of N_2 needed $=$ _____.
Weight, in grams, of N_2 needed (at. wt N:14.0) $=$ _____.

Volume, in liters, of N_2 needed $-$ _____.

ITEM 25

A 0.10-mole sample of Zn is allowed to react with 9.1 g of HCl. The reagent that is present in excess is _____. The reaction will produce _____ mole(s) of $ZnCl_2$ and _____ mole(s) of H_2. Left unreacted is _____ g of _____.

$CH_4 + 2O_2 \rightarrow CO_2 + 2H_2O$

$Zn + 2HCl \rightarrow ZnCl_2 + H_2$

ANSWER 4 two molecules of hydrogen combine with one molecule of acetylene, C_2H_2, to produce one molecule of ethane, C_2H_6

ANSWER 9 2
1 mole of CO_2
2 moles of H_2O

ANSWER 14 the relative numbers of moles (or molecules) of the reactants used and products formed

ANSWER 19 5.0
5.0
5.0 moles (71 g mole^{-1})
  $= 360$ g
5.0 moles (22.4 liters mole^{-1})
  $= 110$ liters

ANSWER 24 2
2
HCl

ANSWER 29

$CH_4 + 2O_2 \rightarrow CO_2 + 2H_2O$
moles methane
  $= 1.00$ liter/22.4 liters mole$^{-1} = 0.0446$
moles H_2O produced
  $= 2 \times 0.0446 = 0.0892$
weight H_2O produced
  $= 0.0892$ mole $\times 18.0$ g mole$^{-1} = 1.61$ g
moles CO_2 produced $= 0.0446$
weight CO_2 produced
  $= 0.0446$ mole $\times 44.0$ g mole$^{-1} = 1.96$ g

(*Turn to page 127.*)

ANSWER 5   2 moles of hydrogen combine with 1 mole of acetylene to produce 1 mole of ethane

(*Item 6 is on page 114.*)

ANSWER 10   20
10 moles
20 moles

(*Item 11 is on page 114.*)

ANSWER 15 $x/2$
$3x/2$

(*Item 16 is on page 114.*)

ANSWER 20 $\frac{1}{2} \times 8.82 = 4.41$
4.41 moles (28.0 g mole^{-1})
$= 123$ g
4.41 moles (22.4 liters mole^{-1})
$= 98.8$ liters

(*Item 21 is on page 114.*)

ANSWER 25   HCl (9.1 g/36.5 g mole^{-1} = 0.25 mole is present; only 0.20 mole is needed)
0.10
0.10
36.5 g mole^{-1} (0.25 − 0.20)
mole = 1.8 g
HCl

(*Item 26 is on page 114.*)

4–2 IONS IN SOLUTION

Because it is often convenient to carry out chemical reactions in liquid solution, you must be able to calculate weight relations between reactants and products, one or more of which may be in solution. Quantities of solutions are more easily measured by volume than by weight. Therefore, it is necessary to relate the volume and concentration of a solution to the number of moles of dissolved compound. This section will supplement Section 4–4 of *Chemical Principles* in describing solutions of ions and showing how to do the necessary concentration and stoichiometry calculations.

Items 54–60 represent the different types of problems encountered in solution stoichiometry. If you can work these correctly, you are probably ready for Section 4–3.

ITEM 1

Combining two or more substances produces a mixture that can be *homogeneous* or *heterogeneous*. A solution is a mixture that has the same composition throughout and therefore can be described as _____.

ITEM 11

The amount of solute in a unit volume of solution is called the *concentration*. The concentration of HCl in a solution containing 6.5 g HCl per liter of solution is _____ g liter^{-1} or _____ g ml^{-1}.

ITEM 21

The number of moles (n) of solute in any given amount of a solution is obtained by multiplying V, the volume in liters, by the number of moles per liter (i.e., the molarity, M). Expressed in symbols, $n =$ _____.

ITEM 31

When NaCl is dissolved in water, each crystal, made of Na$^+$ and Cl$^-$ ions, is broken, or dissociated, so the ions go into solution and are surrounded by _____ molecules.

ITEM 41

Solution stoichiometry involves the weight relations between reactants and products for reactions that occur in solution. For a stoichiometric calculation it is necessary to have a balanced _____.

ITEM 51

In 100 ml of 0.05-molar CuSO$_4$ there is _____ mole of Cu^{2+}.

Solution

Concentration

Na$^+$ ⟵ Cl$^-$

ITEM 2

If a liter of water to which a few crystals of salt are added is stirred well, the salt may dissolve completely and form a mixture that is homogeneous. This mixture can be called a _____.

ITEM 12

For many problems, the most useful concentration is the number of moles of solute per liter of solution. A solution containing 1.00 mole of solute in 500 ml of solution has a concentration of _____ mole(s) per liter.

ITEM 22

A sample of a 0.10-molar solution having a volume of 0.50 liter contains _____ mole(s) of solute.

ITEM 32

We can represent this process as

$$NaCl(crystal) \xrightarrow{H_2O} Na^+(aq) + Cl^-(aq),$$

where (aq) is the abbreviation for "aqueous." $Na^+(aq)$ then represents a *hydrated* sodium ion, an ion that is surrounded by _____ molecules.

ITEM 42

A chemical equation is an attempt to show the amounts of reagents involved in a reaction. If a reaction occurs in an aqueous solution, it is likely that the actual reactants are not molecules but _____ that can be formed by the solution process.

ITEM 52

If excess Zn is added to 100 ml of 0.05-molar $CuSO_4$, how many gram-atoms of Cu will be formed?

NaCl solution

Hydrated

ANSWER 1   homogeneous

ANSWER 11   6.5

$$\frac{6.5 \text{ g liter}^{-1}}{1000 \text{ ml liter}^{-1}}$$

$$= 0.0065$$

ANSWER 21 MV (or VM)

ANSWER 31   water (or solvent)

ANSWER 41   equation

ANSWER 51

$$\frac{100 \text{ ml}}{1000 \text{ ml liter}^{-1}} \times 0.05 \text{ mole liter}^{-1} = 0.005$$

ITEM 3

However, if a kilogram of salt is added to a liter of water, only a part of the salt will dissolve. A visible, physical dividing surface exists between the solid salt and the liquid; the entire mixture is _____.

ITEM 13

A solution containing 6.50 g of $CaCl_2$ (mol wt: 111) in 500 ml of solution has a concentration of _____ mole(s) per liter.

ITEM 23

To prepare 500 ml of a 0.30-molar solution, enough solvent to make 500 ml is added to _____ mole(s) of solute.

ITEM 33

Many other substances form ionic solutions in water. Some, like NaCl(crystal), are already composed of _____ before they are dissolved; others, like HCl(gas), are composed of neutral molecules before they are added to water.

ITEM 43

For instance, if $AgNO_3$ and KCl are dissolved in water, the first processes that occur in the solution are

$$AgNO_3(crystal) \xrightarrow{H_2O} \text{_____}.$$

$$KCl(crystal) \xrightarrow{H_2O} \text{_____}.$$

ITEM 53

If 0.13 g Zn (i.e., _____ g-atom) is added to 100 ml of 0.050-molar $CuSO_4$, how many gram-atoms (and how many grams) of Cu will precipitate?

ANSWER 2   solution

ANSWER 12   1.00 mole/0.500 liter
$$= 2.00 \text{ moles liter}^{-1}$$

ANSWER 22

$n = MV$

0.10 mole liter^{-1} × 0.50 liter = 0.050 mole

ANSWER 32   water

ANSWER 42   (hydrated) ions

ANSWER 52

$$\frac{100 \text{ ml}}{1000 \text{ ml liter}^{-1}} \times 0.05 \text{ mole liter}^{-1}$$

$$= 0.005 \text{ mole} = 0.005 \text{ g-atom}$$

ITEM 4

The entire mixture of Item 3 is composed of solid salt and a liquid containing salt dissolved in water. The liquid part, however, is _____ and is correctly called a _____.

ITEM 14

The concentration in moles of solute per liter of solution is called the *molarity* (M) of the solution. What is the molarity of a solution containing 0.45 mole of solute in 3.0 liters of solution?

ITEM 24

If you want to add 0.30 mole of NaCl to a reaction mixture by adding 0.50-molar NaCl solution, what volume of solution must be added? _____. (It is convenient to recall that $n = MV$, which you can remember by the units involved, and to rearrange this general expression to find the quantity you want.)

ITEM 34

For ionic solids, such as NaCl, we use the term *gram formula weight* to represent the mass of 6.02×10^{23} Cl^- ions and _____ Na^+ ions. Thus, gram formula weight is sometimes used instead of _____ when simple molecules do not exist in the crystal.

ITEM 44

However, the reaction of interest between $AgNO_3$ and KCl is the formation of AgCl, a compound which does not dissolve appreciably in water. The equation for this reaction is written as

$$Ag^+(aq) + Cl^-(aq) \rightarrow AgCl(s)$$

where $AgCl(s)$ (for *solid*) is written to indicate that, for the purpose of stoichiometric calculations, the compound AgCl is *not* _____.

ITEM 54

When Cl_2 is added to a solution of $Fe(NO_3)_2$, the reaction that occurs is represented by the equation $2Fe^{2+} + Cl_2 \rightarrow 2Fe^{3+} + 2Cl^-$. What is the minimum weight of Cl_2 that must be added to 200 ml of 0.750-molar $Fe(NO_3)_2$ solution to oxidize completely the Fe^{2+} to Fe^{3+}?

Molarity

ANSWER 3   heterogeneous

ANSWER 13 $\dfrac{6.50 \text{ g}}{111 \text{ g mole}^{-1}} = 0.0586 \text{ mole}$

$\dfrac{0.0586 \text{ mole}}{500 \text{ ml}} \left(\dfrac{1000 \text{ ml}}{\text{liter}} \right)$

$= 0.117 \text{ mole liter}^{-1}$

ANSWER 23

$0.30 \text{ mole liter}^{-1} \times 0.50 \text{ liter} = 0.15 \text{ mole}$
(i.e., $n = MV = 0.30 \times 0.50 = 0.15$ mole)

ANSWER 33   ions

ANSWER 43 $Ag^+(aq) + NO_3^-(aq)$
$K^+(aq) \; + Cl^-(aq)$

ANSWER 53

$\dfrac{0.13 \text{ g}}{65.4 \text{ g g-atom}^{-1}} = 0.0020 \text{ g-atom Zn.}$

$(0.100 \text{ liter})(0.050 \text{ mole liter}^{-1})$
$= 0.005 \text{ mole } Cu^{2+}.$
0.0020 g-atom Cu will precipitate since Cu^{2+}
is present in excess.
0.0020 g-atom (63.5 g g-atom^{-1}) $= 0.13$ g Cu.

135

In general, that component of a solution present in the largest amount is known as the *solvent.* The solvent can be a gas, a liquid, or a solid, but this section will treat only solutions in which the solvent is a liquid and will emphasize *aqueous* solutions, in which the solvent is _____.

A 0.26-molar H_2SO_4 solution, often written as $0.26M$ H_2SO_4, contains _____ mole(s) of H_2SO_4 per liter of solution.

If a solution is diluted (i.e., if pure solvent is added to it), the volume of solution changes, but the amount of solute _____.

However, we have already stated that the term _____ represents 6.02×10^{23} *anything.* Thus, for simplicity we generally talk of a mole of NaCl and thereby mean _____.

The complete ionic equation for the reaction of $AgNO_3$ and KCl in solution might be written as

$$Ag^+(aq) + NO_3^-(aq) + K^+(aq) + Cl^-(aq) \rightarrow \text{_____}.$$

What is the molarity of Al^{3+} in a solution made by dissolving 12.7 g of $Al_2(SO_4)_3$ in sufficient water to make 100 ml of solution?

Solvent

3

ANSWER 4 homogeneous
solution

ANSWER 14 $\dfrac{0.45 \text{ mole}}{3.0 \text{ liters}} = 0.15 \text{ mole liter}^{-1}$

ANSWER 24

$$V = \frac{n}{M} = \frac{0.30 \text{ mole}}{0.50 \text{ mole liter}^{-1}} = 0.60 \text{ liter}$$

ANSWER 34 6.02×10^{23}
gram molecular weight

ANSWER 44 soluble in water
(or dissociated)

ANSWER 54

Moles Fe^{2+} present
 $= 0.200 \text{ liter} \times 0.750 \text{ mole liter}^{-1}$
 $= 0.150 \text{ mole.}$
Moles Cl_2 needed $= \frac{1}{2} \times 0.150 \text{ mole}$
 $= 0.0750 \text{ mole.}$
Weight $Cl_2 = 0.0750 \text{ mole} \times 70.9 \text{ g mole}^{-1}$
 $= 5.32 \text{ g.}$

ITEM 6

A component of a solution present in lesser amount than the major component is called a *solute*. It can be added to the solvent as a gas, a _____, or a _____.

ITEM 16

A solution is made by dissolving 5.0 g of KOH (mol wt: 56) in enough water to make 0.50 liter of solution. What is the molarity of this solution?

ITEM 26

In 0.750 liter of a 0.500-molar solution, there is (are) _____ mole(s) of solute. If sufficient solvent is added to make the volume 1.00 liter, there will be _____ mole(s) of solute. In the new solution the concentration is _____ mole(s) per liter.

ITEM 36

The ionic solid K_2SO_4 dissolves in water by dissociating into ions as

$$K_2SO_4(crystal) \xrightarrow{H_2O} 2K^+(aq) + SO_4{}^{2-}(aq)$$

Assuming that K_2SO_4 dissociates completely in water, each gram formula weight or mole of K_2SO_4 produces _____ *gram ions* or, as we say, mole(s) of K^+ and _____ gram ions, or mole(s), of SO_4^{2-}.

ITEM 46

However, the NO_3^- and K^+ ions are unchanged during the reaction, and it is customary to omit the unchanged ions. The designations (*s*) and (*aq*) are also sometimes omitted, although you should understand that ions in water solution are always hydrated. Thus, the simplest equation for the reaction that occurs in a solution of $AgNO_3$ and KCl is _____.

ITEM 56

When 25.0 ml of a 0.215-molar solution of K_2SO_4 are diluted to 125 ml, what is the molarity of the resulting solution?

Solute

ANSWER 5   water

ANSWER 15   0.26

ANSWER 25   does not change

ANSWER 35   mole
              6.02×10^{23} Na$^+$ ions
                   and 6.02×10^{23} Cl$^-$ ions

ANSWER 45   AgCl(s) + NO$_3^-$(aq) + K$^+$(aq)

ANSWER 55

Molecular weight of Al$_2$(SO$_4$)$_3$ is 342.
Thus, 12.7 g = 12.7/342 = 0.0371 mole.

Molarity of Al^{3+} = 2 $\times$ $\dfrac{0.0371 \text{ mole}}{0.100 \text{ liter}}$ = 0.742.

ITEM 7

Thus, a solution is a homogeneous mixture of a solvent and one or more _____.

ITEM 17

A solution is made by dissolving 6.4 g of bromine in enough carbon tetrachloride to make 75 ml of solution. What is the molarity of Br_2 in this solution? (Use the periodic table for atomic weights.)

ITEM 27

In a volume V_1 liters of a solution whose molarity is M_1, there are _____ moles of solute. After dilution to a volume V_2 the molarity is M_2. Since the number of moles of solute has not changed, $V_1M_1 =$ _____. This is a convenient expression for doing dilution problems.

ITEM 37

Concentrations of ions in solution are often expressed in terms of molarity. Thus, a 0.62-molar solution of K_2SO_4 contains (assuming complete dissociation) _____ mole(s) of K^+ and _____ mole(s) of SO_4^{2-} per liter.

ITEM 47

In 250 ml of 0.10-molar $AgNO_3$ there is (are) _____ mole(s) of Ag^+. In 400 ml of 0.10-molar NaCl there is (are) _____ mole(s) of Cl^-.

ITEM 57

What is the molarity of NO_3^- in a solution containing 0.600 mole of $Al(NO_3)_3$ in 500 ml of solution?

ANSWER 6   liquid
solid

ANSWER 16 $\dfrac{(5.0/56) \text{ mole}}{0.50 \text{ liter}}$

$= 0.18 \text{ mole liter}^{-1}$

ANSWER 26

$0.500 \text{ mole liter}^{-1} (0.750 \text{ liter}) = 0.375 \text{ mole}$
0.375
0.375

ANSWER 36   2
1

ANSWER 46 $Ag^+ + Cl^- \rightarrow AgCl$

ANSWER 56

$M = \dfrac{0.215M \times 0.0250 \text{ liter}}{0.125 \text{ liter}} = 0.0430 \text{ molar.}$

In an aqueous salt solution, water is the _____ and a salt is the _____.

A solution of HNO_3 and water contains 70.0% HNO_3 by weight (i.e., 70.0% of the weight of the solution is HNO_3 and 30.0% is water). 1.00 ml of this solution weighs 1.42 g. In 1 liter of this solution, which weighs _____ g, the weight of HNO_3 is _____ g. The molarity of HNO_3 in this solution is therefore _____.

In 50 ml of a 0.50-molar solution there is (are) _____ mole(s) of solute. After dilution to 75 ml there is (are) still _____ mole(s) of solute, but now the concentration of the solution is calculated to be _____ molar.

For many purposes it is unimportant to know whether in an ionic solution there is *complete* dissociation of molecules into ions. Therefore, assume in the following items complete dissociation, except where otherwise indicated.

300 ml of a 0.500-molar solution of $Fe_2(SO_4)_3$ contains _____ mole(s) of Fe^{3+} and _____ mole(s) of SO_4^{2-}.

If 250 ml of 0.10-molar $AgNO_3$ and 400 ml of 0.10-molar NaCl are mixed, _____ mole(s) of AgCl will form.

450 ml of 0.10-molar HNO_3 are needed for a reaction. The 450 ml must be made with 70% HNO_3 solution having a density of 1.4 g ml^{-1}. What volume of 70% HNO_3 must be used?

$M_1V_1 = M_2V_2$

ANSWER 7   solutes

ANSWER 17 $\dfrac{(6.4/160) \text{ mole}}{75 \text{ ml}} \left(\dfrac{1000 \text{ ml}}{\text{liter}}\right)$

$= 0.53 \text{ mole liter}^{-1}$

ANSWER 27 $V_1 M_1$
$V_2 M_2$

ANSWER 37 $2 \times 0.62 = 1.24$
0.62

ANSWER 47

$\text{Ag}^+ \ n = \dfrac{250 \text{ ml}}{1000 \text{ ml liter}^{-1}} \times 0.10 \text{ mole liter}^{-1}$

$= 0.025 \text{ mole}$

$\text{Cl}^- \ n = \dfrac{400 \text{ ml}}{1000 \text{ ml liter}^{-1}} \times 0.10 \text{ mole liter}^{-1}$

$= 0.040 \text{ mole}$

ANSWER 57 $\dfrac{3(0.600 \text{ mole})}{0.500 \text{ liter}} = 3.60 \text{ molar.}$

ITEM 9

Volumes of solutions used in chemical studies are usually measured in liters, milliliters (ml), or cubic centimeters (cm³). One ml is equal to one thousandth of a _____, and 1 ml is almost equal to 1 cm³.

ITEM 19

100 ml of an aqueous solution of acetic acid, CH_3COOH, weigh 100 g and contain 1.5% by weight of the acid. What is the molarity of the acetic acid?

ITEM 29

A 1.5-molar solution can be obtained by diluting 500 ml of a 2.0-molar solution to a total volume of _____ liter(s).

ITEM 39

A solution made by dissolving 0.15 mole of NaCl and 0.60 mole of KCl in enough water to make 1.00 liter has a Cl^- concentration of _____ mole(s) per liter.

ITEM 49

If Zn metal is added to an aqueous solution of $Cu(NO_3)_2$, copper metal appears. That is, copper *precipitates* from solution. The net equation for the reaction is written $Zn + Cu^{2+} \rightarrow Zn^{2+} + Cu$, thus indicating that for each atom of Zn that goes into solution _____ atom(s) of Cu precipitate(s).

ITEM 59

What volume of a 0.318-molar Na_2S solution is required to precipitate the Sb^{3+} in 25.0 ml of a 0.124-molar solution of $SbCl_3$? The equation for the reaction is $2Sb^{3+} + 3S^{2-} \rightarrow Sb_2S_3$.

ANSWER 8   solvent
                        solute

ANSWER 18

$$1.42 \text{ g ml}^{-1} \left(\frac{1000 \text{ ml}}{\text{liter}} \right)$$
$$= 1420 \text{ g liter}^{-1}$$
$$0.700 \times 1420 \text{ g} = 994 \text{ g}$$
$$\text{Molarity} = \frac{994 \text{ g liter}^{-1}}{63.0 \text{ g mole}^{-1}}$$
$$= 15.8 \text{ moles liter}^{-1}$$

ANSWER 28

$(0.50 \text{ mole liter}^{-1})\, 0.050 \text{ liter} = 0.025 \text{ mole}$
0.025

$$M_2 = \frac{M_1 V_1}{V_2} = \frac{(0.50 \text{ mole liter}^{-1})(0.050 \text{ liter})}{0.075 \text{ liter}}$$

$= 0.33 \text{ mole liter}^{-1}$

(or $M = 0.025 \text{ mole}/0.075 \text{ liter} = 0.33$)

ANSWER 38

$$\left(\frac{300}{1000} \right) \text{liter } (0.500 \text{ mole liter}^{-1})(2) = 0.300 \text{ mole}$$

$$\left(\frac{300}{1000} \right) \text{liter } (0.500 \text{ mole liter}^{-1})(3) = 0.450 \text{ mole}$$

ANSWER 48   0.025 (since initial moles of $Ag^+ = 0.025$ and moles of $Cl^- = 0.040$)

ANSWER 58

Weight HNO_3 per liter of 70% solution
    $= 0.70 \times 1.4 \text{ g ml}^{-1} \times 1000 \text{ ml liter}^{-1}$
    $= 980 \text{ g liter}^{-1}$.

$$\text{Molarity of 70\% } HNO_3 = \frac{980 \text{ g liter}^{-1}}{63.0 \text{ g mole}^{-1}}$$

$$= 15.6 \text{ moles liter}^{-1}.$$

Volume of 70% HNO_3 needed

$$= \frac{0.45 \text{ liter} \times 0.10M}{15.6M}$$

$= 0.0029 \text{ liter} = 2.9 \text{ ml}.$

ITEM 10

A solution is made by dissolving 1.00 g of NaCl in sufficient water to make 10.0 ml of solution. Each ml of this solution contains _____ g of NaCl.

ITEM 20

The molarity of a solution is the number of _____ of solute per liter of _____.

ITEM 30

A solution of H_2SO_4 and H_2O that is 86% H_2SO_4 by weight has a density of 1.78 g ml^{-1} (i.e., 1.00 ml weighs 1.78 g). What volume of this 86% H_2SO_4 solution must be used to make 500 ml of 6.0-molar H_2SO_4?
Weight of H_2SO_4 per liter of solution = _____.
Molarity of 86% H_2SO_4 solution = _____.
Volume of 86% H_2SO_4 solution needed = _____.

ITEM 40

To what final volume should you dilute 250 ml of 0.15-molar $CaCl_2$ if the final concentration of Cl^- must be 0.10 molar?

ITEM 50

Each mole of Zn that goes into solution produces _____ mole(s) of Cu.

ITEM 60

How many moles of Ag_3PO_4 will be formed when 36.9 ml of 0.256-molar $AgNO_3$ solution are added to 27.4 ml of 0.188-molar Na_3PO_4 solution? The reaction is $3Ag^+ + PO_4^{3-} \rightarrow Ag_3PO_4$.

ANSWER 9 liter

ANSWER 19

wt liter^{-1} = 0.015(1000 g liter^{-1}) = 15 g liter^{-1}

Molarity = $\dfrac{15 \text{ g liter}^{-1}}{60 \text{ g mole}^{-1}}$ = 0.25 mole liter^{-1}

ANSWER 29

$V_2 = \dfrac{M_1 V_1}{M_2} = \dfrac{2.0M \times 0.500 \text{ liter}}{1.5M}$ = 0.67 liter

ANSWER 39

0.15 mole liter^{-1} + 0.60 mole liter^{-1} = 0.75

ANSWER 49 one

ANSWER 59

Moles of Sb^{3+} = 0.0250 liter × 0.124 mole liter^{-1}
= 0.00310 mole.
And moles S^{2-} required = 0.00310($\tfrac{3}{2}$)
= 0.00465.
Thus, the volume of solution required is

$\dfrac{0.00465 \text{ mole}}{0.318 \text{ mole liter}^{-1}}$ = 0.0146 liter = 14.6 ml.

ANSWER 10   0.100

(Item 11 is on page 128.)

ANSWER 20   moles
                 solution

(Item 21 is on page 128.)

ANSWER 30

wt H_2SO_4 per liter

$$= 0.86\ (1.78\ \text{g ml}^{-1})\left(\frac{1000\ \text{ml}}{\text{liter}}\right)$$

$$= 1530\ \text{g liter}^{-1}$$

$$M = \frac{1530\ \text{g liter}^{-1}}{98\ \text{g mole}^{-1}} = 15.6\ \text{moles liter}^{-1}$$

$$V = \frac{0.50\ \text{liter} \times 6.0M}{15.6M} = 0.19\ \text{liter}$$

(Item 31 is on page 128.)

ANSWER 40

$$V_2 = \frac{M_1 V_1}{M_2} = \frac{(0.30M\ \text{Cl}^-)\ 250\ \text{ml}}{0.10M\ \text{Cl}^-} = 750\ \text{ml}$$

(Item 41 is on page 128.)

ANSWER 50   1

(Item 51 is on page 128.)

ANSWER 60

Moles Ag^+ present
 $= 0.256$ mole liter^{-1} (0.0369 liter)
 $= 0.00945$ mole.
Moles PO_4^{3-} present
 $= 0.188$ mole liter^{-1} (0.0274 liter)
 $= 0.00515$ mole.
Thus, PO_4^{3-} is present in excess of the stoichiometric amount, and (0.00945 mole)/3 = 0.00315 mole Ag_3PO_4 will be formed.

Although the stoichiometry of acid and base reactions is fundamentally the same as the stoichiometry of ionic salt reactions examined in this section, we will interrupt briefly our discussion to study acid and base reactions. Then we will return to stoichiometry as it is specifically applied to acids and bases.

4-3 ACID–BASE REACTIONS

The behavior of many chemical compounds can best be correlated by classifying them as acids or bases. Since your study of acids and bases in *Chemical Principles* was in terms of aqueous solutions, aqueous systems will be emphasized in this introduction to acid–base reactions. The definition of acids as hydrogen ion donors and of bases as hydrogen ion acceptors is the definition suggested by Johannes Brønsted.

ITEM 1   Positively charged hydrogen ions, H⁺, can be produced in the gas phase by removing an _____
from a hydrogen atom.

ITEM 9   The H_3O^+ ion is called the *hydronium* (or *hydroxonium*)
ion. It is formed by the transfer of a proton (H^+) from
an acid molecule to a _____ molecule.

ITEM 17   Therefore, the proton-transfer reaction that occurs
when solutions of NaOH and HCl are mixed is
$H_3O^+ + OH^- \rightarrow$ _____, and we see that the
acid and the base in HCl and NaOH solutions are
actually _____ and _____, respectively.

ITEM 25   Any acid–base reaction can be written as a reversible
reaction: conjugate acid of base A + base B ⇆ base
A + conjugate acid of base B. The essential reaction
is the transfer of a _____ from one base to
another.

ITEM 33   Whether this general reaction goes to the left or to
the right depends on the individual acid. For in-
stance, hydrochloric acid is almost 100% ionized:
The reaction $HCl + H_2O$ ⇆ _____ goes almost
entirely to the _____.

ITEM 41   However, other bases can effect the ionization of an
acid. Next to water, the most common base–solvent
for acids is ammonia. The ionization of HCl in NH_3
is written $HCl + NH_3$ ⇆ _____. The two bases
competing for the proton are _____ and
_____.

ITEM 2

Since a hydrogen atom consists of proton and an electron, the species indicated by H^+ in chemical studies is really nothing more than a _____.

ITEM 10

The water molecule may be drawn as $H\!:\!\overset{..}{\underset{}{O}}\!:$
$$ H$$

The dots represent electrons that are bonded or available for bonding. The diagram

$$[H\!:\!\overset{..}{\underset{..}{O}}\!:\!H]^+$$
$$ H$$

represents _____.

ITEM 18

When a base adds a proton, the species formed is an acid. This acid is known as the *conjugate acid* of the base. Thus, H_3O^+ is the conjugate acid of the base _____.

ITEM 26

A molecule of sulfuric acid, H_2SO_4, can donate both its hydrogens to water molecules. The following steps can be written for the reaction of H_2SO_4 with water

$$H_2SO_4 + H_2O \leftrightarrows HSO_4^- + H_3O^+$$
$$HSO_4^- + H_2O \leftrightarrows \underline{}.$$

ITEM 34

In contrast, hydrocyanic acid, HCN, ionizes to the extent of less than 1% in solutions more concentrated than about 10^{-6} molar. The reaction HCN + $H_2O \leftrightarrows$ _____ goes almost entirely to the

_____.

ITEM 42

Even compounds that react as acids in water may serve as bases for the ionization of other acids. For instance, acetic acid can donate one proton (the one attached to oxygen) to water.

$$\overset{\text{O}}{\overset{\|}{CH_3C}}\!-\!OH + H_2O \leftrightarrows \overset{\text{O}}{\overset{\|}{CH_3C}}\!-\!O^- + H_3O^+$$

CH_3COOH is acting as a(n) _____ and H_2O as a(n) _____.

Conjugate acid

ANSWER 1   electron

ANSWER 9   water

ANSWER 17 $2H_2O$
            H_3O^+
            OH^-

ANSWER 25   proton

ANSWER 33 $H_3O^+ + Cl^-$
            right

ANSWER 41 $NH_4^+ + Cl^-$
            Cl^-
            NH_3

An exact description of H^+ in solution is still not possible, but it is certain that the ion is never free but is always associated with molecules of the _____.

Since the oxygen atom of a water molecule has a pair of electrons available for sharing, it can accept a proton. In so doing, it is acting as a _____.

Just as H_3O^+ is the conjugate _____ of the base H_2O, so H_2O is the conjugate _____ of the acid H_3O^+.

In the first reaction, H_2SO_4 is the acid and _____ is its conjugate base. In the second reaction, HSO_4^- is the acid and _____ is its conjugate base.

Just as water serves not only as a solvent for the ionization of an acid but also as the necessary base, water can serve not only as solvent but also, when a base is added, as the _____.

However, if HCl is dissolved in acetic acid, acetic acid can accept a proton.

$$HCl + CH_3\overset{O}{\overset{\|}{C}}-OH \rightleftharpoons CH_3\overset{^+OH}{\overset{\|}{C}}-OH + Cl^-$$

In this system, the two bases competing for the transferable proton are _____ and _____. HCl is acting as a(n) _____ and CH_3COOH as the solvent–_____.

ANSWER 2   proton

ANSWER 10   the hydronium ion

ANSWER 18 H_2O

ANSWER 26 $SO_4^{2-} + H_3O^+$

ANSWER 34 $H_3O^+ + CN^-$
             left

ANSWER 42   acid
             base

ITEM 4

For convenience, let us assume that the hydrogen is always bonded to one other atom by sharing a pair of electrons with that atom. Then, if H^+ ions were formed, they would react immediately with adjacent molecules that have _____ available for _____.

ITEM 12

Similarly, the hydroxide ion, OH^-, is a base because it can accept a _____ as, for example, in the reaction $H_3O^+ + OH^- \rightarrow$ _____.

ITEM 20

The conjugate base of the acid HCN is _____.
The conjugate base of the acid NH_4^+ is _____.

ITEM 28

Of the species H_2SO_4, HSO_4^-, and SO_4^{2-}, which can act most easily both as an acid and as a base?

ITEM 36

For instance, the ionization of ammonia is written

$$NH_3 + H_2O \leftrightarrows NH_4^+ + OH^-$$

Again, the essential reaction is the transfer of a proton between the bases _____ and _____.

ITEM 44

Molecular bases, such as NH_3 and CH_3NH_2 (methyl amine), require an acid for ionization. In aqueous solution, this acid is _____, as shown by the reaction of NH_3:

$$NH_3 + \underline{\hspace{2cm}} \leftrightarrows \underline{\hspace{2cm}}.$$

ANSWER 3   solvent

ANSWER 11   base

ANSWER 19   acid
base

ANSWER 27 HSO_4^-
SO_4^{2-}

ANSWER 35   acid

ANSWER 43 Cl^-

$$CH_3\overset{\displaystyle O}{\overset{\|}{C}}—OH$$

acid
base

ITEM 5

In solution, protons can be transferred from a molecule or an ion in which they share a _____ to another molecule, or ion, that has a free _____.

ITEM 13

In the gas phase, neutral molecules of hydrogen nitrate, HNO_3, exist. The reaction that takes place when neutral molecules of gaseous HNO_3 are dissolved in water is $HNO_3 + H_2O \rightarrow$ _____ $+ NO_3^-$.

ITEM 21

The conjugate base of H_2O is _____. The conjugate acid of OH^- is _____.

ITEM 29

Of the species H_3O^+, H_2O, OH^- (all very important in acid–base studies), which can act most easily both as an acid and as a base?

ITEM 37

In this reaction of NH_3 with H_2O, NH_4^+ is the conjugate _____ of _____ and OH^- is the conjugate _____ of _____.

ITEM 45

Again, however, the Brønsted theory does not require that H_2O be the solvent; any sufficiently strong acid can serve as the ionization medium for a base. Write the equation for the ionization of NH_3 in acetic acid

$$NH_3 + CH_3\overset{\displaystyle O}{\overset{\displaystyle \|}{C}}-OH \leftrightarrows \underline{\qquad}.$$

ANSWER 4   electrons
sharing (or bonding)

ANSWER 12   proton (or hydrogen ion)
$2H_2O$

ANSWER 20 CN^-
NH_3

ANSWER 28 HSO_4^-

ANSWER 36 NH_3
OH^-

ANSWER 44   water
H_2O
$NH_4^+ + OH^-$

ITEM 6

In solution, free H^+ ions do not occur, but they can be _____ from one molecule to another.

ITEM 14

If ammonia gas is dissolved in water, the reaction at the right occurs to an appreciable extent. In this reaction, H_2O is the _____ and NH_3 is the _____.

ITEM 22

Removal of a proton from an acid produces the conjugate base of the acid. Addition of a proton to a base produces the _____.

ITEM 30

Write equations for two reactions, one in which H_2O acts as a base and one in which H_2O acts as an acid. Use HCl as the acid in one reaction and NH_3 as the base in the other reaction.

ITEM 38

When sodium methoxide, CH_3ONa, is dissolved in water, it dissociates into Na^+ and the base CH_3O^-, which has a strong affinity for protons. CH_3O^- reacts as follows

$$CH_3O^- + H_2O \leftrightarrows CH_3OH + \underline{\hspace{2cm}}.$$

In this reaction the proton is transferred between the bases _____ and _____.

ITEM 46

In any chemical system, then, according to the Brønsted definition of acids and bases, a molecule or ion acts as an acid if it _____ and as a base if it _____.

$$NH_3 + H_2O \rightarrow NH_4^+ + OH^-$$

ANSWER 5   pair of electrons
pair of electrons

ANSWER 13 H_3O^+

ANSWER 21 OH^-
H_2O

ANSWER 29 H_2O

ANSWER 37   acid
NH_3
base
H_2O

ANSWER 45 $NH_4^+ + CH_3\overset{\overset{\text{O}}{\|}}{C}{-}O^-$

ITEM 7

According to Brønsted's definitions of acids and bases, an acid is a substance that can donate a proton and a base is a substance that can _____.

ITEM 15

When the ionic compound NaOH is dissolved in water, the solution contains only the ions Na^+ and _____: There are no molecules of NaOH.

ITEM 23

In a reaction of the type $HA + B \rightarrow A^- + HB^+$, we say that HA is acting as a(n) _____ and B as a(n) _____.

ITEM 31

When acid–base reactions, which according to Brønsted theory involve _____ transfers, occur in aqueous solution, the solvent (_____) is not inert; it enters into the reactions.

ITEM 39

In the reaction $H_2O + CH_3O^- \leftrightarrows CH_3OH + OH^-$, CH_3OH is the conjugate _____ of _____.

ANSWER 6   transferred

ANSWER 14   acid (proton donor)
            base (proton acceptor)

ANSWER 22   conjugate acid of the base

ANSWER 30

$HCl + H_2O \rightleftarrows H_3O^+ + Cl^-$ (H_2O is base)
$NH_3 + H_2O \rightleftarrows NH_4^+ + OH^-$ (H_2O is acid)

ANSWER 38 OH^-
            CH_3O^-
            OH^-

ANSWER 46   donates a proton
            accepts a proton

(Turn to page 171.)

ITEM 8

When the gas hydrogen chloride, HCl, is dissolved in water, the reaction $HCl + H_2O \rightarrow Cl^- + H_3O^+$ occurs. In the reaction a proton is transferred from HCl to _____. Therefore, HCl is acting as a(n) _____ and H_2O as a(n) _____.

ITEM 16

When the molecular compound HCl dissolves in water, the reaction $HCl + H_2O \rightarrow$ _____ proceeds to such an extent that few, if any, HCl molecules remain.

ITEM 24

When this reaction $(HA + B \rightarrow A^- + HB^+)$ goes in the opposite direction $(HB^+ + A^- \rightarrow HA + B)$, we say that _____ is acting as an acid and _____ as a base.

ITEM 32

The ionization of an acid in water can be represented as $HA + H_2O \leftrightharpoons$ _____ $+ A^-$ in which the two bases that compete for the proton are _____ and _____.

ITEM 40

The ionization of an acid in solution always requires the presence of a base. In aqueous solutions this base is _____.

ANSWER 7   accept a proton

ANSWER 15   OH$^-$

ANSWER 23   acid
             base

ANSWER 31   proton
             H$_2$O

ANSWER 39   acid
             CH$_3$O$^-$

ANSWER 8 H_2O
acid
base

(Item 9 is on page 152.)

ANSWER 16 $H_3O^+ + Cl^-$

(Item 17 is on page 152.)

ANSWER 24 HB^+
A^-

(Item 25 is on page 152.)

ANSWER 32 H_3O^+
A^-
H_2O

(Item 33 is on page 152.)

ANSWER 40   water

(Item 41 is on page 152.)

4–4 ACID–BASE STOICHIOMETRY

Now that acids and bases have been defined and the proton-transfer reactions that are encountered most often have been described, we can use this background material to study the solution stoichiometry of acid–base reactions. The concepts of normality and equivalent weight, which are especially helpful in quantitative studies of acids and bases, will be a review of Section 4–5 of *Chemical Principles.*

In this section we assume that all acids and bases used as examples are completely ionized in solution. This is valid for our purpose here and has been done in order to avoid, temporarily, the fascinating problems of partial dissociation, which will be discussed in Chapter 16 of *Chemical Principles* and in Review 14 of this book.

Items 27–37 at the end of this section are representative of acid–base stoichiometry problems. If you can solve them, you can probably skip the rest of the section.

ITEM 1

When aqueous solutions of HCl and NaOH are mixed, the reaction can be written $HCl + NaOH \rightarrow NaCl + H_2O$. The actual "net" reaction is $H_3O^+ +$ _____ $\rightarrow$ _____.

ITEM 7

What volume of 0.25-molar NaOH solution would be necessary to provide 0.050 mole of OH^-?

ITEM 13

Since 1 equivalent of an acid can transfer 1 mole of protons to a base, 1 equivalent of H_2SO_4 is _____ of a mole of H_2SO_4.

ITEM 19

A 1-normal (N) solution of an acid or base contains one equivalent per liter of solution. One liter of a 0.5-normal solution of HCl contains _____ equivalent(s) of HCl.

ITEM 25

An equivalent of any base will react with _____ equivalent(s) of an acid in solution.

ITEM 31

How many milliliters of 1.32-normal KOH are required to react with 60 ml of 0.570-molar H_3PO_4?

ITEM 37

A sample of an acid weighing 1.55 g is dissolved in water. If 34.4 ml of 0.480-normal NaOH are required to react completely with the sample, what is the equivalent weight of the acid?

ITEM 2

Each mole of HCl furnishes _____ mole(s) of H_3O^+ in solution. Hence, _____ mole(s) of OH^- is (are) required for complete reaction.

ITEM 8

In 0.50 liter of 0.10-molar H_2SO_4 there is _____ mole of H_2SO_4 so _____ mole of H_3O^+ is available for reaction with a base.

ITEM 14

One molecule of the acid H_3PO_4 can transfer three protons to a base. One mole of H_3PO_4 is _____ equivalent(s) of H_3PO_4.

ITEM 20

A 0.6-normal solution contains _____ of acid or base per liter of solution.

ITEM 26

In 0.15 liter of 0.20-normal K_2CO_3 there is (are) _____ equivalent(s) that will react with _____ equivalent(s) of HCl, or with _____ equivalent(s) of H_2SO_4.

ITEM 32

The *equivalent weight*, E_w, of an acid is the weight of an acid (in grams) that can transfer an Avogadro's number of protons, that is, a "mole" of protons, to a base. The equivalent weight of an acid is therefore equal to the molecular weight divided by _____.

$$H_3O^+ + OH^- \rightarrow 2H_2O$$

ANSWER 1 OH^-
            $2H_2O$

ANSWER 7 $V = \dfrac{n}{M} = \dfrac{0.050 \text{ mole}}{0.25 \text{ mole liter}^{-1}}$

            $= 0.20$ liter

ANSWER 13 $\frac{1}{2}$

ANSWER 19   0.5

ANSWER 25   1

ANSWER 31

N of $H_3PO_4 = 3 \times 0.570 = 1.71$

$V_2 = \dfrac{N_1 V_1}{N_2}$

$ = \dfrac{1.71 \text{ equiv liter}^{-1}(60 \text{ ml})}{1.32 \text{ equiv liter}^{-1}} = 78$ ml

Equivalent weight

ANSWER 37

equiv of NaOH $=$ (0.0344 liter)(0.480 equiv liter^{-1})

$\qquad\qquad = 0.0165$

acid $= 1.55$ g/0.0165 equiv

$\qquad = 94.0$ g equiv^{-1}

ITEM 3

When aqueous solutions of H_2SO_4 and NaOH are mixed, the reaction may be written $H_2SO_4 + 2NaOH \rightarrow Na_2SO_4 + 2H_2O$ or, to show what is actually happening, $H_3O^+ + $ _____ $\rightarrow$ _____.

ITEM 9

Reaction with 0.10 mole H_3O^+ requires _____ mole(s) of OH^-.

ITEM 15

The amount of base that can accept 1 mole of protons is an equivalent of the base. One equivalent of NaOH is _____ mole(s) of NaOH.

ITEM 21

An N-normal solution contains _____ equivalent(s) per liter. The number of equivalents in V liters of an N-normal solution is _____.

ITEM 27

V_1 liters of N_1-normal acid solution contain _____ equivalents. V_2 liters of N_2-normal base contain _____ equivalents.

ITEM 33

The equivalent weight is often a unique property that can aid in the identification of an acid. The equivalent weight of HCl is _____ and of H_3PO_4 is _____. (See periodic table in the inside front cover for atomic weights.)

ANSWER 2   1
1

ANSWER 8   0.50 liter $\times$ 0.10 mole liter^{-1}
$= 0.050$ mole
0.10

ANSWER 14   3

ANSWER 20   0.6 equivalent

ANSWER 26

(0.15 liter)(0.20 equiv liter^{-1}) = 0.030 equiv
0.030
0.030

ANSWER 32   the number of transferable protons per molecule (which is equal to the number of equivalents per mole)

ITEM 4

Each mole of H_2SO_4 can produce _____ moles of H_3O^+ in solution; _____ moles of NaOH are required for complete reaction.

ITEM 10

Since some acid molecules can transfer more than one proton to a base, the number of moles of protons available can be _____ than the number of moles of acid.

ITEM 16

One mole of $Ca(OH)_2$ can furnish 2 moles of OH^- in solution. A mole of $Ca(OH)_2$ is _____ equivalent(s).

ITEM 22

In 2.5 liters of 0.20-normal NaOH there is (are) _____ equivalent(s) (often abbreviated to *equiv* or *eq*) of NaOH.

ITEM 28

Since each equivalent of any acid reacts with an equivalent of any base, the amounts required for complete reaction are related by the equation $V_1N_1 =$ _____.

ITEM 34

Acetic acid

$$CH_3\overset{\overset{\displaystyle O}{\|}}{C}{-}OH$$

can transfer one proton (the one attached to oxygen) to a base such as OH^-. The equivalent weight of acetic acid is _____.

ANSWER 3 OH^-
            $2H_2O$

ANSWER 9   0.10

ANSWER 15   1

ANSWER 21 N
            V liters $\times N$ equivalents liter^{-1}
            $= VN$ equivalents

ANSWER 27 V_1N_1
            V_2N_2

ANSWER 33

$$\frac{36.5 \text{ g mole}^{-1}}{1 \text{ equiv mole}^{-1}} = 36.5 \text{ g equiv}^{-1}$$

$$\frac{98.0 \text{ g mole}^{-1}}{3 \text{ equiv mole}^{-1}} = 32.7 \text{ g equiv}^{-1}$$

ITEM 5

In 0.50 liter of 0.10-molar HCl there is (are) _____ mole(s) of HCl or _____ mole(s) of H_3O^+.

ITEM 11

An *equivalent* of an acid is defined as the amount of acid that will transfer 1 mole of protons to a base. An equivalent of HCl is _____ mole(s) of HCl.

ITEM 17

The carbonate ion, CO_3^{2-}, is a base and can accept two protons to form H_2CO_3, which then decomposes to CO_2 and H_2O. One mole of Na_2CO_3 can furnish _____ mole(s) of CO_3^{2-} that can accept _____ mole(s) of protons.

ITEM 23

In the reaction $H_3O^+ + OH^- \rightarrow 2H_2O$, each mole of OH^- reacts with _____ mole(s) of H_3O^+.

ITEM 29

A 0.500-liter sample of 0.100-normal acid contains _____ equivalent. If this sample of acid is mixed with a 0.200-normal base solution, the volume of base required for complete reaction will be _____ liter(s).

ITEM 35

How many grams of

$$CH_3\overset{\overset{\displaystyle O}{\|}}{C}-OH$$

would be used to make up a solution containing 0.15 equiv in 100 ml of solution? What would be the normality of this solution?

Equivalent

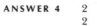

ANSWER 4   2
            2

ANSWER 10   greater

ANSWER 16   2

ANSWER 22
$(2.5 \text{ liters})(0.20 \text{ equiv liter}^{-1}) = 0.50 \text{ equiv}$

ANSWER 28 $V_2 N_2$

ANSWER 34   60.0

ITEM 6

For reaction with this 0.050 mole of H_3O^+, _____ mole of OH^- is required.

ITEM 12

Just as the word "mole" is used for gram molecular weight, the word "equivalent" is used generally instead of "gram equivalent weight." An equivalent is the weight of an acid, expressed in _____, that can transfer 6.02×10^{23} protons to a base.

ITEM 18

Therefore, 1 mole of CO_3^{2-} can furnish _____ equivalent(s) of base.

ITEM 24

An equivalent of acid will produce _____ mole(s) of H_3O^+ in solution. An equivalent of hydroxide base will produce _____ mole(s) of OH^- in solution.

ITEM 30

A 25.0-ml sample of $Ba(OH)_2$ solution required 37.2 ml of 0.110-normal sulfuric acid solution for complete reaction. The normality of the hydroxide solution was _____; the 25.0-ml sample contained _____ mole(s) of $Ba(OH)_2$.

ITEM 36

In 0.0520 liter of 0.204-normal NaOH, there is (are) _____ equivalent(s) of OH^- that will react with _____ equivalent(s) of

$$CH_3\overset{\displaystyle O}{\overset{\displaystyle \|}{C}}-OH$$

or _____ g of

$$CH_3\underset{\displaystyle \|}{\underset{\displaystyle O}{C}}-OH$$

ANSWER 5

$n = MV = (0.50 \text{ liter})(0.10 \text{ mole liter}^{-1})$
   $= 0.050 \text{ mole}$
0.050

ANSWER 11   1

ANSWER 17   1
                2

ANSWER 23   1

ANSWER 29

$(0.500 \text{ liter})(0.100 \text{ equiv liter}^{-1}) = 0.0500 \text{ equiv}$

$V_2 = \dfrac{V_1 N_1}{N_2} = \dfrac{0.0500 \text{ equiv}}{0.200 \text{ equiv liter}^{-1}} = 0.250 \text{ liter}$

ANSWER 35

$(60.0 \text{ g equiv}^{-1})(0.15 \text{ equiv}/100 \text{ ml}) = 9.0$
   $\text{g}/100 \text{ ml}$
$(0.15 \text{ equiv}/100 \text{ ml}) = 1.5 \text{ equiv liter}^{-1}$
Hence, solution is 1.5 normal.

ANSWER 6   0.050

(*Item 7 is on page 172.*)

ANSWER 12   grams

(*Item 13 is on page 172.*)

ANSWER 18   2

(*Item 19 is on page 172.*)

ANSWER 24   1
                  1

(*Item 25 is on page 172.*)

ANSWER 30

$$N_1 = \frac{N_2 V_2}{V_1}$$

$$= \frac{(37.2 \text{ ml})(0.110 \text{ equiv liter}^{-1})}{25.0 \text{ ml}} = 0.164$$

equivalents of $Ba(OH)_2 = VN$
    $= (0.0250 \text{ liter})(0.164 \text{ equiv liter}^{-1})$
    $= 0.00410$
moles of $Ba(OH)_2 = 0.00410/2 = 0.00205$

(*Item 31 is on page 172.*)

ANSWER 36

(0.0520 liter)(0.204 equiv liter^{-1}) = 0.0106
   equiv
0.0106
(0.0106 equiv)(60.0 g equiv^{-1}) = 0.636 g

185

(*Item 37 is on page 172.*)

4-5 HEAT EFFECTS IN CHEMICAL REACTIONS

The heat effects that accompany chemical reactions have much practical and theoretical significance. The study of these effects has practical applications in the burning of fuels for heating purposes, the combustion of gasoline, and other petroleum products for transportation, the use of chemical fuels and oxidants for rockets, and the sustenance of life itself through the controlled release of energy by chemical reactions occurring in plants and animals. In addition, the study of heat effects has led to advances in our understanding of chemical and biochemical reactions, chemical equilibrium, and molecular structure, and, in some measure, has contributed to all topics of current interest in chemistry.

As you have learned in Section 4-6 of *Chemical Principles*, for a given set of conditions, the quantity of heat evolved or absorbed in a chemical reaction is just as definite as is the amount of a product formed. In this section we will enlarge upon the discussion in Section 4-6 of *Chemical Principles* to help you to understand some of the methods for calculating the amount of energy evolved or absorbed in chemical reactions. On completion of the section you will be able to solve problems of this type: The heat of combustion of C(graphite) is −94.052 and C(diamond) is −94.505. Calculate ΔH for the reaction C(graphite) → C(diamond). Items 51–57 will provide a test of your knowledge.

Every chemical compound is characterized by a particular arrangement of atoms in space, and every different arrangement has associated with it a certain amount of potential energy. Therefore, when one compound reacts to form another compound, the new arrangement of atoms will have either a greater or a lesser amount of _____ than the original.

ITEM 11

The equation $A + B \rightarrow C$ does not indicate whether the reaction is exothermic. Using q, rewrite the equation so it represents an exothermic reaction.

ITEM 21

In previous examples, water was formed as a liquid. The heat liberated when 1 mole of water vapor is formed from gaseous oxygen and hydrogen is 57.798 kcal. The thermochemical equation showing the formation of 1 mole of water vapor is _____.

ITEM 31

Another way of saying the same thing is that the net heat evolved or absorbed in the reaction $A \rightarrow C$ is (*independent of, dependent on*) the number and kind of intermediate steps.

ITEM 41

Insert horizontal lines and reagent names, and fill in the blank in the energy diagram at right for the reaction

$$H_2O(l) \rightarrow H_2O(g) \qquad \Delta H = +10.519 \text{ kcal}$$

ITEM 51

Using the data given in the thermochemical equations at the right, tabulate the heats of formation of the compounds below.

Compound	ΔH_f kcal
$H_2O(l)$	
$H_2O(g)$	
$NH_3(g)$	

H $\Delta H = \_\_\_\_\_$ kcal

reagents

$H_2(g) \ + \tfrac{1}{2}O_2(g) \ \rightarrow H_2O(l)$
$\quad\quad\quad\quad\quad\quad\quad \Delta H = -68.32$ kcal
$2H_2(g) + O_2(g) \ \ \rightarrow 2H_2O(g)$
$\quad\quad\quad\quad\quad\quad\quad \Delta H = -115.60$ kcal
$N_2(g) \ + 3H_2(g) \rightarrow 2NH_3(g)$
$\quad\quad\quad\quad\quad\quad\quad \Delta H = -22.08$ kcal

The sum of the potential energy, arising from the _____ of atoms in a sample of a compound, and the kinetic energy, arising from their motion, is known as the *heat content* or *enthalpy*, H, of the sample. Although the absolute value of H is not usually known for a sample of a compound, it is the change in H, which can often be measured, that is important.

ITEM 12

Materials appearing on the left side of a chemical equation are called *reactants*. In an endothermic reaction, heat can be regarded as a _____. For such reactions, the amount of heat (symbol _____) would be written on the _____ side of the equation.

ITEM 22

The heat of combustion of gaseous pentane, C_5H_{12}, is 11.6 kcal g^{-1} when the products are gaseous CO_2 and liquid H_2O. The heat liberated in the combustion of 1 *mole* of pentane under these conditions is _____. The thermochemical equation for the combustion is _____.

ITEM 32

The heat evolved or absorbed in the reaction A → C depends only on the relative heat contents of _____ and _____, and not on whether the reaction is stepwise or direct.

ITEM 42

Fill in the following table:

Reaction	Heat (evolved or absorbed)	ΔH (+ or −)
Endothermic		
Exothermic		

ITEM 52

The heat of formation of a compound, which is given the symbol _____, is defined as the value of ΔH for the reaction in which _____ is formed from _____ at _____ °C and a pressure of _____.

Heat content
  Enthalpy

ANSWER 1   potential energy

ANSWER 11 $A + B \rightarrow C + q$

ANSWER 21

$H_2(g) + \frac{1}{2}O_2(g) \rightarrow H_2O(g) + 57.798$ kcal

ANSWER 31   independent of

ANSWER 41

ANSWER 51

$H_2O(l)$ $\Delta H_f = -68.32$ kcal
$H_2O(g)$ $\Delta H_f = -57.80$ kcal
$NH_3(g)$ $\Delta H_f = -11.04$ kcal

ITEM 3

In the diagram at the right are shown the relative heat contents of equal amounts of compounds A and B. Compound B has a higher heat content than compound A. Therefore, energy must be absorbed by compound _____ in order that compound _____ be formed from it.

ITEM 13

The units in which q is given—the heat units most commonly used in thermochemistry—are *kilocalories.* Since the prefix "kilo" implies 1000, and since 1 calorie is defined as the amount of heat required to raise the temperature of 1 g of water from $14.5°$ C to $15.5°$ C, 1 kilocalorie (kcal) is the amount of heat required to raise the temperature of _____ from $14.5°$ C to $15.5°$ C.

ITEM 23

When 2 moles of gaseous hydrogen iodide (HI) are formed from 1 mole of $H_2(g)$ and 1 mole of $I_2(s)$, 12.40 kcal of heat are absorbed. Write the thermochemical equation for this reaction.

ITEM 33

If the reaction A $\rightarrow$ C is exothermic, the heat content of C must be _____ than that of A.

ITEM 43

One convention for writing thermochemical equations is to write the heat as if it were a reactant or product. Another convention is to write the equation and then to indicate the value of ΔH. Write both kinds of equations for the reaction $CO(g) + \frac{1}{2}O_2(g) \rightarrow CO_2(g)$, which is exothermic by 67.636 kcal.

ITEM 53

The formation of 1 mole of $NaOH(s)$ under standard state conditions from the elements $Na(s)$, $O_2(g)$, and $H_2(g)$ liberates 112.2 kcal of heat. Write an equation and ΔH for the formation of NaOH.

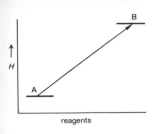

ANSWER 2   arrangement

ANSWER 12   reactant
q
left

ANSWER 22

Heat $= (11.6 \text{ kcal g}^{-1})(72.1 \text{ g mole}^{-1})$
$\quad\quad = 836 \text{ kcal mole}^{-1}$
$C_5H_{12}(g) + 8O_2(g) \rightarrow 5CO_2(g) + 6H_2O(l)$
$\quad\quad\quad\quad\quad\quad\quad\quad\quad\quad + 836 \text{ kcal}$

ANSWER 32   A
C

ANSWER 42

Reaction	Heat	ΔH
Endothermic	Absorbed	+
Exothermic	Evolved	−

ANSWER 52

ΔH_f
1 mole of the compound
its elements in their
    commonly occurring state
25
1 atm

ITEM 4

Conversely, if compound B reacts to form compound A, and A has a lower heat content, it is certain that energy will be _____ in the process.

ITEM 14

When 2 moles of hydrogen are burned, they react with 1 mole of oxygen to form 2 moles of water. If the water is formed as liquid water, 136.634 kcal of heat are liberated for every mole of oxygen reacting; and the reaction, including the heat, can be written as $2H_2(g) + O_2(g) \rightarrow$ _____.

ITEM 24

Calculate the number of kcal of heat required for the formation of 10.0 g of gaseous hydrogen iodide.

ITEM 34

Indicate the relative heat contents of A and C on the diagram at the right by using the information that the reaction A → C is exothermic.

ITEM 44

On the energy diagram at the right, represent the reaction

$$C(s) + 2H_2(g) \rightarrow CH_4(g) \qquad \Delta H = -17.9 \text{ kcal}$$

ITEM 54

The formation of gaseous chlorine atoms from $Cl_2(g)$ under standard state conditions requires 29.0 kcal g-atom^{-1}. Write an equation and ΔH for the formation of Cl atoms.

reagents

reagents

reagents

ANSWER 3   A
               B

ANSWER 13   1000 g of water
                 (very close to 1 liter)

ANSWER 23

$12.40 \text{ kcal} + H_2(g) + I_2(s) \rightarrow 2HI(g)$

ANSWER 33   less

ANSWER 43

$CO(g) + \frac{1}{2}O_2(g) \rightarrow CO_2(g) + 67.636 \text{ kcal}$
$CO(g) + \frac{1}{2}O_2(g) \rightarrow CO_2(g) \qquad \Delta H = -67.636$
$\qquad\qquad\qquad\qquad\qquad\qquad\qquad \text{kcal}$

ANSWER 53

$Na(s) + \frac{1}{2}O_2(g) + \frac{1}{2}H_2(g) \rightarrow NaOH(s)$
$\Delta H = -112.2 \text{ kcal}$

ITEM 5

The energy liberated or absorbed in chemical reactions usually is in the form of heat; therefore, the temperature of a reacting system changes as the reaction proceeds. If heat is liberated by the reaction, the energy warms the reactants and products and the temperature of the system _____. If the temperature falls, it is clear that _____ is being _____ by the reaction.

ITEM 15

The amount of heat liberated or absorbed depends on the physical state of the reagents. Therefore, thermochemical equations indicate physical states. The symbol (g) indicates that the substance is present in the _____ state; the symbol (l) indicates the _____ state; and the symbol (s) indicates the _____ state.

ITEM 25

It is often useful to determine the heat absorbed or liberated in a reaction that can be thought of as the combination of two or more reactions. Thus, when 1 mole of liquid water is formed from $H_2(g)$ and $O_2(g)$, 68.317 kcal of heat are _____; in the further conversion of 1 mole of liquid water to water vapor, 10.519 kcal are _____.

ITEM 35

Another way of expressing the change in heat content is frequently used in thermochemistry: The *heat of reaction*, ΔH, is defined as H(products) $- H$(reactants). [The Greek leter Δ (delta) is commonly used to indicate increments or differences.] If H(products) is greater than H(reactants), will the value of ΔH be positive or negative?

ITEM 45

Calculate the amount of heat liberated by the formation of 5.00 liters of CH_4 at 25°C and 1 atm according to the equation

$$C(s) + 2H_2(g) \rightarrow CH_4(g) \qquad \Delta H = -17.9 \text{ kcal}$$

ITEM 55

The heat of combustion of gaseous pentane, C_5H_{12}, to gaseous CO_2 and liquid H_2O is 836 kcal mole^{-1}. Write an equation, including ΔH, for this combustion.

ANSWER 4 liberated (given off)

ANSWER 14 $2H_2O(l) + 136.634$ kcal

ANSWER 24

$$\frac{10.0 \text{ g}}{128 \text{ g mole}^{-1}} = 0.0781 \text{ mole}$$

$6.20 \text{ kcal} + \frac{1}{2}H_2(g) + \frac{1}{2}I_2(s) \rightarrow HI(g)$
$0.0781 \text{ mole} (6.20 \text{ kcal mole}^{-1}) = 0.484 \text{ kcal}$

ANSWER 34

ANSWER 44

ANSWER 54 $\frac{1}{2}Cl_2(g) \rightarrow Cl(g)$
$\Delta H = +29.0$ kcal

Heat of reaction

ITEM 6

Experimentally, the heat change is determined by observing a system isolated from external heating and cooling. Before the reactants are mixed, the amount of heat required to change the temperature of the system by $1°C$ is measured. Then the reactants are mixed, and the liberated or absorbed heat is determined by measuring the change in ＿＿＿＿＿ of the entire system.

ITEM 16

It is also necessary to indicate reagents that are in solution. The notation $Ag^+(aq)$ indicates that the ion is dissolved in ＿＿＿＿＿.

ITEM 26

From the data at the right, the total reaction by which 1 mole of $H_2O(g)$ is formed from $H_2(g)$ and $O_2(g)$ can be recognized as occurring with the ＿＿＿＿＿ of ＿＿＿＿＿ kcal.

ITEM 36

Then, for an endothermic reaction, in which heat is absorbed and H(products) is ＿＿＿＿＿ than H(reactants), the value of ΔH has a ＿＿＿＿＿ sign.

ITEM 46

It is well to note that, although we have defined ΔH, the heat of reaction, as ＿＿＿＿＿, ΔH is precisely defined as the difference in heat contents of the reaction products and of the reactants at constant pressure and at a definite temperature, with every substance in a definite physical state.

ITEM 56

Calculate the amount of heat released by the combustion of 3.00 g of gaseous pentane (mol wt: 72.1).

thermometer   stirrer

vacuum

$$H_2(g) + \tfrac{1}{2}O_2(g) \rightarrow H_2O(l) + 68.317 \text{ kcal}$$
$$10.519 \text{ kcal} + H_2O(l) \rightarrow H_2O(g)$$

H ΔH

reactants   ⟶   products

ANSWER 5   rises
                      heat
                      absorbed

ANSWER 15   gas
                       liquid
                       solid

ANSWER 25   liberated
                       absorbed

ANSWER 35   positive

ANSWER 45

$$n = \frac{PV}{RT} = \frac{1 \text{ atm (5.00 liters)}}{0.0821 \dfrac{\text{liter atm}}{\text{deg mole}} (298 \text{ deg})}$$

$$= 0.204 \text{ mole}$$

$$0.204 \text{ mole } (17.9 \text{ kcal mole}^{-1}) = 3.65 \text{ kcal}$$

ANSWER 55

$$C_5H_{12}(g) + 8O_2(g) \rightarrow 5CO_2(g) + 6H_2O(l)$$
$$\Delta H = -836 \text{ kcal}$$

ITEM 7

The word "exothermic" comes from the Greek word *exo*, meaning "out of," and *therme*, meaning "heat." Therefore, *exothermic* is used to describe reactions in which heat is _____. As an exothermic reaction proceeds, the temperature of the system _____.

ITEM 17

The equation at the right is another example of a thermochemical equation. It differs from ordinary equations in that it not only includes _____ in the equation but also indicates the _____ of the reagents.

ITEM 27

This result is obtained in a convenient, systematic way if the thermochemical equations for the two steps are written one underneath the other and are then added as if they were algebraic equations. Carry out this procedure with the data at the right to obtain the thermochemical equation for the reaction

$$H_2(g) + \tfrac{1}{2}O_2(g) \rightarrow H_2O(g)$$

ITEM 37

Correspondingly, for an exothermic reaction, in which H(products) is _____ than H(reactants), the value of ΔH has a _____ sign.

ITEM 47

In whatever way thermochemical equations are written, equations of two or more reactions (run under the same conditions of pressure and temperature) can be added or subtracted to give the equation for a new reaction. When two reactions are added, ΔH for the new total reaction will be the _____ of the ΔH's for the individual component reactions.

ITEM 57

The standard heat of formation of $H_2O(l)$ is -68.3 kcal mole^{-1}. The standard heat of formation of sulfur trioxide, $SO_3(g)$, is -94.5 kcal mole^{-1}. Calculate ΔH for the reaction

$$3H_2(g) + SO_3(g) \rightarrow S(s) + 3H_2O(l)$$

Exothermic

$3H_2(g) + 6C(s) + 11.7 \text{ kcal} \rightarrow C_6H_6(l)$

$H_2(g) + \frac{1}{2}O_2(g) \rightarrow H_2O(l) + 68.317 \text{ kcal}$
$10.519 \text{ kcal} + H_2O(l) \rightarrow H_2O(g)$

reactants ⟶ products

A ⟶ B ⟶ C

ANSWER 6   temperature

ANSWER 16   water

ANSWER 26   liberation
$68.317 - 10.519 = 57.798$

ANSWER 36   greater
plus (positive)

ANSWER 46 $H(\text{products}) - H(\text{reactants})$

ANSWER 56

$$\frac{3.00 \text{ g}}{72.1 \text{ g mole}^{-1}} = 0.0416 \text{ mole}$$

$0.0416 \text{ mole } (836 \text{ kcal mole}^{-1}) = 34.8 \text{ kcal}$

ITEM 8

The Greek prefix for "into" is *endo*; hence, reactions that absorb heat are described as _____ reactions. During such reactions, the temperature of the reaction system will _____.

ITEM 18

If the equation at the right were written to show the formation of 1 instead of 2 moles of water (in which case _____ as much heat would be evolved) the thermochemical equation would be _____.

ITEM 28

Similarly, one can subtract equations. Thus, the thermochemical equations for the combustion of C(graphite) and CO(g) are

$$C(graphite) + O_2(g) \rightarrow CO_2(g) + 94.052 \text{ kcal}$$
$$CO(g) + \tfrac{1}{2}O_2(g) \rightarrow CO_2(g) + 67.636 \text{ kcal}$$

Subtraction of the second equation from the first (and moving terms with negative signs to the other side) yields _____.

ITEM 38

The thermochemical equation

$$H_2(g) + \tfrac{1}{2}O_2(g) \rightarrow H_2O(g) + 57.798 \text{ kcal}$$

shows that the heat content of H_2O is _____ than that of $H_2(g) + \tfrac{1}{2}O_2(g)$. Complete the diagram at the right that represents this reaction by adding symbols for the reagents and the value for the heat of reaction. The sign of the value of ΔH must be

_____.

ITEM 48

The reaction C(graphite) $\rightarrow$ C(diamond) is difficult to perform. For this reaction, however, ΔH can be calculated from the heats of combustion of C(graphite) and C(diamond) of -94.052 kcal mole^{-1} and -94.505 kcal mole^{-1}, respectively. Calculate ΔH.

$$2H_2(g) + O_2(g) \rightarrow 2H_2O(l) + 136.634 \text{ kcal}$$

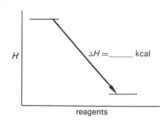

H

$\Delta H = \underline{}$ kcal

reagents

ANSWER 7   liberated
rises

ANSWER 17   heat
physical state

ANSWER 27

$$H_2(g) + \tfrac{1}{2}O_2(g) \rightarrow H_2O(l) + 68.317 \text{ kcal}$$
$$\underline{10.519 \text{ kcal} + H_2O(l) \rightarrow H_2O(g)}$$
$$H_2(g) + \tfrac{1}{2}O_2(g) \rightarrow H_2O(g) + 57.798 \text{ kcal}$$

[The $H_2O(l)$ terms can be cancelled.]

ANSWER 37   less
minus (negative)

ANSWER 47   sum

ANSWER 57

$$H_2(g) + \tfrac{1}{2}O_2(g) \rightarrow H_2O(l) \qquad \Delta H = -68.3 \text{ kcal}$$
$$S(s) \;\; + \tfrac{3}{2}O_2(g) \rightarrow SO_3(g) \qquad \Delta H = -94.5 \text{ kcal}$$

To obtain 3 moles of water and 1 mole S, the second equation must be subtracted from the first equation, which has been multiplied by a factor of 3.

$$3H_2(g) + \tfrac{3}{2}O_2(g) \rightarrow 3H_2O(l) \quad \Delta H = -204.9 \text{ kcal}$$
$$\underline{S(s) \;\;\; + \tfrac{3}{2}O_2(g) \rightarrow SO_3(g) \qquad \Delta H = \;\; -94.5 \text{ kcal}}$$
$$3H_2(g) + SO_3(g) \rightarrow S(s) \qquad \Delta H = -110.4 \text{ kcal}$$
$$\qquad\qquad\qquad\quad + 3H_2O(l)$$

(Turn to page 210.)

203

ITEM 9

Some reactions proceed with very little heat being liberated or absorbed. But temperature changes in most reactions can indicate the liberation of heat (_____ reactions) or the absorption of heat (_____ reactions.)

ITEM 19

The equation that answers Item 18 illustrates the third difference that is sometimes observed when the heat effects accompanying a reaction are shown, namely, that the coefficients are sometimes _____.

ITEM 29

In this way, the heat effects for difficult-to-study reactions can be deduced from data on experimentally convenient reactions, such as combustion reactions. In the example given, the heat evolved when C(graphite) is burned to $CO(g)$ would be difficult to determine experimentally because during the reaction some CO might be further oxidized to _____.

ITEM 39

When ΔH is used to express the change in heat content, the thermochemical equation is written as

$$H_2(g) + \tfrac{1}{2}O_2(g) \rightarrow H_2O(g) \qquad \Delta H = -57.798 \text{ kcal}$$

When this kind of equation is used, it is important to remember that ΔH is defined as _____.

ITEM 49

Complete the energy diagram at the right to represent the relative energies of CO_2, [C(graphite) $+O_2$], and [C(diamond) $+ O_2$]. The diagram should show that diamond has a _____ heat content than graphite.

ANSWER 8   endothermic
               fall

ANSWER 18

half

$$H_2(g) + \tfrac{1}{2}O_2(g) \rightarrow H_2O(l) + 68.317 \text{ kcal}$$

ANSWER 28

$$C(\text{graphite}) + \tfrac{1}{2}O_2(g) \rightarrow CO(g) + 26.416 \text{ kcal}$$

ANSWER 38   less
                negative

ANSWER 48

The combustion equations must be subtracted to yield the desired reaction.

$$C(\text{graphite}) + O_2(g) \rightarrow CO_2(g)$$
$$\Delta H = -94.052 \text{ kcal}$$
$$C(\text{diamond}) + O_2(g) \rightarrow CO_2(g)$$
$$\Delta H = -94.505 \text{ kcal}$$

$$C(\text{graphite}) \rightarrow C(\text{diamond})$$
$$\Delta H = +0.453 \text{ kcal}$$

The general term *reagent* can refer to either a *reactant* or a *product*. Heat can be regarded as a reagent: In an _____ reaction, heat is a product. If q is used to represent the amount of heat liberated, it would be written on the _____ side of the equation for the reaction.

ITEM 20

The *heat of combustion* of a compound is the heat change accompanying the complete combustion (burning in oxygen) of 1 mole of a compound (unless otherwise specified). Either of these equations

$$2H_2(g) + O_2(g) \rightarrow 2H_2O(l) + 136.634 \text{ kcal}$$
$$H_2(g) + \tfrac{1}{2}O_2(g) \rightarrow H_2O(l) + 68.317 \text{ kcal}$$

shows that the heat of combustion of hydrogen is _____ kcal mole^{-1}.

ITEM 30

The procedure of combining reactions to obtain data on a third reaction depends on the fact that the total heat liberated or absorbed in the successive reactions A → B and B → C is the same as in the single, direct reaction A → _____.

ITEM 40

The expression

$$H_2(g) + I_2(s) \rightarrow 2HI(g) \qquad \Delta H = +12.40 \text{ kcal}$$

states that the heat content of $H_2(g) + I_2(s)$ is _____ than that of $2HI(g)$ by _____ kcal. Is the reaction endothermic or exothermic?

ITEM 50

The *heat of formation*, often indicated as ΔH_f, of a compound is defined as the value of ΔH for the reaction in which 1 mole of that compound is formed from its elements in their commonly occurring state at 25° C and 1 atm pressure. Thus, the heat of formation of $HCl(g)$ is _____ kcal mole^{-1}.

Reactants → Products

    Reagents

Heat of combustion

Heat of formation

$\frac{1}{2}H_2(g) + \frac{1}{2}Cl_2(g) \rightarrow HCl(g)$
$\Delta H = -22.1$ kcal

ANSWER 9   exothermic
              endothermic

ANSWER 19   fractions

ANSWER 29 CO_2

ANSWER 39 H(products) $- H$(reactants)

ANSWER 49   greater

ANSWER 10   exothermic
right

(Item 11 is on page 188.)

ANSWER 20   68.317

(Item 21 is on page 188.)

ANSWER 30   C

(Item 31 is on page 188.)

ANSWER 40   less
12.40
endothermic

(Item 41 is on page 188.)

ANSWER 50   −22.1

(Item 51 is on page 188.)

This review has presented many ideas and required much calculation, but this quantitative chemistry is necessary as a basis for everyday laboratory work. Throughout these pages you have seen the importance of the mole concept and the balanced equation in determining the relative amounts of reactants and products, including heat, in a chemical reaction. You have seen how the concentration and volume of a solution are related to the number of moles of solute, and you have learned the theory and stoichiometric terms used most often in acid–base reactions. All this is essential to your further study of chemistry.

REVIEW 5   THE REPRESENTATIVE ELEMENTS

The building of a chemical vocabulary requires not only the memorization of names but also a knowledge of charges, oxidation numbers, and formulas. Using the arrangement of the representative elements in the periodic table as a basis, the first section of this review will help you to become familiar with these elements, their names, their common ions and oxidation numbers, and their simplest compounds. The second section is concerned with the most common anions formed from the representative elements and oxygen.

5–1 THE PERIODIC TABLE AND SIMPLEST COMPOUNDS

The periodic table is of real use to a chemist: It arranges the elements by atomic number, an arrangement that correlates the chemical and physical properties of the elements. As in Section 5–3 of *Chemical Principles*, you will build part of the periodic table and, in doing so, will learn how to name and write formulas for the simplest compounds of the representative elements.

In this chapter you will need to know that electrons of atoms are arranged in energy levels or shells, as mentioned in Section 5–4 of *Chemical Principles*. Energy levels will be discussed in detail in Review 7. For the purposes of this review it is sufficient that you realize that the first shell can contain a maximum of two electrons and the second shell a maximum of eight electrons. Although the higher energy shells can contain more electrons, they reach stability when they are occupied by eight electrons. The properties of atoms are usually determined by the number of electrons in the outermost shell, the highest energy level that is populated by electrons.

If you can write the formulas and names of the metallic oxides of the representative elements and if you can place the representative elements in their proper places in the periodic table, you are already finished with this chapter. The transition metals will be discussed in Review 8.

THE ELEMENTS

1	H	Hydrogen		53	I	Iodine
2	He	Helium		54	Xe	Xenon
3	Li	Lithium		55	Cs	Cesium
4	Be	Beryllium		56	Ba	Barium
5	B	Boron		57	La	Lanthanum
6	C	Carbon		58	Ce	Cerium
7	N	Nitrogen		59	Pr	Praseodymium
8	O	Oxygen		60	Nd	Neodymium
9	F	Fluorine		61	Pm	Promethium
10	Ne	Neon		62	Sm	Samarium
11	Na	Sodium		63	Eu	Europium
12	Mg	Magnesium		64	Gd	Gadolinium
13	Al	Aluminum		65	Tb	Terbium
14	Si	Silicon		66	Dy	Dysprosium
15	P	Phosphorus		67	Ho	Holmium
16	S	Sulfur		68	Er	Erbium
17	Cl	Chlorine		69	Tm	Thulium
18	Ar	Argon		70	Yb	Ytterbium
19	K	Potassium		71	Lu	Lutetium
20	Ca	Calcium		72	Hf	Hafnium
21	Sc	Scandium		73	Ta	Tantalum
22	Ti	Titanium		74	W	Tungsten
23	V	Vanadium		75	Re	Rhenium
24	Cr	Chromium		76	Os	Osmium
25	Mn	Manganese		77	Ir	Iridium
26	Fe	Iron		78	Pt	Platinum
27	Co	Cobalt		79	Au	Gold
28	Ni	Nickel		80	Hg	Mercury
29	Cu	Copper		81	Tl	Thallium
30	Zn	Zinc		82	Pb	Lead
31	Ga	Gallium		83	Bi	Bismuth
32	Ge	Germanium		84	Po	Polonium
33	As	Arsenic		85	At	Astatine
34	Se	Selenium		86	Rn	Radon
35	Br	Bromine		87	Fr	Francium
36	Kr	Krypton		88	Ra	Radium
37	Rb	Rubidium		89	Ac	Actinium
38	Sr	Strontium		90	Th	Thorium
39	Y	Yttrium		91	Pa	Protoactinium
40	Zr	Zirconium		92	U	Uranium
41	Nb	Niobium		93	Np	Neptunium
42	Mo	Molybdenum		94	Pu	Plutonium
43	Tc	Technetium		95	Am	Americium
44	Ru	Ruthenium		96	Cm	Curium
45	Rh	Rhodium		97	Bk	Berkelium
46	Pd	Palladium		98	Cf	Californium
47	Ag	Silver		99	Es	Einsteinium
48	Cd	Cadmium		100	Fm	Fermium
49	In	Indium		101	Md	Mendelevium
50	Sn	Tin		102	No	Nobelium
51	Sb	Antimony		103	Lw	Lawrencium
52	Te	Tellurium		104		

ITEM 1

The atomic number of an element is the same as the number of _____ in the nucleus of each atom of the element and the same as the number of _____ around the nucleus.

ITEM 18

An electron can be added to a halogen atom in two ways. One way is by complete transfer of an electron from an atom of another element. This produces a *halide* ion that has _____ valence electron(s).

ITEM 35

The symbol for the lithium ion is Li^+. Similarly, the sodium ion is written _____. It has the electron arrangement of atoms of the element _____

ITEM 52

The charge on a monatomic ion is its *oxidation state* or *oxidation number*, which is defined as the number of electrons that must be added or removed to convert the ion to a neutral atom. The oxidation number of Ca^{2+} is +2, of Mg^{2+} is _____, and of Cl^- is _____.

ITEM 69

Five elements are characterized by four valence electrons. The atomic numbers and names of these elements are 6, _____; 14, _____; 32, _____; 50, _____; and 82, _____.

ITEM 86

"Arsenious" is the name given to the _____ _____ oxidation state of arsenic. "Arsenic" can refer not only to the name of the element but also to the _____ oxidation state.

ITEM 103

How much of this partial periodic table can you now complete?

Oxidation number

Carbon family

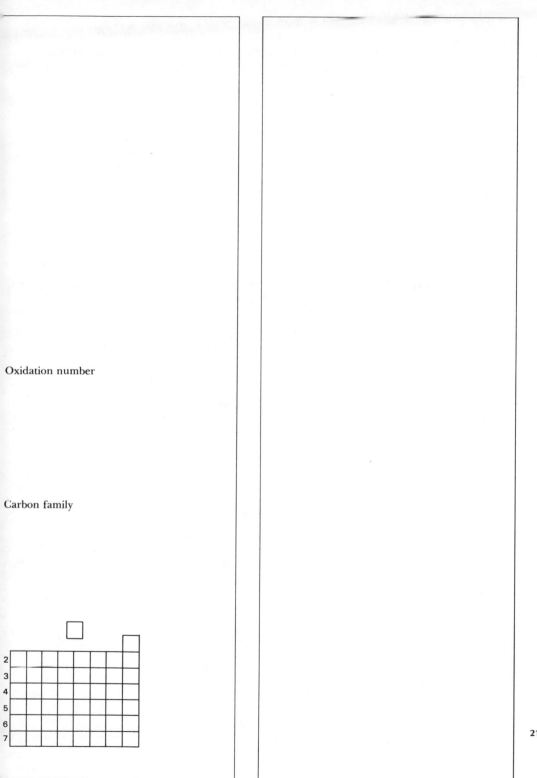

2
3
4
5
6
7

215

ITEM 2

The chemical properties of atoms are dependent on the number of _____ and the energy levels that they occupy.

ITEM 19

A halide ion has _____ more electron(s) than it has protons so each ion has a charge of _____.

ITEM 36

The symbols of the remaining alkali metal cations are _____, _____, _____, and _____. They have the electron arrangements of atoms of the elements _____, _____, _____, and _____, respectively.

ITEM 53

Just as the sum of the ionic charges of an electrically neutral salt must add algebraically to zero, the sum of the oxidation numbers of the ions of a neutral compound must add to _____.

ITEM 70

Enter the symbols for the elements of the carbon family in the diagram at the right.

ITEM 87

Usually the arsenic and antimony halides are named as trihalides or pentahalides. Thus, the chloride compounds of these elements can be named _____, _____, _____, and _____.

(Turn to page 250.)

ANSWER 1   protons
electrons

ANSWER 18   eight

ANSWER 35 Na^+
neon

ANSWER 52 $+2$
-1

ANSWER 69   carbon
silicon
germanium
tin
lead

ANSWER 86 $+3$ (lower)
$+5$ (higher)

ANSWER 103

								He
2	Li	Be	B				F	Ne
3	Na	Mg	Al				Cl	Ar
4	K	Ca	Ga				Br	Kr
5	Rb	Sr	In				I	Xe
6	Cs	Ba	Tl				At	Rn
7	Fr	Ra						

H

217

ITEM 3

The first energy level of an atom can hold a maximum of _____ electrons. The element of atomic number 2, named _____, is a gas that is totally inert to chemical reaction. (Use the table of elements at the beginning of the section as needed.)

ITEM 20

Negative ions are named by replacing "ine" in the element name by "ide"; thus, fluorine becomes _____, chlorine becomes _____, bromine becomes _____, iodine becomes _____, and astatine becomes _____.

ITEM 37

In chemical reactions the valence electrons of alkali metals often are donated to elements of high electron affinity. Each of the ions so formed has _____ electrons in the outermost occupied energy level.

ITEM 54

Since the oxidation number of the barium ion is +2, an ionic compound of barium and chlorine would have the formula _____.

ITEM 71

From its position in the diagram, you can predict that an atom of a carbon family element must share, donate, or accept _____ electrons. An oxidation number of either _____ or _____ might be expected.

ITEM 88

Roman numerals also can be used to indicate the oxidation numbers. In this system, known as *Stock nomenclature*, the arsenic oxidation states are written as _____ and _____.

ANSWER 2   electrons

ANSWER 19   one
                1−

ANSWER 36   K$^+$, Rb$^+$, Cs$^+$, Fr$^+$
                argon
                krypton
                xenon
                radon

ANSWER 53   zero

ANSWER 70

							H			
											He
2	Li	Be	B	C						F	Ne
3	Na	Mg	Al	Si						Cl	Ar
4	K	Ca	Ga	Ge						Br	Kr
5	Rb	Sr	In	Sn						I	Xe
6	Cs	Ba	Tl	Pb						At	Rn
7	Fr	Ra									

ANSWER 87   arsenic trichloride
                arsenic pentachloride
                antimony trichloride
                antimony pentachloride

ITEM 4

The second energy level of an atom can hold a maximum of _____ electrons. The element of atomic number 10, named _____, is also a chemically inert gas.

ITEM 21

The other way in which an electron can be added to the valence shell of a halogen is by sharing. Two electrons (one from each atom) in a molecule of F—F are shared so both atoms have, at least part of the time, _____ valence electron(s).

ITEM 38

The attraction of oppositely charged ions formed by electron transfer between atoms can be called an *ionic* (or *electrovalent*) *bond*. This is in contrast to the bond formed by sharing of electrons, which is called a _____ bond.

ITEM 55

Oxidation numbers are defined also for atoms that form covalent bonds: Two shared electrons are assigned to the atom that has a greater attraction for them. In compounds of a metal and a nonmetal, the _____ has the greater attraction for electrons.

ITEM 72

In fact, the oxidation number of carbon (except in some organic compounds), silicon, and germanium is usually +4. But germanium, tin, and lead have oxidation numbers of both +2 and +4. Write the formulas of the chlorides of the carbon family elements by using the oxidation numbers given.

ITEM 89

With hydrogen the elements of the nitrogen family form compounds in which they have oxidation states of −3 or +3 (depending on whether the nitrogen family element has greater or lesser attraction for electrons than does hydrogen). The formulas of these compounds are _____, _____, _____, _____, and _____.

Ionic bond

ANSWER 3   two
            helium

ANSWER 20   fluoride
            chloride
            bromide
            iodide
            astatide

ANSWER 37   eight, except two in Li^+

ANSWER 54 $BaCl_2$

ANSWER 71   4
            +4
            −4

ANSWER 88   arsenic(III)
            arsenic(V)

ITEM 5

The elements of atomic numbers 18, 36, 54, and 86 have eight electrons in the outermost occupied energy level. These four elements are also extremely unreactive gases. The names of these elements are _____, _____, _____, and _____.

ITEM 22

The sharing of electrons between two atoms produces a *covalent bond.* Just as the bond between atoms in F_2 is covalent, so are the bonds in the other diatomic halogen molecules _____, _____, _____, and _____.

ITEM 39

Crystals of ionic compounds are electrically neutral; thus, the total number of charges on the negative ions must be equal to the total number of charges on the _____ ions.

ITEM 56

For example, electrons can be transferred from beryllium to fluorine, oxygen, and sometimes chlorine so that an ionic bond is formed. With other elements beryllium forms _____ bonds.

ITEM 73

The names of these compounds must reflect the oxidation number of the metal. The easiest way is by addition of a Roman numeral to the metal name; for example, $GeBr_2$ is germanium(II) bromide. Name the tin and lead bromides in this way.

ITEM 90

The diagram (see Item 91) has only one unfilled column. This is the one for the elements containing atoms with six valence electrons. The atomic numbers of these elements are 8, 16, 34, 52, and 84. Their names are _____, _____, _____, _____, and _____.

Covalent bond

Oxygen family

ITEM 6

Thus, there is a special stability associated with atoms in which the outermost energy level populated with electrons, the so-called *valence shell*, contains either the maximum possible number of electrons or _____ of them.

ITEM 23

Place the symbols for the halogen family (atomic numbers 9, 17, 35, 53, 85) and the rare gases (2, 10, 18, 36, 54, 86) in the energy level diagram at the right.

ITEM 40

Since a halide ion has a charge of _____ and an alkali metal ion has a charge of _____, the alkali halide salts have a ratio of metal ions to halide ions of _____.

ITEM 57

In $BeBr_2$ the electrons are attracted more to the bromine atom of a Be—Br bond than to the beryllium atom. Each Br has an oxidation number of -1; Be has an oxidation number of _____.

ITEM 74

Alternatively, the number of halide ions can be specified by prefixes, as in germanium difluoride and germanium tetrafluoride. Name the tin and lead fluorides in this way.

ITEM 91

Complete the diagram at the right with the addition of the symbols of the oxygen family of elements.

	2	3	4	5	6	7

2							
3							
4							
5							
6							
7							

								H	
									He
2	Li	Be	B	C	N		F	Ne
3	Na	Mg	Al	Si	P		Cl	Ar
4	K	Ca	Ga	Ge	As		Br	Kr
5	Rb	Sr	In	Sn	Sb		I	Xe
6	Cs	Ba	Tl	Pb	Bi		At	Rn
7	Fr	Ra						

ANSWER 5
argon
krypton
xenon
radon

ANSWER 22
Cl_2
Br_2
I_2
At_2

ANSWER 39 positive

ANSWER 56 covalent

ANSWER 73
tin(II) bromide
tin(IV) bromide
lead(II) bromide
lead(IV) bromide

ANSWER 90
oxygen
sulfur
selenium
tellurium
polonium

ITEM 7

In other words, atoms containing eight electrons in the valence shell (two electrons for helium) show little tendency to add an electron or to _____ an electron.

ITEM 24

At the top of the halogen column is the empty space for element number 1. For a good reason, a symbol has not yet been put in. Element of atomic number 1, named _____, is unique. Its properties are not similar to those of the halogens or any of the other elements.

ITEM 41

Rare (noble) gas atoms have so little tendency to donate, accept, or share electrons that the elements are composed of single _____.

ITEM 58

All the alkaline earth metals _____, _____, _____, _____, _____, and _____ have _____ electrons in the valence shell and an oxidation number of _____ in compounds.

ITEM 75

Still another system is the use of special names, in which the suffix "ic" indicates the higher of two oxidation states and "ous" indicates the lower. Thus, "stannic" indicates that tin has an oxidation number of _____ and "stannous" indicates that _____.

ITEM 92

Although not as high as those of the halogens, the electron affinities of oxygen and sulfur are high enough that they can accept electrons from metals to form ions. Oxide and sulfide ions have a charge of _____ because _____.

ANSWER 6   eight

ANSWER 23

								He
2							F	Ne
3							Cl	Ar
4							Br	Kr
5							I	Xe
6							At	Rn
7								

ANSWER 40   1−
1+
1/1

ANSWER 57   +2

ANSWER 74   tin difluoride
tin tetrafluoride
lead difluoride
lead tetrafluoride

	H							
								He
2	Li	Be					F	Ne
3	Na	Mg					Cl	Ar
4	K	Ca					Br	Kr
5	Rb	Sr					I	Xe
6	Cs	Ba					At	Rn
7	Fr	Ra						

ANSWER 91

		H							
									He
2	Li	Be	B	C	N	O	F	Ne
3	Na	Mg	Al	Si	P	S	Cl	Ar
4	K	Ca	Ga	Ge	As	Se	Br	Kr
5	Rb	Sr	In	Sn	Sb	Te	I	Xe
6	Cs	Ba	Tl	Pb	Bi	Po	At	Rn
7	Fr	Ra							

ITEM 8

At the right is a crude representation of some of the energy levels in an atom. The first energy level can contain a maximum of _____ electrons. In the top right-hand space, write in the symbol for element number 2.

ITEM 25

Therefore, we have moved the box away from the rest of the chart; now put in the symbol for the first element.

ITEM 42

Because halogen atoms have strong tendencies to accept electrons, the pure halogen elements are comprised of _____ in which atoms share electrons.

ITEM 59

Compounds are usually named as ionic salts, regardless of whether the bonding is ionic or covalent. The "ide" ending and the negative oxidation number are given to the atom that has the greater _____.

ITEM 76

Similarly, "plumbic" indicates that lead has an oxidation number of _____ and "plumbous" indicates that _____.

ITEM 93

All elements except helium, neon, and argon form compounds with bonds to oxygen. In compounds of oxygen with nonmetals, and with some metals, electrons are shared to form _____ bonds.

ANSWER 7   lose

ANSWER 24   hydrogen

ANSWER 41   atoms

ANSWER 58   beryllium
magnesium
calcium
strontium
barium
radium
two
+2

ANSWER 75   +4
tin has an oxidation
number of +2

ANSWER 92   2−
addition of two electrons to
oxygen or sulfur atoms gives
an ion with the electron arrangement of a rare gas

ITEM 9 — Helium is the first of what are called the "rare," "inert," or "noble" gases. Put the symbols of the remaining rare gases in the column at the right of the chart in order of increasing atomic number: 10, 18, 36, 54, 86.

ITEM 26 — In compounds of metals with hydrogen, an electron from the metal becomes bound to a hydrogen atom. The resulting *hydride* ion has a charge of _____ and has the electron arrangement of the element _____.

ITEM 43 — In contrast, a metal crystal is one large molecule composed of positive ions in a cloud of electrons that move freely. This metal structure is possible because the metallic elements have relatively _____ ionization energies.

ITEM 60 — Write the names and formulas (in the form $CaCl_2$) for the iodide salts of the alkaline earth metals. (Note that because alkaline earth metals have only the oxidation number of +2 in compounds, there is no need to indicate in the name that there are two iodide ions per calcium ion.)

ITEM 77 — Give the formula for each of the following: tin(IV) fluoride, _____; germanium(II) bromide, _____; carbon tetraiodide, _____; plumbous chloride, _____; stannic fluoride _____; silicon tetrachloride, _____.

ITEM 94 — The compounds of oxygen are important, and it is useful to know some formulas and names. In nearly all compounds oxygen has the oxidation number of the oxide ion, which is _____. For a neutral compound, the sum of the oxidation numbers on the atoms must be _____.

ANSWER 8 two

ANSWER 25

ANSWER 42   diatomic molecules

ANSWER 59   attraction for electrons

ANSWER 76   +4
              lead has an oxidation
                  number of +2

ANSWER 93   covalent

ITEM 10

Electron affinity is the energy released when an electron is added to a gaseous neutral atom. Would you expect that an electron could be bound to atoms of the rare gases in a chemical reaction?

ITEM 27

H^+, which would be formed by removal of an electron from a hydrogen atom, is never found as the free ion in chemical systems. In H_2 and other hydrogen compounds (except some metal hydrides), electrons are shared so a _____ bond is formed.

ITEM 44

So far, our diagram is filled for the atomic numbers of the rare gases (2, 10, 18, 36, 54, 86) and the elements with atomic numbers that are one more or one less than those of the rare gases. Show these elements in their proper places in the diagram at the right.

ITEM 61

Name the following salts: KF, $SrCl_2$, BaF_2, LiH, $NaBr$, and MgI_2.

ITEM 78

Name the following compounds: SrH_2, $BeBr_2$, $AlBr_3$, SnF_2, $MgCl_2$, PbI_2.

ITEM 95

Write the formulas and names of the oxides of the alkali metals.

Electron affinity

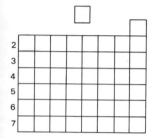

ANSWER 9

							He
2							Ne
3							Ar
4							Kr
5							Xe
6							Rn
7							

ANSWER 26   1—
             helium

ANSWER 43   low

ANSWER 60   beryllium iodide BeI_2
             magnesium iodide MgI_2
             calcium iodide CaI_2
             strontium iodide SrI_2
             barium iodide BaI_2
             radium iodide RaI_2

ANSWER 77 SnF_4
             $GeBr_2$
             CI_4
             $PbCl_2$
             SnF_4
             $SiCl_4$

ANSWER 94   −2
             zero

ITEM 11	Conversely, there are five known elements composed of atoms that contain only seven electrons in the outermost occupied energy level. Would you expect these elements to have a high affinity for electrons?

ITEM 28   Electron affinity is the energy _____.

ITEM 45   Using the diagram in Answer 44 as a guide, write the names of the ionic compounds, or salts, formed by donation of electrons from each alkali metal to the halogen at the end of its row. (Omit francium: It has an unstable nucleus and has been prepared only in trace amounts.)

ITEM 62   Write the formula for each of the following: cesium iodide _____, calcium hydride _____, and radium bromide _____.

ITEM 79   In the diagram at the right enter the symbols of the following: the rare gases, the halogens, the alkali metals, the alkaline earth metals, boron, aluminum, carbon, silicon, germanium, tin, lead.

ITEM 96   Give the formulas and names of the oxides of the alkaline earth metals.

ANSWER 10   No. Atoms of the rare gases have a very stable electron arrangement, so it would require more energy to add an electron than is normally available in chemical reactions.

ANSWER 27   covalent

ANSWER 44

	H							He
2	Li						F	Ne
3	Na						Cl	Ar
4	K						Br	Kr
5	Rb						I	Xe
6	Cs						At	Rn
7	Fr							

ANSWER 61   potassium fluoride
strontium chloride
barium fluoride
lithium hydride
sodium bromide
magnesium iodide

ANSWER 78   strontium hydride
beryllium bromide
aluminum tribromide
tin(II) fluoride, tin difluoride,
   or stannous fluoride
magnesium chloride
lead(II) iodide, lead diiodide,
   or plumbous iodide

ANSWER 95 Li_2O lithium oxide
Na_2O sodium oxide
K_2O potassium oxide
Rb_2O rubidium oxide
Cs_2O cesium oxide
Fr_2O francium oxide

235

ITEM 12

When electrons are added to atoms that have only seven electrons in the valence shell, energy is released. The resulting anions are stable because there are _____ electrons in the valence shell of the ions.

ITEM 29

Whereas energy is released when electrons are added to atoms of some elements, removing an electron from the influence of the positively charged nucleus always requires _____.

ITEM 46

The formulas of these salts can be written as LiF, Li$^+$F$^-$, or (LiF)$_x$, in which x is an indeterminate number. Write formulas of the type LiF for the rest of the salts in Item 45.

ITEM 63

Atoms of five of the elements have three valence electrons. These elements have the atomic numbers 5, 13, 31, 49, and 81. Their names are _____, _____, _____, _____, and _____.

ITEM 80

Atoms of five elements have five valence electrons. The atomic numbers of these elements are 7, 15, 33, 51, and 83. Their names are _____, _____, _____, _____, and _____.

ITEM 97

The formula for aluminum trioxide is _____.

Boron family

Nitrogen family

ANSWER 11   Yes. If an electron is added, there will be eight electrons in the valence shell; this will yield the stable electron arrangement of a rare gas.

ANSWER 28   released when an electron is added to a gaseous, neutral atom

ANSWER 45   lithium fluoride
sodium chloride
potassium bromide
rubidium iodide
cesium astatide

ANSWER 62   CsI
CaH_2
$RaBr_2$

ANSWER 79

									H		
											He
2	Li	Be	B	C			F	Ne
3	Na	Mg	Al	Si			Cl	Ar
4	K	Ca	Ga	Ge			Br	Kr
5	Rb	Sr	In	Sn			I	Xe
6	Cs	Ba	Tl	Pb			At	Rn
7	Fr	Ra						

ANSWER 96   BeO   beryllium oxide
MgO   magnesium oxide
CaO   calcium oxide
SrO   strontium oxide
BaO   barium oxide
RaO   radium oxide

ITEM 13   The atomic numbers of the rare gas elements are 2, 10, 18, 36, 54, and 86. The atomic numbers of the five elements that have seven electrons in the valence shell are _____.

ITEM 30   The energy required to remove an electron from a neutral, gaseous atom is called the *ionization energy*. Would you expect an element of the helium family to have a high or a low ionization energy?

ITEM 47   There are six elements that have two electrons in the valence shell and the rest of the electrons in an inert gas arrangement. It is not difficult to predict that ions formed from these elements would have a charge of _____.

ITEM 64   Write the symbols of the nitrogen family of elements in the diagram at the right.

ITEM 81   The symbols of the nitrogen family of elements are placed in the diagram as at the right.

ITEM 98   Give the formula for each of the following: silicon dioxide, _____; tin monoxide, _____; stannic oxide, _____; stannous sulfide, _____; plumbous oxide, _____; and carbon disulfide, _____.

Ionization energy

ANSWER 12   eight

ANSWER 29   energy

ANSWER 46   NaCl
             KBr
             RbI
             CsAt

ANSWER 63   boron
             aluminum
             gallium
             indium
             thallium

ANSWER 80   nitrogen
             phosphorus
             arsenic
             antimony
             bismuth

ANSWER 97 Al_2O_3

								H		
										He
2	Li	Be							F	Ne
3	Na	Mg							Cl	Ar
4	K	Ca							Br	Kr
5	Rb	Sr							I	Xe
6	Cs	Ba							At	Rn
7	Fr	Ra								

								H		
										He
2	Li	Be	B	C					F	Ne
3	Na	Mg	Al	Si					Cl	Ar
4	K	Ca	Ga	Ge					Br	Kr
5	Rb	Sr	In	Sn					I	Xe
6	Cs	Ba	Tl	Pb					At	Rn
7	Fr	Ra								

ITEM 14

Write the names of the elements containing seven electrons in the outermost occupied energy level.

ITEM 31

However, six of the known elements have an atomic number that is one greater than those of the rare gases. These elements have relatively low ionization energies because _____.

ITEM 48

The atomic numbers of these elements, the *alkaline earth metals*, are 4, 12, 20, 38, 56, and 88. The names of the alkaline earth metals are _____,

_____, _____, _____, _____,

and _____.

ITEM 65

The elements of the boron family, except boron itself, are metals. With nonmetals they form ionic or covalent compounds in which the oxidation number of the metal can be predicted to be _____.

ITEM 82

From the diagram in Answer 81 it is clear that if atoms of these elements gain three electrons, they will have eight valence electrons. You can predict that elements of the nitrogen family could have an oxidation number of _____.

ITEM 99

The formulas and names of the arsenic oxides are As_2O_3: arsenic trioxide, arsenic(III) oxide, or arsenious oxide; and _____.

Alkaline earth metals

ANSWER 13   9, 17, 35, 53, 85

ANSWER 30   High, because removal of an electron would result in a less stable electron arrangement. A large amount of energy is required to remove an electron from a rare gas atom.

ANSWER 47   2+

ANSWER 64

	H							He
2	Li	Be	B				F	Ne
3	Na	Mg	Al				Cl	Ar
4	K	Ca	Ga				Br	Kr
5	Rb	Sr	In				I	Xe
6	Cs	Ba	Tl				At	Rn
7	Fr	Ra						

ANSWER 81

	H							He
2	Li	Be	B	C	N		F	Ne
3	Na	Mg	Al	Si	P		Cl	Ar
4	K	Ca	Ga	Ge	As		Br	Kr
5	Rb	Sr	In	Sn	Sb		I	Xe
6	Cs	Ba	Tl	Pb	Bi		At	Rn
7	Fr	Ra						

ANSWER 98 SiO_2
SnO
SnO_2
SnS
PbO
CS_2

ITEM 15

These elements are known collectively as the *halogen* family. Place the symbols for the halogens in rows 2 to 6 of column 7 in the diagram, in order of increasing atomic number: 9, 17, 35, 53, 85.

ITEM 32

Atoms of elements numbered 3, 11, 19, 37, 55, and 87 have one valence electron. These elements, known as the *alkali metals*, are named _____,

_____, _____, _____, _____,

and _____.

ITEM 49

Enter the symbols for the alkaline earth metals in column 2 of the diagram at the right.

ITEM 66

Aluminum is by far the most important of the boron family metals. Write the formulas for the compounds of aluminum and the halogens. (Omit astatine: It has an unstable nucleus and is extremely rare.)

ITEM 83

Nitrogen and phosphorus have an oxidation number of -3 in some compounds. The symbol for the nitride ion is _____ and for the phosphide ion is _____.

ITEM 100

The formulas and names of the antimony oxides are _____.

Alkali metals

ANSWER 14 fluorine
chlorine
bromine
iodine
astatine

ANSWER 31 removal of one electron leaves an ion with the electron arrangement of a rare gas atom

ANSWER 48 beryllium
magnesium
calcium
strontium
barium
radium

ANSWER 65 $+3$

ANSWER 82 -3

ANSWER 99

As_2O_5: arsenic pentoxide, arsenic(V) oxide, or arsenic oxide (least preferable)

ITEM 16

The electrons in the outermost occupied energy level are called *valence electrons.* Halogen atoms have _____ valence electrons, and atoms of the inert gases have _____ valence electrons.

ITEM 33

Enter the symbols for the alkali metals in column 1 of the chart at the right in order of increasing atomic number: 3, 11, 19, 37, 55, 87.

ITEM 50

Two electrons can be donated from calcium atoms to atoms of high electron affinity. A halogen atom can accept only _____ electron(s).

ITEM 67

The names of aluminum compounds should include a reference to the number of halogen atoms. (It can form polyatomic ions containing four halide ions.) Thus, the prefix "tri" is used, as in aluminum trifluoride. Name the other three important halides of aluminum.

ITEM 84

The formula for sodium nitride is _____, and the formula for calcium phosphide is _____.

ITEM 101

The diagram at the right of the representative elements will be a partial periodic table if the group numbers are added. The group number is the same as the number of valence electrons. It is written in Roman numerals I to VII, followed by the letter "A," at the top of each column. Add group numbers.

						H	
							He
2						F	Ne
3						Cl	Ar
4						Br	Kr
5						I	Xe
6						At	Rn
7							

							H		
									He
2	Li	Be	B	C	N	O	F	Ne	
3	Na	Mg	Al	Si	P	S	Cl	Ar	
4	K	Ca	Ga	Ge	As	Se	Br	Kr	
5	Rb	Sr	In	Sn	Sb	Te	I	Xe	
6	Cs	Ba	Tl	Pb	Bi	Po	At	Rn	
7	Fr	Ra							

ANSWER 15

						He
2					F	Ne
3					Cl	Ar
4					Br	Kr
5					I	Xe
6					At	Rn
7						

ANSWER 32　lithium
sodium
potassium
rubidium
cesium
francium

ANSWER 49

					H			
								He
2	Li	Be					F	Ne
3	Na	Mg					Cl	Ar
4	K	Ca					Br	Kr
5	Rb	Sr					I	Xe
6	Cs	Ba					At	Rn
7	Fr	Ra						

ANSWER 66　AlF_3
$AlCl_3$
$AlBr_3$
AlI_3

ANSWER 83　N^{3-}
P^{3-}

ANSWER 100　Sb_2O_3:　antimony trioxide
　or antimony(III) oxide
Sb_2O_5:　antimony pentoxide
　or antimony(V) oxide

ITEM 17
The chemical properties of all the halogens are very similar: They often react with other substances in such a way that _____ is added to the valence shell.

ITEM 34
When a lithium atom loses one electron, the resulting ion has the electron arrangement of the element _____. The lithium ion has a charge of _____.

ITEM 51
Thus, in an ionic compound of calcium and chlorine, the ratio of chloride ions to calcium ions must be _____ and the formula would be _____.

ITEM 68
Boron is not a metal, a fact from which one can deduce that the ionization energies for the three valence electrons are relatively _____. A boron atom does not donate electrons to other atoms but shares electrons to form _____ bonds in strange and interesting molecules.

ITEM 85
But nitrogen and phosphorus can have any oxidation number from -3 to $+5$; the oxidation number of arsenic, antimony, and bismuth can be $+3$ or $+5$. (The reasons must be bypassed here.) Write the formulas of the bromides of arsenic and antimony.

ITEM 102
In the diagram at the right shade with pencil the spaces filled with symbols of metallic elements. Half-fill the spaces of the "borderline" semimetallic elements germanium, arsenic, antimony, selenium, and tellurium.

ANSWER 16   seven
                 eight

ANSWER 33

	H							He
2	Li						F	Ne
3	Na						Cl	Ar
4	K						Br	Kr
5	Rb						I	Xe
6	Cs						At	Rn
7	Fr							

ANSWER 50   one

ANSWER 67   aluminum trichloride
                 aluminum tribromide
                 aluminum triiodide

ANSWER 84 Na_3N
                 Ca_3P_2

ANSWER 101

	H							
	IA	IIA	IIIA	IVA	VA	VIA	VIIA	He
2	Li	Be	B	C	N	O	F	Ne
3	Na	Mg	Al	Si	P	S	Cl	Ar
4	K	Ca	Ga	Ge	As	Se	Br	Kr
5	Rb	Sr	In	Sn	Sb	Te	I	Xe
6	Cs	Ba	Tl	Pb	Bi	Po	At	Rn
7	Fr	Ra						

	H							
	IA	IIA	IIIA	IVA	VA	VIA	VIIA	He
2	Li	Be	B	C	N	O	F	Ne
3	Na	Mg	Al	Si	P	S	Cl	Ar
4	K	Ca	Ga	Ge	As	Se	Br	Kr
5	Rb	Sr	In	Sn	Sb	Te	I	Xe
6	Cs	Ba	Tl	Pb	Bi	Po	At	Rn
7	Fr	Ra						

ANSWER 17   one electron

(Item 18 is on page 214.)

ANSWER 34   helium
1+

(Item 35 is on page 214.)

ANSWER 51   2/1
$CaCl_2$ or $Ca^{2+}(Cl^-)_2$
or $(CaCl_2)_x$

(Item 52 is on page 214.)

ANSWER 68   high
covalent

(Item 69 is on page 214.)

ANSWER 85 $AsBr_3$
$AsBr_5$
$SbBr_3$
$SbBr_5$

(Item 86 is on page 214.)

ANSWER 102

	H						
IA	IIA	IIIA	IVA	VA	VIA	VIIA	He
2 Li	Be	B	C	N	O	F	Ne
3 Na	Mg	Al	Si	P	S	Cl	Ar
4 K	Ca	Ga	Ge	As	Se	Br	Kr
5 Rb	Sr	In	Sn	Sb	Te	I	Xe
6 Cs	Ba	Tl	Pb	Bi	Po	At	Rn
7 Fr	Ra						

(Item 103 is on page 214.)

By now you need not have memorized the periodic table of the representative elements, but you should know the positions of the more common elements and the relationship between the position of an element and its usual oxidation number.

5-2 NAMES AND FORMULAS OF THE POLYATOMIC ANIONS

The nonmetals and semimetals of the representative elements can be bonded covalently to oxygen in molecules and polyatomic ions. Some of the possible anions are found so often in minerals and common chemicals that it is important to know their names and to be able to write formulas for compounds in which they occur. This section provides practice in writing the names and formulas of the important representative element anions. More of these anions are given in Table 3–4 of *Chemical Principles.*

The name of a polyatomic ion depends on the oxidation state of the element that is combined with oxygen. For this reason it is necessary for you to know that the oxidation number of oxygen in all the anions is −2. Further, the sum of the oxidation numbers of the atoms in an ion must be equal to the charge on the ion.

If you can answer correctly Items 37–40 at the end of the section, there is no reason for you to do the rest of the items.

ITEM 1

The anion formed by the combination of an oxide ion with hydrogen is the hydroxide ion for which the symbol is _____. Remembering that NH_4^+ is the ammonium ion, name the following compounds: LiOH, Al(OH)$_3$, Mg(OH)$_2$, NH$_4$OH.

ITEM 8

Name the following ions: ClO_4^-, ClO_2^-, ClO^-, ClO_3^-.

ITEM 15

The acids corresponding to the chlorine anions are *hypochlorous*, HClO (or HOCl, which indicates the structure); *chlorous*, HClO$_2$; *chloric*, HClO$_3$; and *perchloric*, _____.

ITEM 22

Write formulas for the compounds sodium thiosulfate _____, calcium sulfite _____, magnesium sulfate _____, cesium sulfide _____, lithium iodate _____, and potassium hydrogen sulfite _____.

ITEM 29

Give the names corresponding to K$_3$PO$_4$, NaH$_2$PO$_4$, Mg$_3$(PO$_4$)$_2$, CaHPO$_4$, Ca(H$_2$PO$_4$)$_2$.

ITEM 36

Write the formulas of the following: magnesium borate, ammonium carbonate, potassium hydrogen sulfate, sodium chlorate.

ITEM 2   As a monatomic ion, a halogen has the oxidation
                              number _____. When a halogen (except
                              fluorine) is bonded to one or more oxygen atoms, it
                              has other oxidation numbers.

ITEM 9   Write formulas for the following compounds: lithium
                              hypochlorite, _____; potassium perchlorate,
                              _____; magnesium chlorate, _____; am-
                              monium chlorite, _____; beryllium chloride,
                              _____.

ITEM 16   It is apparent that "ous" in the acid name is con-
                              verted to _____ in the anion name; and "ic"
                              in the acid name is converted to _____ in the
                              anion name.

ITEM 23   Give the names corresponding to the formulas
                              $(NH_4)_2SO_4$, BaS_2O_3, $CsHSO_4$, $Mg(ClO)_2$.

ITEM 30   Write the formulas for the sodium salts containing
                              the anions nitrite, sulfite, phosphate, perchlorate,
                              and hypobromite.

ITEM 37   Write the formulas of the lithium compounds con-
                              taining the anions thiosulfate, iodate, borate, hydro-
                              gen sulfate, and bicarbonate.

ANSWER 1 OH^-
            lithium hydroxide
            aluminum trihydroxide
                (or aluminum hydroxide)
            magnesium hydroxide
            ammonium hydroxide

ANSWER 8   perchlorate
            chlorite
            hypochlorite
            chlorate

ANSWER 15 $HClO_4$

ANSWER 22 $Na_2S_2O_3$
            $CaSO_3$
            $MgSO_4$
            Cs_2S
            $LiIO_3$
            $KHSO_3$

ANSWER 29   potassium phosphate
            (or tripotassium phosphate)
            sodium dihydrogen
                phosphate
            magnesium phosphate
            calcium hydrogen phosphate
            calcium dihydrogen
                phosphate

ANSWER 36 $Mg_3(BO_3)_2$
            $(NH_4)_2CO_3$
            $KHSO_4$
            $NaClO_3$

ITEM 3

For example, in the *hypochlorite* ion, ClO⁻, oxygen has an oxidation number of −2, so Cl must have an oxidation number of _____.

ITEM 10

Name the following compounds: $NaClO$, $Ca(ClO_3)_2$, NH_4ClO_4, $KClO_2$.

ITEM 17

The names and formulas of the iodine acids are *hypoiodous*, _____; _____, _____; _____, _____; and _____, _____.

ITEM 24

The two important nitrogen–oxygen anions are derived from *nitric acid,* HNO_3, and *nitrous acid,* HNO_2. The ion NO_3^- is named _____, and NO_2^- is named _____.

ITEM 31

Phosphorous acid is H_2HPO_3. As you might expect, all the anions derived from it contain the word _____.

ITEM 38

Write the formulas of the magnesium compounds containing the ions nitrate, hydrogen phosphate, bromide, bromite, and sulfite.

ANSWER 2   −1

ANSWER 9   LiClO (or LiOCl)
            $KClO_4$
            $Mg(ClO_3)_2$
            NH_4ClO_2
            $BeCl_2$

ANSWER 16   "ite"
            "ate"

ANSWER 23

ammonium sulfate (or diammonium sulfate)
barium thiosulfate
cesium hydrogen sulfate (cesium acid sulfate
    or cesium bisulfate)
magnesium hypochlorite

ANSWER 30 $NaNO_2$
            Na_2SO_3
            Na_3PO_4
            $NaClO_4$
            NaOBr (or NaBrO)

ANSWER 37 $Li_2S_2O_3$
            $LiIO_3$
            Li_3BO_3
            $LiHSO_4$
            $LiHCO_3$

The oxidation number of Cl in the *chlorite* ion, ClO_2^-, is _____; in the *chlorate* ion, ClO_3^-, it is _____; and in the *perchlorate* ion, ClO_4^-, it is _____.

ITEM 11

By analogy with the chlorine–oxygen anions, you realize that the name of BrO^- is *hypobromite*, that of BrO_2^- is _____, that of BrO_3^- is _____, and that of BrO_4^- is _____.

ITEM 18

When H_2SO_4 reacts with bases, either one or two hydrogen ions can be donated to bases, so two anions are possible.
$$H_2SO_4 + OH^- \rightarrow H_2O + HSO_4^-$$
$$HSO_4^- + OH^- \rightarrow \underline{\hspace{2cm}}.$$

ITEM 25

Give the names of the following compounds: $Ca(NO_2)_2$, $Ba(NO_3)_2$, K_2SO_3, MgS_2O_3, KNO_2.

ITEM 32

One hydrogen in H_2HPO_3 is bonded to phosphorus and cannot be donated to a base. Thus, there are only two anions possible: *phosphite*, HPO_3^{2-}, and *hydrogen phosphite*, _____.

ITEM 39

Write the formulas of the aluminum compounds containing the ions sulfate, sulfide, phosphate, hydroxide, and perchlorate.

ANSWER 3   +1

ANSWER 10   sodium hypochlorite
calcium chlorate
ammonium perchlorate
potassium chlorite

ANSWER 17   HIO (or HOI)
iodous, HIO_2
iodic, HIO_3
periodic, HIO_4

ANSWER 24   nitrate
nitrite

ANSWER 31   phosphite

ANSWER 38 $Mg(NO_3)_2$
$MgHPO_4$
$MgBr_2$
$Mg(BrO_2)_2$
$MgSO_3$

ITEM 5

You notice that the names of the anions with the two lower oxidation states of Cl, hypochlorite and chlorite, have the suffix "ite" and the two higher oxidation state names, chlorate and _____, have the suffix _____.

ITEM 12

Write the names of the following compounds: $Mg(BrO_2)_2$, $LiBrO$, $KBrO_4$, $Ca(BrO_3)_2$.

ITEM 19

The anion SO_4^{2-} is named *sulfate*, and HSO_4^- is named *hydrogen sulfate* (sometimes *acid sulfate* or *bisulfate*). The formula for calcium sulfate is _____, and the one for calcium hydrogen sulfate is _____.

ITEM 26

Write formulas for the following: magnesium perchlorate, sodium nitrate, sodium nitride, sodium nitrite, lithium sulfite.

ITEM 33

Noting this exception to the usual nomenclature, write the formula for sodium phosphite and the formula for sodium hydrogen phosphite.

ITEM 40

Write the formulas of each of the following anions: borate, carbonate, dihydrogen phosphate, thiosulfate, bicarbonate, hypochlorite.

ANSWER 4   +3
+5
+7

ANSWER 11   bromite
bromate
perbromate

ANSWER 18 $H_2O + SO_4{}^{2-}$

ANSWER 25   calcium nitrite
barium nitrate
potassium sulfite
magnesium thiosulfate
potassium nitrite

ANSWER 32 $HHPO_3{}^-$ (or $H_2PO_3{}^-$)

ANSWER 39 $Al_2(SO_4)_3$
Al_2S_3
$AlPO_4$
$Al(OH)_3$
$Al(ClO_4)_3$

ITEM 6

The prefix "hypo" indicates a lower oxidation state than the "ite" anion. For chlorine–oxygen anions, *hypochlorite* indicates the Cl oxidation number _____ and the formula _____; *chlorite* indicates the oxidation number _____ and the formula _____.

ITEM 13

Similarly, IO_3^- is named *iodate*, and IO_4^- is named _____. IO^- is named _____, and IO_2^- is named _____.

ITEM 20

The names and formulas for the potassium salts containing the two sulfate ions are _____, _____; and _____, _____.

ITEM 27

Phosphoric acid, H_3PO_4, can donate three hydrogen ions to bases. Therefore, there are three phosphate ions: the *normal phosphate*, PO_4^{3-}; *hydrogen phosphate*, HPO_4^{2-}; and *dihydrogen phosphate*, _____.

ITEM 34

Three important anions remaining are *carbonate*, CO_3^{2-}; *bicarbonate* (or *hydrogen carbonate*), HCO_3^-; and *borate*, BO_3^{3-}. The two acids from which they are derived are named _____ and _____ and have the formulas _____ and _____, respectively.

ANSWER 5   perchlorate
            "ate"

ANSWER 12   magnesium bromite
            lithium hypobromite
            potassium perbromate
            calcium bromate

ANSWER 19 $CaSO_4$
            $Ca(HSO_4)_2$

ANSWER 26 $Mg(ClO_4)_2$
            $NaNO_3$
            Na_3N
            $NaNO_2$
            Li_2SO_3

ANSWER 33 Na_2HPO_3
            $NaHHPO_3$ (or NaH_2PO_3)

ANSWER 40 BO_3^{3-}
            CO_3^{2-}
            $H_2PO_4^-$
            $S_2O_3^{2-}$
            HCO_3^-
            ClO^-

ITEM 7

The prefix "per" indicates a higher oxidation state than the "ate" anion. For chlorine anions, *chlorate* indicates the oxidation number _____ and the formula _____; *perchlorate* indicates the oxidation number _____ and the formula _____.

ITEM 14

Name the following: NH_4BrO_3, $CsIO_4$, $NaBrO$, KIO_3, $Ca(IO)_2$.

ITEM 21

Other important sulfur anions are *sulfite*, SO_3^{2-}; *hydrogen sulfite* (*acid sulfite* or *bisulfite*), HSO_3^-; and *thiosulfate*, $S_2O_3^{2-}$. Give the formulas and names of the lithium salts containing these anions.

ITEM 28

Write formulas for the following: disodium hydrogen phosphate _____, potassium dihydrogen phosphate _____, magnesium dihydrogen phosphate _____, sodium phosphate (or trisodium phosphate) _____, calcium phosphate _____.

ITEM 35

Write the names of the compounds $CaCO_3$, K_3BO_3, $Mg(HCO_3)_2$.

ANSWER 6   +1
              ClO^-
              +3
              ClO_2^-

ANSWER 13   periodate
              hypoiodite
              iodite

ANSWER 20

potassium sulfate (or dipotassium sulfate),
      K_2SO_4
potassium hydrogen sulfate (or potassium acid
      sulfate or potassium bisulfate), $KHSO_4$

ANSWER 27 $H_2PO_4^-$

ANSWER 34   carbonic
              boric
              H_2CO_3
              H_3BO_3

ANSWER 7 $+5$
                 ClO_3^-
                 $+7$
                 ClO_4^-

(*Item 8 is on page 252.*)

ANSWER 14   ammonium bromate
                  cesium periodate
                  sodium hypobromite
                  potassium iodate
                  calcium hypoiodite

(*Item 15 is on page 252.*)

ANSWER 21

Li_2SO_3, lithium sulfite (or dilithium sulfite)
$LiHSO_3$, lithium hydrogen sulfite, (lithium
       acid sulfite or lithium bisulfite)
$Li_2S_2O_3$, lithium thiosulfate

(*Item 22 is on page 252.*)

ANSWER 28 Na_2HPO_4
                  KH_2PO_4
                  $Mg(H_2PO_4)_2$
                  Na_3PO_4
                  $Ca_3(PO_4)_2$

(*Item 29 is on page 252.*)

ANSWER 35   calcium carbonate
                  potassium borate
                       (or tripotassium borate)
                  magnesium bicarbonate
                       (or magnesium hydrogen
                       carbonate)

(*Item 36 is on page 252.*)

REVIEW 6   BALANCING REDOX EQUATIONS

The ability to balance chemical equations is essential to understanding chemical reactions. Balanced equations show the relative numbers of ions and molecules that are involved in a chemical reaction and that are therefore necessary for calculations of relative weights of reagents and products. Balanced equations also provide the first step for quantitative treatments of chemical equilibria and electrochemistry.

Many simple equations often can be balanced by inspection, but equations involving oxidation and reduction may be difficult to balance so directly. An easy system for balancing such equations is the ion–electron method discussed in *Chemical Principles*, Section 6–4.

This review provides a step-by-step development of the method and practice in balancing equations. When you have completed the items, you will be able to balance any reaction involving oxidation and reduction by this method, once you know what the reactants and products are.

It is assumed in this review that you already have learned how to assign oxidation numbers to the atoms of an ion or a molecule. This procedure is discussed in detail in Section 6–2 of *Chemical Principles*, and a short review is included here.

ASSIGNMENT OF OXIDATION NUMBERS

Oxidation numbers provide a "bookkeeping" procedure for counting the electrons that can be associated with, or assigned to, each atom of a molecule or ion. An oxidation number of zero implies that the atom in a molecule or ion is assigned the same number of electrons as it has in the free atom. Negative values of oxidation numbers correspond to a greater number of electrons than in the neutral atom, whereas positive values correspond to a smaller number of electrons.

The rules for assigning oxidation numbers to atoms in molecules or ions can be summarized as follows.

(1) The atoms in an element, such as He, H_2, O_2, S_8, C, Zn, Li, have an oxidation number of zero.

(2) Simple, one-atom ions, such as Cl^-, Zn^{2+}, Li^+, have oxidation numbers equal to the charge on the ion. (This means that the alkali metals, except as the element or when combined with each other, have an oxidation number of +1. The alkaline earth metals form only 2+ ions and have oxidation numbers of +2.)

(3) Except for H_2 and the metal hydrides, the oxidation number of the hydrogen atom in any molecule or ion is +1. In the metal hydrides, such as NaH and CaH_2, H is assigned the value −1.

(4) Except for O_2, O_3 (ozone), OF_2, peroxides, and the superoxides (KO_2, RbO_2, CsO_2), the oxidation number of the oxygen atom in any molecule or ion is −2. In peroxides, such as HOOH, the oxygen atoms are assigned the oxidation number −1, and in the superoxides, $-\frac{1}{2}$.

(5) When two nonmetal atoms are bonded in an ion or molecule, the nonmetal considered the most negative is assigned an oxidation number of the same value as its most common negative ion. Which of the two atoms is more negative depends on the positions of the elements in the periodic table: The element either above or to the right of the other is more negative. For example, in OF_2, F is assigned the oxidation number −1, and O has the oxidation number +2.

(6) The algebraic sum of the oxidation numbers of all the atoms in a molecule must be zero. For example, for CH_4, since each H has an oxidation number of +1, the carbon atom

must have the value -4 to give a total value for the molecule of zero.

(7) The sum of the oxidation numbers of all the atoms of an ion must equal the charge on the ion. For the sulfate ion SO_4^{2-}, since each oxygen has an oxidation number of -2, the sulfur atom in SO_4^{2-} must have an oxidation number of $+6$. Then the total for the ion is -2, which is equal to the charge on the ion.

To test whether you know and understand these rules, whether you can assign oxidation numbers, and whether you are ready to start balancing equations, assign oxidation numbers to the atoms in each of the following examples:

(1) N_2 (2) NH_3 (3) H_2O_2 (4) Na_2CO_3

(5) CO_3^{2-} (6) Ce_2O_3 (7) HBr (8) BrO^-

(9) $KMnO_4$ (10) MnO_2 (11) $Cr_2O_7^{2-}$ (12)

PCl_3 (13) ClF (14) $P(OH)_3$ (15) C_2H_6.

ANSWERS

(1) N has an oxidation number of zero (Rule 1).

(2) H has an oxidation number of $+1$ (Rule 3), and to make the total of the oxidation numbers of the molecule equal to zero, N must have an oxidation number of -3 (Rule 6).

(3) This is a peroxide. Each H has an oxidation number of $+1$; each O has an oxidation number of -1 (Rule 4).

(4) Each Na has an oxidation number of $+1$; each O has an oxidation number of -2. For the total of the molecule to be zero, the carbon atom must be assigned the value $+4$ (Rule 6).

(5) Each O is -2, and C must be $+4$ to make the total for the ion equal to the ion's charge (Rule 7).

(6) Each O is -2, and each cerium atom must be $+3$ to give a total for the molecule of zero.

(7) Since each H is $+1$, Br must be -1.

(8) Since O is -2, Br must be $+1$ so the charge on the ion is -1.

(9) Since each O is -2 and K is $+1$, Mn must be $+7$ to give a total of zero for the molecule.

(10) Since each O is -2, Mn must be $+4$.

(11) Since each O is −2, each Cr must be +6 for the total of the oxidation numbers to be equal to the charge on the ion.

(12) Cl is to the right of phosphorus in the periodic table; therefore, Cl is assigned its usual negative charge of −1 and P must be +3, so the total for the molecule is zero.

(13) F is above Cl in the periodic table, so F is assigned the value −1 and Cl is +1.

(14) Each O is −2 and each H is +1, so the total of 3 OH^- is −3. Therefore, P must be +3, so the total for the molecule will be zero.

(15) Each H is +1; each C in this compound is then −3.

The word *redox* describes a reaction in which electrons are transferred from one substance to another. It is derived from the words _____duction and _____dation.

The equation for a half-reaction is balanced if, on each side of the equation, there are the same number of atoms of each element and the same net charge. The net charge is determined by adding the charges on the ions and the electrons. In the preceding equation (Answer 14) the charge on each electron is, of course, _____, and on Fe^{3+} it is _____.

Because the charge is not equal on the two sides of the equation, we can infer that some additional charged species is involved in the half-reaction. If the reaction occurs in basic aqueous solution, we generally assume that OH^- ions are involved. Rewrite the equation at the right and add enough OH^- ions to balance the charges.

Check the number of oxygen atoms on both sides. Is the equation completely balanced?

Completely balance the equation with respect to atoms and check it.

In this equation, if H^+ is changed to H_3O^+, the final equation is _____.

$$\overset{+5}{NO_3^-} + 3e^- \rightarrow \overset{+2}{NO}$$

$$3Cu + 8H^+ + 2NO_3^- \rightarrow$$
$$3Cu^{2+} + 2NO + 4H_2O$$

ITEM 2

Oxidation numbers help us to keep track of the number of electrons associated with a particular atom or ion. Since in redox reactions _____ are transferred from one reagent to another, the _____ of the atoms of the reagents change.

ITEM 16

Therefore, in the equation $Fe^{3+} + 3e^- \rightarrow Fe$, the net charge on each side is _____. This equation is balanced with respect to atoms, electrons, and net charge.

ITEM 30

If the half-reaction at the right occurs in acidic solution, H_3O^+ is the reagent that is generally assumed to be involved, but H_3O^+ is usually abbreviated to H^+. Rewrite the equation to show this addition.

ITEM 44

Again, the same basic procedure has been followed: first, assignment of _____ and balancing of the number of _____ of the element being reduced or _____; second, addition of _____ to balance the change in _____.

ITEM 58

Balance the half-reaction for the reduction $H_3AsO_4 \rightarrow HAsO_2$ (acidic solution) with respect to electrons, charge, and atoms.

ITEM 72

Check the total equation. Is it balanced with respect to both charge and atoms?

$+5 \qquad\qquad +2$

$NO_3^- + 3e^- \rightarrow NO$

ANSWER 1   re
oxi

ANSWER 15   1−
3+

ANSWER 29 $+5 \qquad\qquad +2$
$NO_3^- + 3e^- \rightarrow NO + 4OH^-$

ANSWER 43   Yes
(left: 8)
(right: 8)

ANSWER 57

$\qquad\quad 0 \quad\; +5$
$6H_2O + I_2 \rightarrow 2IO_3^- + 10e^- + 12H^+$

ANSWER 71

$3Cu + 8H_3O^+ + 2NO_3$
$\qquad \rightarrow 3Cu^{2+} + 2NO + 12H_2O$

If a reagent loses electrons, its oxidation number is increased. In the example $Cu^+ - e^- \rightarrow Cu^{2+}$, the oxidation number of copper increases from _____ to _____; Cu^+ has been *oxidized* to Cu^{2+}.

ITEM 17

In the equation

$$\overset{0}{Cr} + 4\overset{-2+1}{OH^-} \rightarrow \overset{+3-2}{CrO_2^-} + 2\overset{+1-2}{H_2O} + 3e^-$$

the net charge on the left is _____ and on the right is _____.

ITEM 31

For reactions that occur in acidic solution, equations are balanced by adding H^+. For reactions occurring in basic solution, _____ ions are added to balance charge.

ITEM 45

The third step has been to balance the charge on both sides of the equation by adding _____ for reactions in acidic solution or _____ for reactions in basic solution. Next, the number of H atoms has been balanced by adding _____. Finally, the equation has been checked by counting _____.

ITEM 59

Completely balance the equation for the half-reaction $HSnO_2^- \rightarrow Sn(OH)_6^{2-}$ (basic solution).

The overall reaction is a combination of two half-reactions. You must recognize the two half-reactions (after assignment of oxidation numbers), balance the half-reactions separately, and finally combine them so the number of electrons produced in one half-reaction equals the number consumed in the other.

ITEM 73

Assign oxidation numbers to the atoms in the reaction $Cl_2 \rightarrow Cl^- + HClO$ (acidic solution).

ANSWER 2   electrons
                 oxidation numbers

ANSWER 16   left: $(3+) + 3(1-) = 0$
                 right: 0

ANSWER 30 $+5$ $+2$
                 $NO_3^- + 3e^- + 4H^+ \rightarrow NO$

ANSWER 44   oxidation numbers
                 atoms
                 oxidized
                 electrons
                 oxidation number

ANSWER 58

$+1+5-2$ $+1+3-2$
$H_3AsO_4 \rightarrow HAsO_2$
$2e^- + H_3AsO_4 \rightarrow HAsO_2$
$2H^+ + 2e^- + H_3AsO_4 \rightarrow HAsO_2$
$2H^+ + 2e^- + H_3AsO_4 \rightarrow HAsO_2 + 2H_2O$

ANSWER 72   Yes.

It is customary to write equations showing the *addition* of electrons to the appropriate side and to place the oxidation number of each atom above its symbol. Rewrite the equation at the right for the oxidation of Cu^+ in this way.

ITEM 18

A simple example will illustrate how a half-reaction is balanced: To begin balancing the half-reaction $Cl_2 \rightarrow Cl^-$, first assign oxidation numbers to the reagents.

ITEM 32

The equation at the right is balanced with respect to electrons and charge. It is not balanced with respect to _____.

ITEM 46

In basic aqueous solution $Be_2O_3^{2-}$ can be converted to Be. Write this much of the equation and assign oxidation numbers.

ITEM 60

Metallic silver dissolves in nitric acid to give Ag^+ and NO. To begin balancing the equation for this reaction, assign oxidation numbers to the atoms.

ITEM 74

In this reaction, part of the Cl_2 is reduced to _____ and part is oxidized to _____.

$Cu^+ - e^- \rightarrow Cu^{2+}$

$$\overset{+5}{NO_3^-} + 3e^- + 4H^+ \rightarrow \overset{+2}{NO}$$

$Ag + NO_3^- \rightarrow Ag^+ + NO$

ANSWER 3 $+1$
                $+2$

ANSWER 17   left: $4(1-) = 4-$
                right: $(1-) + 3(1-) = 4-$

ANSWER 31 OH^-

ANSWER 45 H^+
                OH^-
                H_2O
                oxygen atoms

ANSWER 59

$$\overset{+1+2-2}{HSnO_2^-} \rightarrow \overset{+4-2+1}{Sn(OH)_6^{2-}}$$
$$HSnO_2^- \rightarrow Sn(OH)_6^{2-} + 2e^-$$
$$3OH^- + HSnO_2^- \rightarrow Sn(OH)_6^{2-} + 2e^-$$
$$H_2O + 3OH^- + HSnO_2^- \rightarrow Sn(OH)_6^{2-} + 2e^-$$

ANSWER 73 $\overset{0}{Cl_2} \rightarrow \overset{-1}{Cl^-} + \overset{+1+1-2}{HClO}$

When an atom or ion is oxidized, its oxidation number is _____ creased.

Next, balance the number of atoms of the element being oxidized or reduced.

If the reaction occurs in aqueous solution, H_2O molecules may be involved as reactants or products. Balance the hydrogen atoms in the equation by adding an appropriate number of H_2O molecules.

Is the half-reaction $Be_2O_3^{2-} \rightarrow Be$ a reduction or an oxidation?

The element undergoing oxidation is _____. Therefore, the easily balanced oxidation half-reaction is _____.

The two balanced half-reactions are

$$2e^- + Cl_2 \rightarrow 2Cl^-$$
$$2H_2O + Cl_2 \rightarrow 2HClO + 2e^- + 2H^+$$

They combine to give the total balanced equation _____.

Additional examples of redox equations follow. Balance each equation, using the method outlined in this chapter. The steps in balancing each equation appear on the page following the question. Practice on these equations until you have mastered the procedure and can balance them without help.

$$+5 \qquad\qquad\qquad +2$$
$$NO_3^- + 3e^- + 4H^+ \rightarrow NO$$

ANSWER 4 $\quad +1 \qquad +2$
$$Cu^+ \rightarrow Cu^{2+} + e^-$$

ANSWER 18 $\quad 0 \qquad -1$
$$Cl_2 \rightarrow Cl^-$$

ANSWER 32 $\quad$ the number of atoms
of H and O

ANSWER 46 $\quad +2-2 \qquad 0$
$$Be_2O_3^{2-} \rightarrow Be$$

ANSWER 60 $\quad 0 \quad +5-2 \qquad +1 \quad +2-2$
$$Ag + NO_3^- \rightarrow Ag^+ + NO$$

ANSWER 74 $\qquad -1$
$$Cl^- \text{ (Cl)}$$
$$\qquad\quad +1$$
$$HClO \text{ (Cl)}$$

281

ITEM 6

Complete the equation at the right. Show the oxidation of H^- to H_2 by adding electrons to the appropriate side and assigning oxidation numbers.

ITEM 20

The oxidation numbers are used in balancing electrons: Since each of the Cl atoms shows a decrease in oxidation number from _____ to _____, a total of _____ electrons must be picked up by Cl_2. Rewrite the equation to show the addition of these electrons.

ITEM 34

If the equation is balanced also with respect to oxygen atoms, the equation is completely balanced. Check this.
Number of O atoms on left: _____.
Number of O atoms on right: _____.

ITEM 48

After assignment of oxidation numbers, the next step is to balance _____.

ITEM 62

The element undergoing reduction is _____.
The unbalanced half-reaction is _____.

ITEM 76

$$H_2S + Cr_2O_7^{2-} \rightarrow S + Cr^{3+} \quad \text{(acid solution)}$$

(Use the summary on page 202 if you need it.)

$2H^- \rightarrow H_2$

ANSWER 5   in

ANSWER 19   0   −1
$Cl_2 \rightarrow 2Cl^-$

ANSWER 33

+5   +2
$NO_3^- + 3e^- + 4H^+ \rightarrow NO + 2H_2O$

ANSWER 47   reduction

ANSWER 61   Ag
     0   +1
$Ag \rightarrow Ag^+ + e^-$

0   +5−2   +1   +2−2
$Ag + NO_3^- \rightarrow Ag^+ + NO$

ANSWER 75

$2H_2O + 2Cl_2 \rightarrow 2Cl^- + 2HClO + 2H^+$
or
$H_2O + Cl_2 \rightarrow Cl^- + HClO + H^+$
or
$2H_2O + Cl_2 \rightarrow Cl^- + HClO + H_3O^+$

ITEM 7

Reduction of a reagent corresponds to an increase in the number of electrons assigned to an atom of the reagent. Therefore, when an atom is reduced, its oxidation number is _____.

ITEM 21

This equation has been balanced with respect to atoms and electrons. What is the net charge on each side?

ITEM 35

Tabulate the steps that have been taken to balance the half-reaction treated in the preceding items: (a) Assign oxidation numbers and balance the number of atoms of the element being oxidized or reduced. (b) Add _____ to balance the change in oxidation number. (c) Add _____ or _____ to balance the charge. (d) Add _____. (e) Check by seeing that the oxygen atoms are balanced.

ITEM 49

Then the equation becomes _____.

ITEM 63

Balance this half-reaction.

ITEM 77

$$ClO^- + CrO_2^- \rightarrow Cl^- + CrO_4^{2-} \quad \text{(basic solution)}$$

$$+2 \qquad 0$$
$$Be_2O_3{}^{2-} \rightarrow Be$$

ANSWER 6 $\quad -1 \qquad 0$
$$2H^- \rightarrow H_2 + 2e^-$$

ANSWER 20 $\quad 0$
$\qquad\qquad\qquad\quad -1$
$\qquad\qquad\qquad\quad$ two
$\qquad\qquad\qquad\quad 0 \qquad\qquad -1$
$\qquad\qquad\qquad$ $Cl_2 + 2e^- \rightarrow 2Cl^-$

ANSWER 34 $\quad$ left: 3
$\qquad\qquad\qquad$ right: 3

ANSWER 48 $\quad$ the number of atoms of Be
$\qquad\qquad\qquad$ (the element being reduced)

ANSWER 62 $\quad$ nitrogen
$\qquad\qquad\qquad +5 \qquad +2$
$\qquad\qquad\qquad$ $NO_3^- \rightarrow NO$

ANSWER 76

$$H_2S + Cr_2O_7{}^{2-} \rightarrow S + Cr^{3+} \text{ (acid solution)}$$

$$-2 \quad 0$$
$$H_2S \rightarrow S + 2H^+ + 2e^-$$
$$+6 \qquad\qquad\qquad\qquad\qquad +3$$
$$Cr_2O_7{}^{2-} + 14H^+ + 6e^- \rightarrow 2Cr^{3+} + 7H_2O$$

$$3H_2S \rightarrow 3S + 6H^+ + 6e^-$$
$$\underline{Cr_2O_7{}^{2-} + 14H^+ + 6e^- \rightarrow 2Cr^{3+} + 7H_2O}$$
$$3H_2S + Cr_2O_7{}^{2-} + 8H^+ \rightarrow 3S + 2Cr^{3+} + 7H_2O$$
or $\quad 3H_2S + Cr_2O_7{}^{2-} + 8H_3O^+ \rightarrow 3S + 2Cr^{3+} + 15H_2O$

285

Write the equation and include oxidation numbers for the reduction of Cu^{2+} to Cu^+.

ITEM 22

Balance the equation for the half-reaction $S_8 \rightarrow S^{2-}$ by first assigning oxidation numbers and balancing atoms.

ITEM 36

In acidic solution, $S_2O_3^{2-}$ can be converted to SO_4^{2-}. Assign oxidation numbers in the half-reaction

$$S_2O_3^{2-} \rightarrow SO_4^{2-}$$

ITEM 50

The next step is to add _____. The equation becomes _____.

ITEM 64

To obtain the balanced total equation, the half-reactions must be added so that the electrons of each half-reaction cancel. For the electrons to cancel in the two half-reactions at the right, the oxidation equation must be multiplied by _____.

ITEM 78

$Zn + NO_3^- \rightarrow Zn^{2+} + NH_4^+$ (acid solution)

$Ag \rightarrow Ag^+ + e^-$

$NO_3^- + 3e^- + 4H^+ \rightarrow NO + 2H_2O$

ANSWER 7   decreased

ANSWER 21   left: $2-$
right: $2-$

ANSWER 35   electrons
H^+
OH^-
H_2O to balance number
of H atoms

ANSWER 49 $+2$ $\quad\quad\quad$ 0
$Be_2O_3^{2-} \rightarrow 2Be$

ANSWER 63

$+5$ $\quad\quad$ $+2$
$NO_3^- \rightarrow NO$
$3e^- + NO_3^- \rightarrow NO$
$4H^+ + 3e^- + NO_3^- \rightarrow NO + 2H_2O$

ANSWER 77

$ClO^- + CrO_2^- \rightarrow Cl^- + CrO_4^{2-}$ (basic solution)

$+3$ $\quad\quad\quad\quad\quad$ $+6$
$CrO_2^- + 4OH^- \rightarrow CrO_4^{2-} + 2H_2O + 3e$
$\quad +1$ $\quad\quad\quad\quad\quad$ -1
$\quad ClO^- + H_2O + 2e^- \rightarrow Cl^- + 2OH^-$

$\quad\quad\quad 2CrO_2^- + 8OH^- \rightarrow 2CrO_4^{2-} + 4H_2O + 6e^-$
$3ClO^- + 3H_2O + 6e^- \quad \rightarrow 3Cl^- \quad + 6OH^-$
$\overline{2CrO_2^- + 3ClO^- + 2OH^- \rightarrow 2CrO_4^{2-} + 3Cl^- + H_2O}$

The relation between oxidation and reduction and the loss or gain of electrons by an element is as follows: When an element loses electrons, it is _____; conversely, when it gains electrons, it is _____.

Since each S atom must add _____ electrons to become S^{2-}, the total number of electrons picked up by S_8 is _____. Rewrite the equation and add electrons to the appropriate side.

Is this an oxidation or a reduction half-reaction?

Once the number of electrons is balanced, it is necessary to balance _____.

Addition of the two half-reactions gives the total equation, which is _____.

$NO_2 \rightarrow NO_3^- + NO$ (acid solution)

ANSWER 8

$$\overset{+2}{Cu^{2+}} + e^- \to \overset{+1}{Cu^+}$$

ANSWER 22

$$\overset{0}{S_8} \to 8\overset{-2}{S^{2-}}$$

ANSWER 36

$$\overset{+2-2}{S_2O_3^{2-}} \to \overset{+6-2}{SO_4^{2-}}$$

ANSWER 50   electrons

$$\overset{+2}{Be_2O_3^{2-}} + 4e^- \to 2\overset{0}{Be}$$

ANSWER 64   3

$3Ag \to 3Ag^+ + 3e^-$
$NO_3^- + 3e^- + 4H^+ \to NO + 2H_2O$

ANSWER 78

$Zn + NO_3^- \to Zn^{2+} + NH_4^+$
$\overset{0}{Zn} \quad \overset{+2}{} \qquad \overset{+5}{NO_3^-} \qquad \overset{-3}{NH_4^+}$
$Zn \to Zn^{2+} + 2e^- \qquad NO_3^- + 10H^+ + 8e^- \to NH_4^+ + 3H_2O$

$$4Zn \to 4Zn^{2+} + 8e^-$$
$$\underline{NO_3^- + 10H^+ + 8e^- \to NH_4^+ + 3H_2O}$$
$$4Zn \;+ NO_3^- + 10H^+ \quad \to 4Zn^{2+} + NH_4^+ + 3H_2O$$

or

$$4Zn \;+ NO_3^- + 10H_3O^+ \to 4Zn^{2+} + NH_4^+ + 13H_2O$$

289

ITEM 10

Thus, oxidation corresponds to a(n) ——————— in oxidation number; reduction corresponds to a(n) ——————— in oxidation number.

ITEM 24

Is the equation balanced with respect to charge?

ITEM 38

Balance this half-reaction with respect to the number of atoms of the element being oxidized.

ITEM 52

Since this reaction is carried out in basic solution, the charge is balanced by ———————. Do this.

ITEM 66

To change H^+ to H_3O^+, how many H_2O molecules must be added to each side of the equation? Then the equation becomes ———————.

ITEM 80

$$MnO_4^- + H_2C{=}CH_2 \rightarrow MnO_2 + H_2C{-}CH_2$$

(basic solution) $\qquad\qquad$ OH OH

This can also be written as

$$MnO_4^- + C_2H_4 \rightarrow MnO_2 + C_2H_6O_2$$

$$+2 \qquad +6$$
$$S_2O_3{}^{2-} \rightarrow SO_4{}^{2-}$$

$$+2 \qquad\qquad 0$$
$$Be_2O_3{}^{2-} + 4e^- \rightarrow 2Be$$

ANSWER 9   oxidized
                 reduced

ANSWER 23   two
                 16
                 $0 \qquad\qquad -2$
                 $S_8 + 16e^- \rightarrow 8S^{2-}$

ANSWER 37   oxidation

ANSWER 51   the charge

ANSWER 65

$$3Ag + NO_3{}^- + 4H^+ \rightarrow 3Ag^+ + NO + 2H_2O$$

ANSWER 79

$NO_2 \rightarrow NO_3{}^- + NO$ (acid solution)
$+4 \qquad\qquad +5$
$NO_2 + H_2O \rightarrow NO_3{}^- + 2H^+ + e^-$
$\qquad +4 \qquad\qquad\qquad +2$
$\qquad NO_2 + 2H^+ + 2e^- \rightarrow NO + H_2O$

$\qquad 2NO_2 + 2H_2O \rightarrow 2NO_3{}^- + 4H^+ + 2e^-$
$\qquad \underline{NO_2 + 2H^+ + 2e^- \rightarrow NO + H_2O}$

or $\quad 3NO_2 + \ H_2O \rightarrow 2NO_3{}^- + NO \ + 2H^+$
$\qquad 3NO_2 + 3H_2O \rightarrow 2NO_3{}^- + NO \ + 2H_3O^+$

When Cl^- ions are converted to Cl_2, the oxidation number of chlorine increases from _____ to _____. Is this conversion a reduction or an oxidation?

ITEM 25

To begin balancing the equation for the half-reaction $NO_3^- \rightarrow NO$, we first assign _____ to each element. The equation now is _____.

ITEM 39

The half-reaction must now be balanced with respect to the number of electrons. Add electrons to balance the change in oxidation number of the two S atoms.

ITEM 53

Now the equation must be balanced with respect to _____. The equation becomes _____.

ITEM 67

Another example is the reaction of copper with nitric acid: $Cu + NO_3^- \rightarrow Cu^{2+} + NO$. Assign oxidation numbers to the atoms that you expect are involved in oxidation and reduction. The two half-reactions are
(oxidation) _____
(reduction) _____.

(*Item 81 is on page 294.*)

ANSWER 10 increase
decrease

ANSWER 24 Yes
(left: 16−)
(right: 16−)

ANSWER 38 +2   +6
$S_2O_3^{2-} \rightarrow 2SO_4^{2-}$

ANSWER 52 adding OH^-
+2   0
$Be_2O_3^{2-} + 4e^- \rightarrow 2Be + 6OH^-$

ANSWER 66

Four.
$3Ag + NO_3^- + 4H_3O^+ \rightarrow 3Ag^+ + NO + 6H_2O$

ANSWER 80

$MnO_4^- + H_2C{=}CH_2 \rightarrow MnO_2 + H_2C{-}CH_2$ (basic solution)

with OH OH

−2   −1
$C_2H_4 + 2OH^- \rightarrow C_2H_6O_2 + 2e^-$
+7   +4
$2H_2O + MnO_4^- + 3e^- \rightarrow MnO_2 + 4OH^-$

$3C_2H_4 + 6OH^- \rightarrow 3C_2H_6O_2 + 6e^-$
$4H_2O + 2MnO_4^- + 6e^- \rightarrow 2MnO_2 + 8OH^-$
───────────────────────────────────
$3C_2H_4 + 4H_2O + 2MnO_4^- \rightarrow 3C_2H_6O_2 + 2MnO_2 + 2OH^-$

293

Write an equation to represent the oxidation of two chloride ions to Cl_2.

The element undergoing reduction is _____.

In its present form, the equation has a net charge on the left of _____ and a net charge on the right of _____.

Check this equation. Is it balanced?

The balanced equations for the two half-reactions are _____.

$Al + OH^- \rightarrow Al\,(OH)_4^- + H_2$ (basic solution)

ANSWER 11   −1
                  0
                  Oxidation

ANSWER 25   oxidation numbers
                  +5−2   +2−2
                  $NO_3^- \rightarrow NO$

ANSWER 39   +2   +6
                  $S_2O_3^{2-} \rightarrow 2SO_4^{2-} + 8e^-$

ANSWER 53

H atoms
+2   0
$Be_2O_3^{2-} + 4e^- + 3H_2O \rightarrow 2Be + 6OH$

ANSWER 67   0   +5   +2   +2
                  $Cu + NO_3^- \rightarrow Cu^{2+} + NO$
                  (oxidation) $Cu \rightarrow Cu^{2+}$
                  (reduction) $NO_3^- \rightarrow NO$

Write an equation for the reduction of the ion Sn^{4+} to metallic Sn.

ITEM 27

Since this equation is balanced with respect to the number of atoms of the element being reduced, the next step is to add electrons to the appropriate side. The N atom shows a decrease in oxidation number from _____ to _____ and therefore must pick up _____ electrons. Rewrite the equation to show the addition of these electrons.

ITEM 41

Since this reaction occurs in acidic solution, H^+ ions are added to balance the _____. The equation becomes _____.

ITEM 55

In acid solution, I_2 can be converted to IO_3^-. Carry out the steps necessary to balance the half-reaction with respect to electrons.

ITEM 69

In order for the electrons to cancel when the two equations are added, the oxidation half-reaction must be multiplied by _____ and the reduction half-reaction by _____.

$$+2 \qquad +6$$
$$S_2O_3{}^{2-} \rightarrow 2SO_4{}^{2-} + 8e^-$$

ANSWER 12 $\quad -1 \qquad 0$
$$2Cl^- \rightarrow Cl_2 + 2e^-$$

ANSWER 26 $\quad$ nitrogen

ANSWER 40 $\quad$ left: $\quad 2-$
$\qquad\qquad$ right: $2(2-) + 8(1-) = 12-$

ANSWER 54 $\quad$ Yes
$\qquad\qquad$ (left: $\quad 6O$)
$\qquad\qquad$ (right: $6O$)

ANSWER 68

$$Cu \rightarrow Cu^{2+} + 2e^-$$
$$4H^+ + 3e^- + NO_3{}^- \rightarrow NO + 2H_2O$$

ANSWER 81

$Al + OH^- \rightarrow Al(OH)_4{}^- + H_2$ $\quad$ (basic solution)

$0 \qquad\qquad +3$
$Al + 4OH^- \rightarrow Al(OH)_4{}^- + 3e^-$
$\qquad\quad +1 \qquad\qquad\qquad 0$
$\qquad 2OH^- + 2e^- + 2H_2O \rightarrow H_2 + 4OH^-$
$\qquad$ or
$\qquad 2H_2O + 2e^- \rightarrow H_2 + 2OH^-$

$\qquad\quad 2Al + 8OH^- \rightarrow 2Al(OH)_4{}^- + 6e^-$
$\underline{\qquad\quad 6H_2O + 6e^- \quad \rightarrow 3H_2 + 6OH^- \qquad\qquad}$
$2Al + 6H_2O + 2OH^- \rightarrow 2Al(OH)_4{}^- + 3H_2$

297

ITEM 14

Equations such as these are known as *half-reactions*. A half-reaction represents only a reduction or only an oxidation and shows, as part of the balanced equation, the electrons lost or gained by an atom. Write the half-reaction for the reduction of Fe^{3+} to Fe.

ITEM 28

The equation is balanced now with respect to electrons associated with N, the element undergoing reduction; the next step is to balance the net charge. As the equation stands, the net charge on the left is _____ and on the right it is _____.

ITEM 42

The equation is now unbalanced with respect to _____, so _____ is added to the _____ side. The equation then becomes _____.

ITEM 56

Balance the equation with respect to charge.

ITEM 70

The addition step is _____.

$Cu \rightarrow Cu^{2+} + 2e^-$

$4H^+ + 3e^- + NO_3^- \rightarrow NO + 2H_2O$

ANSWER 13 $\begin{matrix} +4 & & 0 \end{matrix}$

$Sn^{4+} + 4e^- \rightarrow Sn$

ANSWER 27 $+5$

$+2$

3

$\begin{matrix} +5 & & +2 \end{matrix}$

$NO_3^- + 3e^- \rightarrow NO$

ANSWER 41

charge

$\begin{matrix} +2 & & +6 \end{matrix}$

$S_2O_3^{2-} \rightarrow 2SO_4^{2-} + 8e^- + 10H^+$

ANSWER 55 $\begin{matrix} 0 & +5 \end{matrix}$

$I_2 \rightarrow IO_3^-$

$I_2 \rightarrow 2IO_3^-$

$I_2 \rightarrow 2IO_3^- + 10e^-$

ANSWER 69 3

2

ANSWER 14   +3   0
$$Fe^{3+} + 3e^- \rightarrow Fe$$

(Item 15 is on page 272.)

ANSWER 28 $(1-) + 3(1-) = 4-$
                0

(Item 29 is on page 272.)

ANSWER 42

H and O atoms
H_2O
left

         +2   +6
$$5H_2O + S_2O_3^{2-} \rightarrow 2SO_4^{2-} + 8e^- + 10H^+$$

(Item 43 is on page 272.)

ANSWER 56   0   +5
$$I_2 \rightarrow 2IO_3^- + 10e^- + 12H^+$$

(Item 57 is on page 272.)

ANSWER 70

$$3Cu \rightarrow 3Cu^{2+} + 6e^-$$
$$\underline{8H^+ + 6e^- + 2NO_3^- \rightarrow 2NO + 4H_2O}$$
$$3Cu + 8H^+ + 2NO_3^- \rightarrow 3Cu^{2+} + 2NO + 4H_2O$$

(Item 71 is on page 272.)

SUMMARY OF STEPS FOR BALANCING REDOX EQUATIONS

(1) Write down the main reactants and products.

(2) Assign oxidation numbers.

(3) Separate the oxidation and reduction half-reactions.

(4) Balance the half-reactions with respect to
   (a) the number of atoms of the element undergoing oxidation or reduction;
   (b) electrons by adding electrons to the electron-deficient side of the equation;
   (c) charge by adding H^+ ions or OH^- ions;
   (d) H and O atoms by adding H_2O.

(5) Multiply the half-reactions by appropriate numbers so that, when they are added, the electrons cancel.

(6) Add the half-reactions and check for balance.

REVIEW 7 ELECTRONS IN ATOMS

One of the great successes of physical science in the twentieth century was the development of a model for the electronic structure of the atom. The model was derived from information obtained by the study of atomic spectra and from extensive quantum mechanical calculations. Neither of these will be treated here, but atomic spectra are discussed briefly in Section 7–2 and a short introduction to the quantum mechanical calculations is presented in Sections 7–3 through 7–6 of *Chemical Principles*.

In this review you will learn some of the results of these calculations that are particularly important for understanding the chemical behavior of atoms. This will serve as a review of Section 7–7 of *Chemical Principles* and also as an introduction to Chapter 8 of that text. When you have finished the chapter, you will be able to predict the approximate arrangement in space of an atom's electrons and to indicate the relative energies of these electrons. This knowledge will allow you to predict the electron configurations of the elements of the first two rows of the periodic table.

ITEM 1

Although an electron of an atom does not occupy a fixed position relative to the nucleus, there is a region of space in the neighborhood of the nucleus in which the probability of finding an electron of an atom is relatively high. We can say, for example, that there is some "most probable distance" between an electron and the _____ of an atom.

ITEM 14

For the hydrogen atom, the energies of the allowed electronic states are given by the expression $E = -313.5/n^2$ kcal mole^{-1} or $E = -13.58/n^2$ electron volts (eV). Calculate the energies for the $n = 2, 3, 4$, and ∞ levels for the hydrogen atom, and show these in the diagram at the right.

ITEM 27

The value of n for an electron determines the degree to which its orbital extends from the nucleus. For small values of n, the orbital is relatively small: There is a high probability that the electron will be located relatively _____ to the nucleus.

ITEM 40

The shape of an orbital depends on the _____ quantum number, represented by the symbol _____, which can have values _____. (We shall see that the energy of the electron can also depend, to a small extent, on this quantum number.)

ITEM 53

On the coordinate axes at the right, make sketches representing orbitals to show that only one s orbital exists but that three p orbitals, differing in their orientation, occur.

ITEM 66

The *Pauli exclusion principle* states that only one electron of an atom can have any given combination of all four quantum numbers. Since $s = \pm\frac{1}{2}$, an orbital identified by any given combination of n, l, and m can be occupied by no more than _____ electrons.

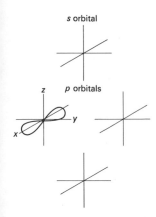

s orbital

p orbitals

ITEM 2

In addition, an electron has some amount of energy: the kinetic energy of its motion plus potential energy arising from the electrostatic force of attraction between it and the positively charged _____.

ITEM 15

The difference in energy between the $n = 1$ and the $n = 2$ states of hydrogen is _____ kcal mole^{-1}. Therefore, if an electron in the $n = 1$ state absorbed (i.e., gained) this much energy, the value of n for the new state would be _____.

ITEM 28

The smallest orbital will be that corresponding to $n =$ _____, whereas the largest will be that corresponding to $n =$ _____.

ITEM 41

The energy of an electron depends primarily on its distance from the nucleus, and the distance is determined by the value of _____, the _____ quantum number.

ITEM 54

Since the three p orbitals can be drawn along the $x, y,$ and z axes, they are often labeled p_x, _____, and _____.

ITEM 67

In an energy level diagram, an electron is often represented by an arrow indicating one of the two possible spins. Show ten electrons in their lowest energy arrangement in the energy levels at the right by adding additional arrows to represent electrons.

$3d_{xy}$ $3d_{xz}$ $3d_{yz}$ $3d_{x^2-y^2}$ $3d_{z^2}$

$3p_x$ $3p_y$ $3p_z$

$3s$

$2p_x$ $2p_y$ $2p_z$

$2s$

$\uparrow\downarrow$ $1s$

ANSWER 1   nucleus

ANSWER 14

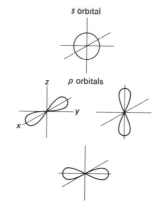

ANSWER 27   close

ANSWER 40   azimuthal

l

$0, 1, 2, \ldots, n-1$

ANSWER 53

ANSWER 66   two

ITEM 3   Together, the most probable distance from the nucleus and the energy describe, in part, the state of an electron of an atom. If the state of an electron were to change, both the _____ and the _____ would change.

ITEM 16   Conversely, if a hydrogen atom having its electron in the $n = 2$ state emits 235.1 kcal mole^{-1} of energy, n will become _____.

ITEM 29   In fact, in the limit where $n = \infty$, there is no interaction between the _____ and the _____. They are completely separated.

ITEM 42   When many electrons are present in an atom, their orbitals penetrate one another. The extent to which an electron is influenced by the nucleus then depends on both the size and the shape of its orbital. For many-electron atoms, therefore, the energy of a particular electron is determined not only by the value of n, but also by the value of _____.

ITEM 55   Orbitals with $l = 2$, that is, _____ orbitals, can have any one of _____ orientations, each orientation corresponding to a different value of the quantum number _____.

ITEM 68   The atomic number of fluorine is 9. In the diagram at the right, indicate the arrangement of nine electrons in a fluorine atom in the ground state and label the occupied levels.

Spatial representations of all d orbitals are shown at the beginning of Review 10.

— — — — —
— — —
—
— —
—

—
—

ANSWER 2   nucleus

ANSWER 15   235.1
2

ANSWER 28   1
∞

ANSWER 41 n
principal

ANSWER 54 p_y
p_z

ANSWER 67

—$3d_{xy}$ —$3d_{xz}$ —$3d_{yz}$ —$3d_{x^2-y^2}$ —$3d_{z^2}$
—$3p_x$ —$3p_y$ —$3p_z$
—$3s$
⇅ $2p_x$ ⇅ $2p_y$ ⇅ $2p_z$
⇅ $2s$
⇅ $1s$

309

ITEM 4

Since the states available to an electron are governed by the laws of quantum mechanics, the numbers used to identify these states are known as ＿＿＿＿＿ numbers.

ITEM 17

An atom is in the *ground state* when its electrons have the lowest possible energy. The electron of a hydrogen atom in the ground state has a principal quantum number of ＿＿＿＿＿.

ITEM 30

The quantum number n, which can have the values ＿＿＿＿＿, is primarily responsible for determining the ＿＿＿＿＿ of the electron and the size of the ＿＿＿＿＿ occupied by the electron.

ITEM 43

For instance, s electrons shield p electrons from the attraction of the nucleus. Thus, for a given value of n, p electrons have slightly ＿＿＿＿＿ energy than s electrons.

ITEM 56

For a given value of n there is (are) only ＿＿＿＿＿ s orbital(s), but there are ＿＿＿＿＿ p orbitals, differing only in their ＿＿＿＿＿ in space.

ITEM 69

The arrangement, or *configuration*, of the electrons in fluorine can also be represented by the notation $1s^2 2s^2 2p_x^2 2p_y^2 2p_z^1$, or $1s^2 2s^2 2p^5$, in which the superscripts indicate the number of electrons in that quantum state. At the right, indicate diagrammatically, and with this notation, the electronic configuration of sodium (at. no. = 11).

ANSWER 3 most probable distance from the nucleus

energy

ANSWER 16 1

ANSWER 29 electron

nucleus

ANSWER 42 l

ANSWER 55 d

five

m

ANSWER 68

‐‐ ‐‐ ‐‐ ‐‐ ‐‐
‐‐ ‐‐ ‐‐

$\uparrow\downarrow$ $2p_x$ $\uparrow\downarrow$ $2p_y$ $\uparrow$ $2p_z$
$\uparrow\downarrow$ $2s$
$\uparrow\downarrow$ $1s$

ITEM 5

The first of the four quantum numbers that specify the _____ and the _____ of an electron is called the *principal quantum number* and is denoted by the symbol n.

ITEM 18

If energy is absorbed by a hydrogen atom in the ground state, the value of n will _____. Then the atom is in an *excited state*.

ITEM 31

The shape of the region in which the probability of the electron being located is high (i.e., the shape of the _____) is determined by the value of a second quantum number, the *azimuthal quantum number l*.

ITEM 44

Similarly, p electrons have somewhat lower energy than d electrons, and so forth. The energy is principally determined, however, by the value of _____.

ITEM 57

Since the energy of an electron in an atom is independent of the orientation of the orbital (so long as the atom is not subjected to an electric or magnetic field), electrons with different values of m have the same _____.

ITEM 70

The electronic configuration of oxygen (at. no. $= 8$) in the ground state is $1s^2 2s^2 2p_x^2 2p_y^1 2p_z^1$. (The repulsion between two electrons causes them to occupy two different orbitals of the same energy whenever possible; such unpaired electrons have the same spin.) Represent the ground state configuration of oxygen in the diagram at the right.

ANSWER 4   quantum

ANSWER 17   1

ANSWER 30   1, 2, 3, . . . , ∞
energy
orbital

ANSWER 43   higher

ANSWER 56   one
three
direction

ANSWER 69

$\uparrow$ $3s$

$\uparrow\downarrow$ $2p_x$ $\uparrow\downarrow$ $2p_y$ $\uparrow\downarrow$ $2p_z$

$\uparrow\downarrow$ $2s$

$\uparrow\downarrow$ $1s$

$1s^22s^22p_x^22p_y^22p_z^23s^1$ (or $1s^22s^22p^63s^1$)

ITEM 6

The principal quantum number, symbol _____,
can have integral values from 1 to ∞. This is indicated
by writing $n = 1, 2,$ _____.

ITEM 19

In the diagram at the right, draw a vertical arrow to
represent the change in energy level when a hydrogen atom in the ground state absorbs 278.7 kcal
mole^{-1} of energy.

ITEM 32

The solutions of the quantum mechanical equation
that describes the behavior of an electron in a hydrogen atom show that l can have integral values from
zero to one less than the value of n; that is, $l =$
_____.

ITEM 45

For atoms with several electrons, each state with n
greater than one is split into different levels depending on the number of l values possible. Complete
the labeling of the diagram at the right.

ITEM 58

The energy level diagram at the right has lines corresponding to some of the states available to an electron in an atom. Complete the labeling.

ITEM 71

Using the notation s, p_x, and so on, write the electronic configurations of carbon (at. no. = 6) and
nitrogen (at. no. = 7).

principal
quantum
number

azimuthal
quantum
number

energy ⟶

$n=3$ ————————

————————

$n-2$ ———————— $p(l=1)$

       ———————— $s(l=0)$

$n=1$ ———————— $s(l=0)$

$3d_{xy}$ $3d_{xz}$ $3d_{yz}$ $3d_{x^2-y^2}$ $3d_{z^2}$

$n=3$ ——   ——   ——   ——   ——

$2p_x$

$n=2$ ——   ——   ——

$n=1$ $1s$ ——

ANSWER 18   increase

ANSWER 31   orbital

ANSWER 44 n

ANSWER 57   energy

ANSWER 70

——   ——   ——   ——   ——

——   ——   ——

$\uparrow\downarrow$ $2p_x$ $\uparrow$ $2p_y$ $\uparrow$ $2p_z$

$\uparrow\downarrow$ $2s$

$\uparrow\downarrow$ $1s$

315

If the state of an electron is that specified by a small value of n, the electron is relatively near the nucleus and has a relatively low _____.

ITEM 20

In the diagram at the right, indicate the change in energy level when a hydrogen atom having an electron in the $n = 3$ state emits 43.6 kcal mole^{-1}.

ITEM 33

Thus, when an electron has a principal quantum number of 1, l must be _____; if $n = 2$, l can be _____ or _____; if $n = 3$, l can be _____, _____, or _____.

ITEM 46

A convenient abbreviation of the orbital notation consists of writing $1s$ instead of $n = 1$, $l = 0$; $2s$ for $n = 2$, $l = 0$; $2p$ for $n = 2$, $l = 1$, and so forth. Use this abbreviated notation to label the energy levels at the right, as is done for the $1s$ level.

ITEM 59

All s orbitals have a _____ shape; the shape of all p orbitals can be represented by _____. The size of an orbital is dependent on the value of _____.

ITEM 72

The electronic configurations of heavier elements are obtained in the same way. Electrons are "placed" in orbitals in order of increasing energy. However, the simple energy level diagram must be modified, as shown at the right, when we include $n = 4$ levels. Indicate in the diagram at the right the configuration of potassium (at. no. = 19).

1s

4p ___ ___ ___
3d ___ ___ ___ ___ ___
4s ___
3p ___ ___ ___
3s ___
2p ___ ___ ___
2s ___
1s ___

ANSWER 6 n
$$3, \ldots, \infty$$

ANSWER 19

ANSWER 32 $0, 1, 2, \ldots, n-1$

ANSWER 45

principal quantum number	azimuthal quantum number

$n = 3$ —— $d(l = 2)$
—— $p(l = 1)$
—— $s(l = 0)$

$n = 2$ —— $p(l = 1)$
—— $s(l = 0)$

$n = 1$ —— $s(l = 0)$

ANSWER 58

$$n = 3 \begin{cases} \underline{3d_{xy}}\ \underline{3d_{xz}}\ \underline{3d_{yz}}\ \underline{3d_{x^2-y^2}}\ \underline{3d_{z^2}} \\ \underline{3p_x}\ \underline{3p_y}\ \underline{3p_z} \\ \underline{3s} \end{cases}$$

$$n = 2 \begin{cases} \underline{2p_x}\ \underline{2p_y}\ \underline{2p_z} \\ \underline{2s} \end{cases}$$

$$n = 1 \quad \underline{1s}$$

ANSWER 71   C $1s^2 2s^2 2p_x^{\ 1} 2p_y^{\ 1}$
N $1s^2 2s^2 2p_x^{\ 1} 2p_y^{\ 1} 2p_z^{\ 1}$

317

ITEM 8

The state in which the electron has the lowest energy and is nearest the nucleus is that state specified by $n = \underline{\hspace{2cm}}$.

ITEM 21

The only energies that an electron of a hydrogen atom can have are those calculated by using the formula $E = -313.5/n^2$ kcal mole^{-1}, where n, known as the $\underline{\hspace{2cm}}$, is an integer. Thus, the smallest amount of energy that a ground state hydrogen atom can absorb is $\underline{\hspace{2cm}}$.

ITEM 34

Electrons that undergo transitions to states with $l = 0$ emit energy and produce spectral lines that are sometimes described as *sharp*. The first letter, *s*, of this word is often used to indicate an electronic state where $l = \underline{\hspace{2cm}}$.

ITEM 47

We have now dealt with two of the four quantum numbers necessary to describe the behavior of an electron in an atom. These are the $\underline{\hspace{2cm}}$ quantum number, having values $\underline{\hspace{2cm}}$, and the $\underline{\hspace{2cm}}$ quantum number, having values $\underline{\hspace{2cm}}$.

ITEM 60

In addition to the three quantum numbers introduced so far, the $\underline{\hspace{2cm}}$, the $\underline{\hspace{2cm}}$, and the $\underline{\hspace{2cm}}$ quantum numbers, a final one is necessary to describe the behavior of an electron in an atom.

ITEM 73

Show the electronic configuration of arsenic (at. no. = 33) on the diagram at the right and by means of the notation s, p_x, and so forth.

$$\text{energy, kcal mole}^{-1}$$

0 ——— $n=\infty$
——— $n=3$
−50
−78.4 ——— $n=2$
−100
−150
−200
−250
−300
−313.5 ——— $n=1$
−350

4p — — —
3d — — — — —
4s —
3p — — —
3s —
2p — — —
2s —
1s —

ANSWER 7   energy

ANSWER 20

energy, kcal mole⁻¹

0 ——— $n=\infty$
——— $n=4$
−50 ——— $n=3$
↓ ——— $n=2$
−100
−150
−200
−250
−300
−313.5 ——— $n=1$
−350

ANSWER 33   0
0, 1
0, 1, 2

ANSWER 46

——— energy

——— 3d
——— 3p
——— 3s

——— 2p
——— 2s

——— 1s

ANSWER 59   spherical
dumbbells
n

ANSWER 72

4p —   —   —
3d —   —   —   —   —
4s ↑
3p ↿⇂   ↿⇂   ↿⇂
3s ↿⇂
2p ↿⇂   ↿⇂   ↿⇂
2s ↿⇂
1s ↿⇂

319

ITEM 9

For larger values of the principal quantum number, the distance of the electron from the nucleus is _____, and the energy is _____.

ITEM 22

Using the formula $E = -313.5/n^2$ kcal mole^{-1} for the allowed energies of an electron of a hydrogen atom, calculate the energy emitted when an electron changes from a state with $n = 4$ to one with $n = 2$.

ITEM 35

Similarly, since l values of 1, 2, and 3 were related to series of spectral lines described as *principal, diffuse,* and *fundamental,* the letters _____, _____, or _____ generally are written to indicate l values of 1, 2, or 3, respectively.

ITEM 48

Although s orbitals are spherically symmetric and cannot be oriented in any particular direction, it is clear that _____ orbitals (and, in fact, all orbitals with higher values of l) can be oriented along different directions.

ITEM 61

An electron is sometimes pictured as spinning about an axis through its center. With this picture, it can spin either counterclockwise, conventionally represented by an arrow pointing up, or it can spin _____, represented by ↓.

ITEM 74

All the orbitals of any one value of n are generally called, collectively, a *shell.* Helium and neon, elements that are not known to react chemically, are characterized by completed shells of electrons, as shown by their respective electronic configurations, _____ and _____. (*For the atomic numbers of He and Ne see the periodic table in the inside front cover.*)

s orbital

p orbital

ANSWER 8   1

ANSWER 21   principal quantum number
235.1 kcal mole^{-1}

ANSWER 34   0

ANSWER 47   principal
1, 2, 3, . . . , ∞
azimuthal
0, 1, 2, . . . , $n-1$

ANSWER 60   principal
azimuthal
magnetic

ANSWER 73

$4p$	↑	↑	↑	
$3d$	↑↓	↑↓	↑↓	↑↓	↑↓
$4s$	↑↓			
$3p$	↑↓	↑↓	↑↓	
$3s$	↑↓			
$2p$	↑↓	↑↓	↑↓	
$2s$	↑↓			
$1s$	↑↓			

$1s^2 2s^2 2p^6 3s^2 3p^6 4s^2 3d^{10} 4p_x^1 4p_y^1 4p_z^1$

ITEM 10

At the right is a set of lines representing the energies of the lowest allowed states of an electron of an atom. Label these with appropriate values of the principal quantum number.

ITEM 23

At room temperature, atoms are generally in their ground states, which means that states with the _____ possible values of n will be occupied by electrons.

ITEM 36

If the principal quantum number of an electron is 4, the value of the azimuthal quantum number will be designated by one of the integers _____, or by one of the letters _____.

ITEM 49

The energy of an electron of an atom placed in a magnetic field depends, to some extent, on the direction of its orbital relative to the field. The different possible orientations are designated by the quantum number, m, known as the *magnetic quantum number*. It determines the _____ in which an orbital lies.

ITEM 62

Because there are only two different spin states that an electron can have, the quantum number s that identifies these states can have only _____ values.

ITEM 75

This special chemical stability apparently is characteristic of electronic configurations in which eight electrons (completing both s and p orbitals) are placed in the outermost occupied shell. Thus, the elements Ar and Kr have only a slight tendency to react chemically. Their electronic configurations are _____ and _____.

ANSWER 9   greater
             higher

ANSWER 22

$E_{n=4} = -313.5/16 = -19.6$ kcal mole^{-1}
$E_{n=2} = -313.5/4 = -78.4$ kcal mole^{-1}
$E_{n=4} - E_{n=2} = 58.8$ kcal mole^{-1}

ANSWER 35 p
              d
              f

ANSWER 48 p

ANSWER 61   clockwise

ANSWER 74 $1s^2$
              $1s^2 2s^2 2p^6$

ITEM 11

The energy of an electron for $n = \infty$ was assigned the value zero when the theory of atomic structure was worked out. Therefore, for smaller values of n, for which the energy is ——————, the value of the energy will have a —————— sign.

ITEM 24

An atom in an excited state can return to the ground state by —————— energy.

ITEM 37

The shape of the orbital for any s electron ($l = 0$) is often represented by a diffuse sphere having the nucleus as its center. The size of the sphere is determined by the value of ——————.

ITEM 50

The allowed values of m are 0 and the positive and negative integers that are less than or equal to the value of l. Complete the table of m values at the right.

ITEM 63

The values of the spin quantum number, which determines the angular momentum of the spinning electron, can be only $+\frac{1}{2}$ or $-\frac{1}{2}$. Thus, we write —————— $= \pm\frac{1}{2}$.

ITEM 76

Fluorine, chlorine, and bromine are chemically alike in that they easily add one electron to form a negative ion. Their electronic configurations suggest that this tendency is related to their needing only one electron to complete a p orbital. The configurations of the atoms are F ——————; Cl ——————; Br ——————.

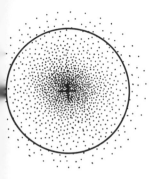

l		m	
0		0	
1	−1	0	+1
2	__ __	0	__ __

ITEM 12

For some atoms only one electron need be considered. The energy, E, of this electron is given by $E = -k/n^2$, where the constant, k, depends on the atom being considered. For $n = 1$, $E =$ _____; for $n = 2$, $E =$ _____, and for $n = \infty$, $E =$ _____.

ITEM 25

The principal quantum number n determines not only the _____ of an electron but also its _____ from the nucleus.

ITEM 38

The region in which there is a relatively high probability of finding a p electron ($l =$ _____) is dumbbell shaped, as shown at the right. (This representation is the easiest to draw but a more correct representation is shown in Figure 7–21 of *Chemical Principles*.)

ITEM 51

For a p electron ($l = 1$), there are three possible values of m: _____, _____, or _____.

ITEM 64

The allowed values of the four quantum numbers that describe electron behavior can be arranged as in the table at the right. Extend this table to show all the possible quantum number combinations for $n = 2$ and $n = 3$.

ITEM 77

Similarly, oxygen and sulfur easily add two electrons to form negative ions. Compare the electronic configurations of neutral oxygen and sulfur with those of the doubly charged negative ions.

O _____ S _____

O^{2-} _____ S^{2-} _____

$E = -k/n^2$

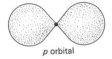

p orbital

$n = 1 \quad l = 0 \quad m = \quad 0 \quad s = \pm\frac{1}{2}$
$n = 2 \quad l = 0 \quad m = \quad 0 \quad s =$
$\qquad l = 1 \quad m = +1 \quad s =$
$\qquad l = 1 \quad m = \quad\quad s =$
$\qquad l = 1 \quad m =$
$n = 3 \quad l = 0$
$\qquad l =$

ANSWER 11   lower
             negative

ANSWER 24   emitting (or losing)

ANSWER 37 n

ANSWER 50 $-2, -1, 0, +1, +2$

ANSWER 63 s

ANSWER 76 $1s^2 2s^2 2p^5$
             $1s^2 2s^2 2p^6 3s^2 3p^5$
             $1s^2 2s^2 2p^6 3s^2 3p^6 4s^2 3d^{10} 4p^5$

ITEM 13

In the diagram at the right, draw horizontal lines to represent the energies of states corresponding to $n = 2, 3, 4$, and ∞.

ITEM 26

The region in space occupied by an electron is called its *orbital*. More specifically, an orbital is the region in space where there is appreciable probability of finding the _____ .

ITEM 39

A p electron most likely would be located in the regions suggested by the lobes of the dumbbell. The probability of its being located in regions perpendicular to the axis of the dumbbell would be relatively _____ .

ITEM 52

Similarly, a d electron can have the values of m: _____ , that is, a total of _____ different values.

ITEM 65

The total number of possible combinations of quantum numbers with $n = 1$ is 2; the number of combinations with $n = 2$ is _____ and with $n = 3$ is _____ .

ITEM 78

Conversely, the elements Li, Na, and K easily lose one electron to form a positive ion, as might be inferred from their electronic configurations: Li _____ ; K _____ ; Na _____ .

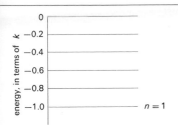

ANSWER 12 $-k$
               $-\frac{1}{4} k$
               0

ANSWER 25   energy
               most probable distance

ANSWER 38   1

ANSWER 51 $-1, 0, +1$

ANSWER 64

$n=1$	$l=0$	$m=\ \ 0$	$s=\pm\frac{1}{2}$
$n=2$	$l=0$	$m=\ \ 0$	$s=\pm\frac{1}{2}$
	$l=1$	$m=+1$	$s=\pm\frac{1}{2}$
	$l=1$	$m=\ \ 0$	$s=\pm\frac{1}{2}$
	$l=1$	$m=-1$	$s=\pm\frac{1}{2}$
$n=3$	$l=0$	$m=\ \ 0$	$s=\pm\frac{1}{2}$
	$l=1$	$m=+1$	$s=\pm\frac{1}{2}$
	$l=1$	$m=\ \ 0$	$s=\pm\frac{1}{2}$
	$l=1$	$m=-1$	$s=\pm\frac{1}{2}$
	$l=2$	$m=+2$	$s=\pm\frac{1}{2}$
	$l=2$	$m=+1$	$s=\pm\frac{1}{2}$
	$l=2$	$m=\ \ 0$	$s=\pm\frac{1}{2}$
	$l=2$	$m=-1$	$s=\pm\frac{1}{2}$
	$l=2$	$m=-2$	$s=\pm\frac{1}{2}$

ANSWER 77

O	$1s^2 2s^2 2p^4$
O^{2-}	$1s^2 2s^2 2p^6$
S	$1s^2 2s^2 2p^6 3s^2 3p^4$
S^{2-}	$1s^2 2s^2 2p^6 3s^2 3p^6$

ANSWER 13

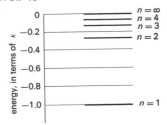

(*Item 14 is on page 304.*)

ANSWER 26   electron

(*Item 27 is on page 304.*)

ANSWER 39   low

(*Item 40 is on page 304.*)

ANSWER 52 $-2, -1, 0, +1, +2$
five

(*Item 53 is on page 304.*)

ANSWER 65   8
18

(*Item 66 is on page 304.*)

ANSWER 78   Li $1s^2 2s^1$
Na $1s^2 2s^2 2p^6 3s^1$
K $1s^2 2s^2 2p^6 3s^2 3p^6 4s^1$

REVIEW 8   THE TRANSITION METALS

In Review 5 you built a periodic table for the representative elements. As you did this, you learned how to write the formulas and names of the ionic, or mostly ionic, compounds formed from these elements. In Review 8 you will use electronic configurations as a basis for learning about the most important of the transition metals, the elements that involve the filling of the d orbitals. To do this review you must be familiar with the material of Reviews 5 and 7 so that you know the ground rules for naming compounds and for writing electronic configurations.

At the end of the review you will be able to predict formulas and write names for the compounds of the first row of transition elements in the periodic table and for silver, cadmium, and mercury. Although Stock nomenclature is by far the most convenient, you will learn the common names for the ions, too. Since there may be as many as three choices for the name of a given compound, you should try to give at least two names, where appropriate. The important thing is that you can write at least one correct name.

This material is a review of Table 6–2 and the relevant parts of Sections 8–1 and 8–4 in *Chemical Principles.* If you can list the important oxidation states of the transition metals and write formulas and names for the metal oxides, you are already sufficiently familiar with the transition metals and can skip this review.

ITEM 1

The order of filling orbitals with electrons is
$$1s2s2p3s3p4s3d4p5s4d5p6s4f5d6p \ldots$$
The s orbitals contain a maximum of _____ electrons, the p orbitals a maximum of _____ electrons, and the d orbitals a maximum of _____ electrons.

ITEM 12

The energy required to remove completely four electrons from an atom is exorbitant, so the free Ti^{4+} ion is not formed. However, in the compound TiO_2, named _____, titanium has an oxidation number of _____.

ITEM 23

Name the following compounds: CrO_3, Cr_2O_3, V_2O_5, $Sc(NO_3)_3$, TiO.

ITEM 34

The most important oxidation state of iron is $+3$ and exists as the *ferric* ion, Fe^{3+}. Write the names and formulas of the sulfate salts of iron(II) and iron(III).

ITEM 45

Element number 29 is copper. The electronic configuration is $1s^2 2s^2 2p^6 3s^2 3p^6 4s^1 3d^{10}$. Again there is an irregularity in the filling of orbitals. We could expect copper to have an oxidation number of _____ so the $3d$ orbital would remain completely filled.

ITEM 56

The symbols for the zinc, cadmium, and both mercury ions are _____, _____, _____, and _____.

ITEM 2

Calcium, element number 20, has the electronic configuration ＿＿＿＿＿＿. It is not a transition element, but a representative element, because there are no electrons partially filling a ＿＿＿＿＿ orbital.

ITEM 13

In the compound TiO, named ＿＿＿＿＿, titanium has an oxidation number of ＿＿＿＿＿. The electrons considered to be transferred or partially transferred are the ones from the ＿＿＿＿＿ orbital(s).

ITEM 24

The twenty-fifth element, manganese, has the electronic configuration $1s^2 2s^2 2p^6 3s^2 3p^6 4s^2 3d^5$. (Note that the $4s$ orbital again has two electrons.) The maximum oxidation state for manganese is ＿＿＿＿＿.

ITEM 35

The maximum oxidation state of a transition element is equal to the number of unpaired electrons in the outermost occupied d orbital plus the number of electrons in the outermost occupied s orbital. Thus, the maximum oxidation number of iron is ＿＿＿＿＿.

ITEM 46

Compounds containing the *cuprous* ion Cu^+ are known (and include the principal ores of copper), but the principal oxidation state of copper is $+2$, which occurs as the *cupric* ion Cu^{2+}. Write the common names and formulas for the chlorides and oxides of copper(I) and copper(II).

ITEM 57

Write the formulas of the following compounds: cadmium oxide, ＿＿＿＿＿; zinc nitrate, ＿＿＿＿＿; mercurous fluoride, ＿＿＿＿＿; mercuric sulfide, ＿＿＿＿＿; chromous chloride, ＿＿＿＿＿.

ANSWER 1   two
           six
           ten

ANSWER 12   *titanium dioxide,*
              titanium(IV) oxide,
              or *titanic oxide*
           +4

ANSWER 23

chromium trioxide or chromium(VI) oxide
chromic oxide or chromium(III) oxide
vanadium pentoxide or vanadium(V) oxide
scandium trinitrate or scandium(III) nitrate
titanium monoxide, titanium(II) oxide,
      or titanous oxide

ANSWER 34

ferrous sulfate [iron(II) sulfate] $FeSO_4$
ferric sulfate [iron(III) sulfate] $Fe_2(SO_4)_3$

ANSWER 45   +1

ANSWER 56 Zn^{2+}
               Cd^{2+}
               Hg^{2+}
               Hg_2^{2+}

ITEM 3

Atoms of calcium usually react by donating electrons of the _____ orbital to elements of high electron affinity. The resulting ion has the symbol _____.

ITEM 14

Name the compounds $TiCl_4$, TiF_2, and $ScBr_3$.

ITEM 25

Manganese has all oxidation numbers from 0 through +7, but the principal oxidation number is +7, found in the *permanganate* anion, MnO_4^-. The corresponding acid has the formula _____ and the name _____.

ITEM 36

Write the formula of each of the following: ferric chloride, _____; ferrous sulfite, _____; chromic oxide, _____; lithium chromate, _____; ferric sulfide, _____.

ITEM 47

Silver, atomic number 47, is beneath copper in the periodic table and has an analogous electronic configuration: ten electrons in the $4d$ and one electron in the $5s$ orbital. The principal ion is Ag^+ and is formed by _____.

ITEM 58

Name the following compounds: $HgSO_4$, $AgNO_3$, FeO, $Cu(OH)_2$, TiO_2, H_2CrO_4.

ANSWER 2 $1s^2 2s^2 2p^6 3s^2 3p^6 4s^2$
             d

ANSWER 13   *titanium monoxide,*
                 titanium(II) oxide,
                 or *titanous oxide*
             +2
             $4s$

ANSWER 24   +7

ANSWER 35   +6 (It occurs only in the rare
             ferrate ion, FeO_4^{2-}.)

ANSWER 46   cuprous chloride, CuCl
             cupric chloride, $CuCl_2$
             cuprous oxide, Cu_2O
             cupric oxide, CuO

ANSWER 57   CdO
             $Zn(NO_3)_2$
             Hg_2F_2
             HgS
             $CrCl_2$

ITEM 4

The electronic configuration of Ca^{2+}, with 18 electrons, is _____. This is also the configuration of the element _____, which belongs to the family of _____ elements.

ITEM 15

Element number 23, vanadium, has the electronic configuration _____. The maximum oxidation number is expected to be _____.

ITEM 26

One important compound of manganese is MnO_2, named _____, in which manganese has the oxidation number _____.

ITEM 37

Cobalt has the atomic number 27 and the electronic configuration _____.

ITEM 48

Write formulas for the four important silver halides.

ITEM 59

Write the principal oxidation states of the following elements: iron, _____; copper, _____; mercury, _____; cobalt, _____; nickel, _____; zinc, _____; silver, _____.

ANSWER 3 $4s$
             Ca^{2+}

ANSWER 14

titanium tetrachloride, titanium(IV) chloride,
    or titanic chloride
titanium difluoride, titanium(II) fluoride,
    or titanous fluoride
scandium tribromide or scandium(III)
    bromide

ANSWER 25 $HMnO_4$
               permanganic

ANSWER 36 $FeCl_3$
               $FeSO_3$
               Cr_2O_3
               Li_2CrO_4
               Fe_2S_3

ANSWER 47   donation of the $5s$ electron to
               an element of high electron
               affinity

ANSWER 58

mercuric sulfate or mercury(II) sulfate
silver nitrate
ferrous oxide or iron(II) oxide
cupric hydroxide or copper(II) hydroxide
titanium dioxide, titanium(IV) oxide,
    or titanic oxide
chromic acid

ITEM 5

Atoms or ions are especially stable when the valence shell contains _____ electrons, thus filling the outermost occupied _____ and _____ orbitals.

ITEM 16

The principal oxidation number of vanadium is +5. It occurs in the vanadate anion, VO_4^{3-}, and in vanadium pentoxide, which has the formula _____.

ITEM 27

The *manganate* ion is MnO_4^{2-}, the only ion in which manganese has an oxidation number of _____.

ITEM 38

In the cobalt atom there are _____ unpaired electrons in the d orbitals. The maximum oxidation number would be _____.

ITEM 49

The principal oxidation state of copper is _____, and that of silver is _____. Write formulas for the sulfides corresponding to these oxidation states and name them.

ITEM 60

Write formulas for the following compounds: scandium oxide, _____; potassium permanganate, _____; vanadium pentoxide, _____; nickel sulfate, _____; manganese dioxide, _____.

ANSWER 4 $1s^2 2s^2 2p^6 3s^2 3p^6$
argon
rare gas
     (noble gas or inert gas)

ANSWER 15 $1s^2 2s^2 2p^6 3s^2 3p^6 4s^2 3d^3$
+5

ANSWER 26   manganese dioxide
         or manganese(IV) oxide
+4

ANSWER 37 $1s^2 2s^2 2p^6 3s^2 3p^6 4s^2 3d^7$

ANSWER 48   AgF
AgCl
AgBr
AgI

ANSWER 59   +2 and +3
+2
+1 and +2
+3
+2
+2
+1

343

Element number 21, scandium, has the electronic configuration _____.

The electronic configuration of chromium, element 24, is $1s^22s^22p^63s^23p^64s^13d^5$. How is it different than what would have been expected from the configuration of Sc, Ti, and V?

Name the following compounds: TiO_2, Na_2CrO_4, $Ca(MnO_4)$, $Mg(MnO_4)_2$, $K_2Cr_2O_7$.

However, the principal oxidation state of cobalt occurs in the *cobaltic* ion Co^{3+}. The *cobaltous* ion Co^{2+} is found in cobaltous oxide, which has the formula _____, and in a few other compounds.

Zinc has 30 electrons in the electronic configuration _____.

Write formulas and names for the sulfides of silver, iron, cadmium, nickel, and zinc.

ANSWER 5   eight
s
p

ANSWER 16 V_2O_5

ANSWER 27 $+6$

ANSWER 38   3
$+5$

ANSWER 49 $+2$
$+1$
CuS, cupric sulfide
    or copper(II) sulfide
Ag_2S, silver sulfide
    or silver(I) sulfide

ANSWER 60 Sc_2O_3
$KMnO_4$
V_2O_5
$NiSO_4$
MnO_2

ITEM 7

Scandium can be expected to donate _____ electrons from the orbitals _____ and _____ to yield an ion with a charge of _____.

ITEM 18

The maximum oxidation number of chromium is _____. This is the oxidation number assigned to chromium in two important anions: CrO_4^{2-}, named *chromate*, and $Cr_2O_7^{2-}$, named *dichromate*.

ITEM 29

Write the formulas of the following compounds: manganese dioxide, chromic oxide, vanadium pentoxide, sodium dichromate, sodium permanganate.

ITEM 40

The common name and formula of cobalt(III) sulfate is _____.

ITEM 51

The removal of _____ electrons from a zinc atom leaves an ion in which the $n = 3$ level is filled and higher levels are empty. It is not surprising that the zinc ion has a charge of _____.

ITEM 62

In the first row of transition elements, electrons fill the _____ orbitals from scandium to zinc. Can you name all the first-row transition elements?

ANSWER 6 $1s^2 2s^2 2p^6 3s^2 3p^6 4s^2 3d^1$

ANSWER 17   The $3d$ orbital contains not one but two additional electrons because one has been transferred from the $4s$ orbital.

ANSWER 28   titanium dioxide,
                titanium(IV) oxide,
                or titanic oxide
            sodium chromate
            calcium manganate
            magnesium permanganate
            potassium dichromate

ANSWER 39   CoO

ANSWER 50 $1s^2 2s^2 2p^6 3s^2 3p^6 4s^2 3d^{10}$

ANSWER 61

Ag_2S, silver sulfide or silver(I) sulfide
FeS, ferrous sulfide or iron(II) sulfide
Fe_2S_3, ferric sulfide or iron(III) sulfide
CdS, cadmium sulfide
NiS, nickel sulfide
ZnS, zinc sulfide

ITEM 8

The oxidation number +3, as found in the ion Sc^{3+}, is by far the most common state of scandium. The ion has 18 electrons in the configuration _____.

ITEM 19

Chromium has an oxidation number of +6 not only in the two anions, CrO_4^{2-}, named _____, and $Cr_2O_7^{2-}$, named _____, but also in the compound CrO_3, named *chromium trioxide* or, in Stock nomenclature, _____.

ITEM 30

There are _____ d orbitals for any value of n greater than _____. Each of the orbitals can contain a maximum of two electrons, one with spin quantum number _____ and the other with spin quantum number _____.

ITEM 41

The properties of iron, cobalt, and nickel are quite similar. The usual oxidation state of nickel (atomic number 28, electronic configuration _____) is +2, as in the *nickelous* ion, Ni^{2+}.

ITEM 52

Similar electronic configurations for cadmium ($\ldots 5s^2 4d^{10}$) and mercury ($\ldots 6s^2 5d^{10}$) suggest that the principal oxidation number of cadmium should be _____, and that of mercury should be _____.

ANSWER 7 three
4s
3d
3+

ANSWER 18 +6

ANSWER 29 MnO_2
Cr_2O_3
V_2O_5
$Na_2Cr_2O_7$
$NaMnO_4$

ANSWER 40 cobaltic sulfate, $Co_2(SO_4)_3$

Ni

Zn
Cd
Hg

ANSWER 51 2
2+

ANSWER 62 3d
scandium   iron
titanium   cobalt
vanadium   nickel
chromium   copper
manganese   zinc

ITEM 9

Elements do not always lose enough electrons to yield an ion with a rare gas configuration, in which the outermost occupied _____ and _____ orbitals are _____.

ITEM 20

Write the formulas for the compounds potassium dichromate, potassium chromate, chromium trioxide, vanadium pentafluoride, and chromic acid.

ITEM 31

As electrons fill the orbitals, from scandium to manganese, each new electron goes in a different d orbital. In manganese, all the $3d$ orbitals contain _____ electron(s).

ITEM 42

The principal oxidation numbers of iron are _____ and _____. The principal oxidation number of cobalt is _____, and that of nickel is _____.

ITEM 53

In fact, the prediction is correct: Cadmium has oxidation states only of 0 and _____; mercury shares or donates _____ electrons per atom in all compounds.

ANSWER 8 $1s^2 2s^2 2p^6 3s^2 3p^6$

ANSWER 19   chromate
dichromate
chromium(VI) oxide

ANSWER 30   5
2
$+\frac{1}{2}$
$-\frac{1}{2}$

ANSWER 41 $1s^2 2s^2 2p^6 3s^2 3p^6 4s^2 3d^8$

ANSWER 52 $+2$
$+2$

ITEM 10

In general, the first electrons to be lost from an atom are those with the highest value of n. The rare Sc^{2+} ion has the electronic configuration _____.

ITEM 21

There are compounds in which chromium has oxidation states from 0 to +6. Two important ions are Cr^{3+}, named *chromic*, and Cr^{2+}, named *chromous*. Write the formulas for chromic oxide and chromous chloride.

ITEM 32

The electronic configuration of iron, element number 26, is _____. You know that one of the d orbitals will contain _____ electron(s) and four of them will contain _____ electron(s).

ITEM 43

Name the following compounds: $Ni(NO_3)_2$, Fe_2O_3, $Co(OH)_3$, $FeBr_2$, Cr_2O_3.

ITEM 54

However, mercury occurs in two oxidation states. *Mercuric* is the name of the +2 state. The +1 state is named _____.

ANSWER 9   *s*
                 p
                 filled

ANSWER 20 $K_2Cr_2O_7$
                 K_2CrO_4
                 CrO_3
                 VF_5
                 H_2CrO_4

ANSWER 31   one

ANSWER 42   +2
                 +3
                 +3
                 +2

ANSWER 53   +2
                 two

ITEM 11

Titanium, element number 22, has the electronic configuration $1s^22s^22p^63s^23p^64s^23d^2$. The maximum oxidation number of this ion is expected to be _____ by transferral of electrons from the _____ and _____ orbitals.

ITEM 22

The positive oxidation states possible for chromium are _____. The +6 state is found in the anion _____, which is named _____, and in the ion _____, which is named _____.

ITEM 33

The first electrons to be donated from an iron atom to an element of high electron affinity are the ones in the _____ orbital. The ion that results has the symbol _____ and is called the *ferrous* ion.

ITEM 44

Write the formulas corresponding to ferrous carbonate, _____; ferric hydroxide, _____, nickelous sulfide, _____; cobaltic chloride, _____.

ITEM 55

The mercurous ion is actually Hg_2^{2+}, in which there is a covalent bond between the two atoms. The formula for mercurous chloride is therefore _____.

ANSWER 10 $1s^2 2s^2 2p^6 3s^2 3p^6 3d^1$

ANSWER 21 Cr_2O_3
$CrCl_2$

ANSWER 32 $1s^2 2s^2 2p^6 3s^2 3p^6 4s^2 3d^6$
two
one

ANSWER 43

nickel nitrate, nickel dinitrate,
    nickel(II) nitrate or nickelous nitrate
ferric oxide or iron(III) oxide
cobaltic hydroxide, cobalt(III) hydroxide,
    or cobalt trihydroxide
ferrous bromide, iron(II) bromide,
    or iron dibromide
chromic oxide or chromium(III) oxide

ANSWER 54   mercurous

ANSWER 11   +4
                    $4s$
                    $3d$

(Item 12 is on page 334.)

ANSWER 22   +1 through +6
                    CrO_4^{2-}
                    chromate
                    $Cr_2O_7^{2-}$
                    dichromate

(Item 23 is on page 334.)

ANSWER 33 $4s$
                    Fe^{2+}

(Item 34 is on page 334.)

ANSWER 44 $FeCO_3$
                    $Fe(OH)_3$
                    NiS
                    $CoCl_3$

(Item 45 is on page 334.)

ANSWER 55 Hg_2Cl_2 (The empirical formula is $HgCl$, but the formula Hg_2Cl_2 is a better representation of the structure.)

(Item 56 is on page 334.)

REVIEW 9 THE STRUCTURE OF MOLECULES

"What holds the atoms together in molecules?" has been, and is, one of the most fascinating questions in chemistry. The answer to that question is far beyond the scope of this book, but Lewis diagrams and orbital diagrams are extremely useful in answering the question on a pictorial level. Section 9–1 will describe the bonding in ions and molecules by Lewis diagrams. Section 9–2 will use orbital diagrams and electronic configurations to describe the simplest diatomic molecules. Section 9–3 will teach you how to draw orbital diagrams for polyatomic molecules composed of the representative elements.

9–1 LEWIS DIAGRAMS

The chemical properties of an element are determined primarily by the number of electrons in the valence shell of the atom. A convenient method for representing these valence electrons and their participation in chemical bonding is the simple *Lewis diagram*, named after the American chemist G. N. Lewis. The explanation of the way in which these diagrams are drawn and the way in which they indicate the role of the valence electrons in the formation of ions or molecules will be a review of Section 9–1 of *Chemical Principles*. An understanding of these simple diagrams is of value because they provide a convenient bookkeeping system for electrons. The diagrams show the role, bonding or nonbonding, of electrons in many molecules, and they suggest the number of atoms that can be bound by covalent or ionic bonds in these molecules.

After studying the Lewis-diagram method for representing molecules and ions, you will be able to show that, for example, the simplest compound of nitrogen and hydrogen should be NH_3, rather than some other ratio of N to H, and that there is an unshared pair of valence electrons in the molecule. If you can do Items 94 through 97, you probably already understand how to draw Lewis diagrams.

ITEM 1	Two electrons can occupy a $1s$ orbital. A filled $1s$ orbital, indicated by $1s^2$, is the ground state configuration of the element _____.
ITEM 17	The fluorine atom in its ground state has one of its electrons unpaired, as is evident from its electronic configuration _____ or its Lewis diagram _____.
ITEM 33	The term *covalent* is used for bonds whose pairs of electrons are _____ between atoms.
ITEM 49	A molecule of HCN has a triple bond. Its Lewis diagram is _____, which can be simplified to _____.
ITEM 65	The Lewis diagram for water is _____. The formal charge on each atom is _____, and the sum of all these formal charges is _____.
ITEM 81	Boron trifluoride reacts with ions or molecules that have unshared pairs of electrons. For instance, BF_3 reacts with fluoride ion to form $(BF_4)^-$. Draw the Lewis diagram for this ion and insert formal charge signs where needed.
ITEM 97	Draw Lewis diagrams and show formal charges for the following compounds. Assume that only s and p orbitals are involved in the bonding.

$$\text{dimethyl sulfone, } H_3C\overset{\displaystyle O}{\underset{\displaystyle O}{-S-}}CH_3$$

dimethyl sulfoxide, $H_3C\overset{\displaystyle O}{S}CH_3$

aluminum tetrachloride ion, $[Al(Cl_4)]^-$

ITEM 2

The next noble gas elements below helium are neon and argon. Their electronic configurations are _____ and _____, respectively.

ITEM 18

Since the remaining halogens appear under fluorine in the periodic table (inside front cover), each also has _____ valence electron(s).

ITEM 34

The Lewis diagrams for hydrogen and oxygen atoms, _____ and _____, can show that H_2O forms as a result of covalent bonding between hydrogen and oxygen.

ITEM 50

In each of the molecules considered so far, every covalent bond between two atoms has been a shared pair of electrons. Each atom is considered to have contributed _____ electron(s) to the pair.

ITEM 66

In the presence of a strong base, a hydrogen ion, H^+, can be removed from H_2O. The Lewis diagram of the resulting ion is _____.

ITEM 82

A similar reaction of BF_3 occurs with NH_3 to form the molecule H_3NBF_3. Draw the Lewis diagram and insert formal charge signs where necessary.

ANSWER 1   He

ANSWER 17

$1s^2 2s^2 2p_x^2 2p_y^2 2p_z^1$ (or $1s^2 2s^2 2p^5$)

:F· (the unpaired electron can be written in any position)

ANSWER 33   shared

ANSWER 49   H:C⋮⋮N: or H:C⋮⋮N:

H—C≡N:

ANSWER 65   H:O:H or H—O—H

zero

zero

ANSWER 81

ANSWER 97

365

ITEM 3

If the term *valence electrons* implies those with the highest value of n in an atom, we see that to fill the s and p orbitals of the valence shell, as occurs for Ne and Ar, takes _____ electrons.

ITEM 19

By analogy with the diagram for fluorine, the Lewis diagrams of chlorine, bromine, iodine, and astatine can be written, without determining their electronic configurations, as _____, _____, _____, and _____.

ITEM 35

The Lewis diagram for H_2O is _____.

ITEM 51

For instance, the combination of four hydrogen atoms and one carbon atom gives CH_4 (Lewis diagram _____). Each bond is formed by one electron from _____ and one electron from _____.

ITEM 67

In the OH^- ion the number of valence electrons assigned to oxygen is _____. The neutral oxygen atom has _____ valence electrons. The formal charge on oxygen in OH^- is _____.

ITEM 83

Although you may have never encountered a compound of phosphorus and bromine, you could combine the Lewis diagrams at the right to predict that a possible compound of these elements might be _____.

: P·   : Br·

ANSWER 2 $1s^2 2s^2 2p^6$
$1s^2 2s^2 2p^6 3s^2 3p^6$

ANSWER 18   seven

ANSWER 34   H·
· Ö·

ANSWER 50   one

ANSWER 66 $\left[:\ddot{O}:H \right]^-$

ANSWER 82

$$
\begin{array}{ccc}
 & :\!\ddot{F}\!: & H \\
 & | & | \\
:\!\ddot{F}\!-\!\overset{\ominus}{B}\!-\!\overset{\oplus}{N}\!-\!H \\
 & | & | \\
 & :\!\ddot{F}\!: & H
\end{array}
$$

ITEM 4

Lack of chemical reactivity is a characteristic of atoms with a complete valence *octet* of s and p electrons, as illustrated by the noble gases _____ and _____.

ITEM 20

The Lewis diagram for oxygen can be written by deriving its electronic configuration, which is _____, or by noting that it comes before fluorine in the periodic table and, therefore, must have _____ valence electrons.

ITEM 36

Fluorine can achieve an octet by the formation of a covalent bond, as in F_2, having the Lewis diagram _____, or by accepting an electron (as from a sodium atom) with the formation of an _____ bond. The Lewis diagram of NaF is _____.

ITEM 52

From the Lewis diagram of CH_4, assign to each atom one electron from each pair it shares with another atom. This formal assignment of shared electrons gives carbon _____ valence electrons and each hydrogen _____.

ITEM 68

The Lewis diagram of CH_3CH_2Cl is _____.

ITEM 84

PBr_3 is one compound of phosphorus and bromine. However, PBr_5 is also a known compound. In PBr_5, the bonding probably involves the $3d$ orbitals as well as _____ and _____ orbitals.

P $1s^2 2s^2 2p^6 3s^2 3p^3$

ANSWER 3   eight

ANSWER 19   :Cl· :Br· :I· :At·

ANSWER 35

$$H:\overset{..}{\underset{..}{O}}:H$$ (or $\overset{\overset{\textstyle H}{}}{:\overset{..}{\underset{..}{O}}:H}$ etc., since Lewis diagrams are not really intended to show molecular shapes)

ANSWER 51

$$H:\overset{\overset{\textstyle H}{}}{\underset{\underset{\textstyle H}{}}{C}}:H$$

carbon
hydrogen

ANSWER 67   seven
            six
            −1

ANSWER 83   :Br—P—Br:
                 |
               :Br:

ITEM 5

In He, only *s* electrons can be accommodated and only _____ valence electrons are present.

ITEM 21

Lewis diagrams for atoms can be drawn either by first writing the _____ for the atom or by noting the position of the element in the _____.

ITEM 37

The sodium atom can achieve an octet of valence electrons by _____ one electron.

ITEM 53

The Lewis diagram for NH_3 is _____.

ITEM 69

The Lewis diagram of chloride ion, Cl^-, is _____.

ITEM 85

When *d* orbitals participate in bonding, Lewis diagrams are not particularly helpful in predicting the existence of compounds since the number of electrons, including shared electrons, in the valence shell of an atom can be more than _____.

ANSWER 4   Ne
Ar
(to a lesser extent,
Kr and Xe also)

ANSWER 20 $1s^2 2s^2 2p_x^2 2p_y^{\,2} 2p_z^{\,1}$
six

ANSWER 36   :F̈:F̈:
ionic (or electrovalent)
$[Na]^+\ [:\ddot{F}:]^-$

ANSWER 52   four (for carbon)
one (for hydrogen)

ANSWER 68

H H
H:C̈:C̈:C̈l: or   H—C—C—C̈l:
H H

H H   H H

ANSWER 84 $3s$
$3p$

ITEM 6

The electronic configurations of lithium, sodium, and potassium (at right) show that each of these elements has _____ valence electron(s).

ITEM 22

Lewis diagrams show the number of outer s and p electrons. Therefore, these diagrams are not generally used for representing atoms that have electrons in partially filled _____ or _____ orbitals.

ITEM 38

In contrast, a sodium atom does not form an octet by sharing electrons. This is consistent with the fact that sodium does not form strong _____ bonds.

ITEM 54

From the Lewis diagram at the right for NH_3, assign to each atom half of the electrons it shares with other atoms plus all its unshared valence electrons. On this basis, the nitrogen atom has _____ valence electrons and each hydrogen has _____.

ITEM 70

If Cl^- is removed from the molecule CH_3CH_2Cl, the Lewis diagram of the resulting ion is _____.

ITEM 86

Lewis diagrams, then, are used mostly for molecules containing "light" elements in which the bonding can be described by a valence shell with no more than either _____ or _____ electrons.

Li $1s^2 2s^1$
Na $1s^2 2s^2 2p^6 3s^1$
K $1s^2 2s^2 2p^6 3s^2 3p^6 4s^1$

H : N̈ : H   or   H—N̈—H
    N |
                      H

ANSWER 5   two

ANSWER 21   electronic configuration
              periodic table

ANSWER 37   donating
              (or transferring)

ANSWER 53   H : N̈ : H   or   H—N̈—H
                  N |
                                     H

ANSWER 69 $[\,:\ddot{C}l:\,]^-$

ANSWER 85   eight

ITEM 7

A useful convention is to let the chemical symbol stand for the nucleus and all inner, nonvalence electrons. Then the outer electrons are represented by dots. Such a diagram, an example of a *Lewis diagram,* for lithium is Li·. Corresponding diagrams for sodium and potassium are _____ and _____.

ITEM 23

Atoms often react with other atoms to achieve a complete outer shell, that is, a complete octet. For example, a sodium atom, with the Lewis diagram shown at the right, tends to _____ one electron, thereby becoming the ion Na^+.

ITEM 39

From the Lewis diagram for nitrogen at the right it is apparent that a nitrogen atom needs to share _____ pairs of electrons to achieve an octet.

ITEM 55

This *formal* assignment of electrons to atoms of a molecule or ion, in which we assign _____ electron from each shared pair plus _____ unshared valence electrons, is the first step in determining the *formal charge* of an atom.

ITEM 71

Add (+) or (−) signs to the diagram at the right (the ion treated in Item 70) to indicate the formal charges.

ITEM 87

For instance, Lewis diagrams predict correctly that helium and neon will not donate or accept electrons because the valence shells, holding _____ and _____ electrons, respectively, are filled.

Li $1s^22s^1$
Na $1s^22s^22p^63s^1$
K $1s^22s^22p^63s^23p^64s^1$

Na ·

: N ·

$$H-\underset{\underset{H}{|}}{\overset{\overset{H}{|}}{C}}-\underset{\underset{H}{|}}{\overset{\overset{H}{|}}{C}}$$

ANSWER 6   one

ANSWER 22   *d*
                 f

ANSWER 38   covalent

ANSWER 54   five (for nitrogen)
                 one (for hydrogen)

ANSWER 70

$$\left[H : \overset{\overset{H}{\cdot\cdot}}{\underset{\underset{H}{\cdot\cdot}}{C}} : \overset{\overset{H}{\cdot\cdot}}{\underset{\underset{H}{\cdot\cdot}}{C}} \right]^{+} \quad \text{or} \quad \left[H - \overset{\overset{H}{|}}{\underset{\underset{H}{|}}{C}} - \overset{\overset{H}{|}}{\underset{\underset{H}{|}}{C}} \right]^{+}$$

ANSWER 86   two
                 eight

ITEM 8

The electronic configurations of the alkaline earth elements (at right) indicate that each has _____ valence electron(s).

ITEM 24

Similarly, a halogen such as fluorine, with Lewis diagram _____, might acquire one electron to become the fluoride ion, for which the Lewis diagram is _____.

ITEM 40

The octet is completed if nitrogen forms covalent compounds with other elements. For example, the Lewis diagram of NH_3 is _____ and of NF_3 is _____.

ITEM 56

If an atom is assigned more or less valence electrons than it possesses as a neutral atom, it carries a positive or negative formal charge. If it is assigned fewer electrons than it has as a neutral atom, its formal charge is positive; if it has more electrons, its formal charge is _____.

ITEM 72

A chemical reaction might remove an H^+ ion from a hydrocarbon molecule. If this happened to an ethane molecule, C_2H_6, the Lewis diagram of the resulting ion, including the formal charge sign, would be _____.

ITEM 88

Conversely, such diagrams are worthless in predicting the existence or the composition of compounds of krypton or xenon, such as KrF_2 and XeO_3, for which Lewis diagrams would have to show more than _____ electrons in the outer shell of the central atom.

Be $1s^2 2s^2$

Mg $1s^2 2s^2 2p^6 3s^2$

Ca $1s^2 2s^2 2p^6 3s^2 3p^6 4s^2$

Kr $1s^2 2s^2 2p^6 3s^2 3p^6 4s^2 3d^{10} 4p^6$

Xe $1s^2 2s^2 2p^6 3s^2 3p^6 4s^2 3d^{10} 4p^6 5s^2 4d^{10} 5p^6$

ANSWER 7   Na·

                K·

ANSWER 23   lose (or donate)

ANSWER 39   three

ANSWER 55   one

                     all

ANSWER 71

(formal charges are often circled as ⊕ or ⊖)

ANSWER 87   two

                     eight

ITEM 9

Diagrams showing the valence electrons, that is, Lewis diagrams, of the alkaline earth elements beryllium, magnesium, and calcium are ·Be· or Be:, _____, and _____ .

ITEM 25

A sodium atom and a fluorine atom both can achieve complete octets of valence electrons by the _____ of one electron from the sodium atom to the fluorine atom.

ITEM 41

The Lewis diagram for N_2 at the right shows another way that three pairs of electrons can be shared to give _____ electrons about each nitrogen atom.

ITEM 57

In the neutral N and H atoms there are _____ and _____ valence electrons, respectively.

ITEM 73

Neutral molecules also can have atoms with formal charges, for example, trimethylamine oxide, $(CH_3)_3NO$. Its Lewis diagram is shown at the right. The formal charge on the nitrogen is _____ . The formal charge on the oxygen is _____ .

ITEM 89

The ion I_3^- (in which there are a total of 22 outer electrons) is known. We conclude, since a Lewis diagram with octets cannot be drawn (verify this), that _____ orbitals may be involved in the bonding.

:N::N:

$$
\begin{array}{ccc}
\text{H} & \ddot{\text{O}}\text{:} & \text{H} \\
| & | & | \\
\text{H}\!-\!\text{C}\!-\!\!\!-\!\!\text{N}\!-\!\!\!-\!\text{C}\!-\!\text{H} \\
| & | & | \\
\text{H} & \text{H}\!-\!\text{C}\!-\!\text{H} & \text{H} \\
& | & \\
& \text{H} &
\end{array}
$$

ANSWER 8   two

ANSWER 24   :F̈:

:F̈:⁻ or, as ions are usually written, [:F̈:]⁻

ANSWER 40   H:N̈:H   :F̈:N̈:F̈:
                    Ḧ   :F̈:

ANSWER 56   negative

ANSWER 72
$$
\begin{array}{cc}
\text{H} & \text{H} \\
| & | \\
\text{H}\!-\!\text{C}\!-\!\text{C}\text{:}^{\ominus} \\
| & | \\
\text{H} & \text{H}
\end{array}
$$

(any H might be removed)

ANSWER 88   eight

The normal hydrogen atom, with the electronic configuration _____, has one valence electron and has the Lewis diagram _____.

In a similar way, one calcium atom (Lewis diagram _____) must transfer _____ electrons to become the positive ion Ca^{2+}.

In the ethylene molecule, C_2H_4, two pairs of electrons are shared between the carbon atoms. The Lewis diagram _____ can be drawn to show that each atom acquires a completed outer shell.

In NH_3 the number of valence electrons assigned to N and H are _____ and _____, respectively. Thus, the formal charges of N and H in NH_3 are both _____.

Draw Lewis diagrams and insert formal charge signs where needed for the following:
hydrogen cyanide, HCN
formamide, $HCNH_2$

O

formate ion, HCO^-

O

the trichloromethane anion, $^-CCl_3$
the amide ion, $^-NH_2$.

A Lewis diagram for the sulfuric acid molecule, H_2SO_4, whose atoms are arranged as

O
HOSOH
O

can be drawn so the sulfur atom need not use d orbitals. Draw this diagram and assign formal charges.

ANSWER 9   ·Mg· or Mg:
             ·Ca· or Ca:

ANSWER 25   transfer

ANSWER 41   eight

ANSWER 57   five
             one

ANSWER 73   +1
             −1

ANSWER 89 d

ITEM 11

The ground state electronic configuration of the carbon atom is _____. There are _____ valence electrons.

ITEM 27

Many ions can be recognized as resulting from the tendency of an atom to achieve a complete _____ of electrons by the transfer of electrons.

ITEM 43

In a molecule of formaldehyde, H_2CO, two pairs of electrons are shared between the carbon and the oxygen to give the Lewis diagram _____.

ITEM 59

A molecule of NH_3 can share both of its nonbonded valence electrons with a hydrogen ion. The ion $(NH_4)^+$ that is formed has the Lewis diagram _____.

ITEM 75

The Lewis diagrams written thus far have been for molecules or ions in which only s and _____ orbitals are needed to describe the bonding. And each of the atoms, through transfer or _____ of electrons, has attained a completed valence shell or octet.

ITEM 91

Other diagrams for sulfuric acid, such as the one at the right, are also reasonable because the _____ atom uses d orbitals and can accommodate more than _____ valence electrons.

ANSWER 10 $1s^1$
H·

ANSWER 26   Ca   or   Ca:
two

ANSWER 42
H H
H:C::C:H

ANSWER 58   five
one
zero

ANSWER 74   H—C≡N:

H—C—N⟨H⟩(H) (with :O: below C, H's on N)

H—C—Ö:⊖ (with :O: double bonded below)

:C̈l—C̈⊖—C̈l: (with :C̈l: below)

⊖:N̈—H (with H below)

:Ö:
‖
H—Ö—S—Ö—H
‖
:Ö:

ANSWER 90
:Ö:⊖
│
H—Ö—S²⊕—Ö—H
│
:Ö:⊖

383

ITEM 12

The Lewis diagram for carbon is $\cdot\overset{\cdot}{C}\cdot$. Here we notice that Lewis diagrams do not distinguish between s and _____ electrons.

ITEM 28

When electrons are transferred from one atom to another, the compounds that result contain charged species, that is, _____. The bond holding the groups together in such cases is referred to as an _____ bond.

ITEM 44

In the formaldehyde molecule each hydrogen atom has a share of two electrons. The total number of electrons that each carbon and each oxygen atom has, shared plus unshared, in its outer shell is _____.

ITEM 60

From the Lewis diagram for $(NH_4)^+$, assign one electron from each bond to each atom of the bond. Each hydrogen atom will be assigned _____ electron(s), and the nitrogen atom will be assigned _____ electron(s).

ITEM 76

The tendency of atoms to achieve a complete shell or octet can be useful for predicting the composition of compounds. For example, a nitrogen atom has the Lewis diagram _____, from which it is apparent that this atom must obtain a share of _____ more electrons to attain an octet.

ITEM 92

Thus, a kind of Lewis diagram can be drawn when _____ orbitals are involved, but it is not as useful because the octet rule need not be obeyed.

ANSWER 11 $1s^22s^22p^2$ (or $1s^22s^22p_x^{1}2p_y^{1}$)
four

ANSWER 27   octet (or valence shell)

ANSWER 43

$$\text{H:C::\overset{..}{O}:}\quad \text{with } H \text{ above } C$$

ANSWER 59

$$\left[\; \begin{array}{c} H \\ \overset{..}{H:N:H} \\ H \end{array} \;\right]^{+}$$

ANSWER 75 p
sharing

ANSWER 91   sulfur
eight

385

ITEM 13   Fill in the remaining Lewis diagrams of the first-row elements in the table at the right.

ITEM 29   An alternative way in which completed outer shells or octets are attained is illustrated by two hydrogen atoms (Lewis diagram _____) that combine by sharing their electrons, thereby forming H_2, represented by $H:H$.

ITEM 45   A shared pair of electrons often is denoted by a line, as in H—H. With this modification the Lewis diagram for HF is _____.

ITEM 61   Since in $(NH_4)^+$ the nitrogen atom is assigned one less valence electron than it possesses as a neutral atom, the formal charge on nitrogen in $(NH_4)^+$ is _____.

ITEM 77   Therefore, the simplest neutral molecule having no unpaired electrons that can be formed from N atoms and H atoms has the Lewis diagram _____.

ITEM 93   According to the rule for writing Lewis diagrams, the two diagrams at the right are equally good. Lewis diagrams do not attempt to indicate the _____ of molecules.

Li	Be	B	C	N	O	F	Ne

Li· ·Be· ‗ ·Ċ· ‗ ‗ ‗ :N̈e:

ANSWER 12   *p*

ANSWER 28   ions
ionic (or electrovalent)

ANSWER 44   eight

ANSWER 60   one (for hydrogen)
four (for nitrogen)

ANSWER 76   ·N̈·
three

ANSWER 92   *d*

H:Ö:H   H
         :O̤:H

The maximum number of outer s and p electrons, as illustrated by neon, is _____. Its complete octet of electrons can be shown as dots arranged neatly in pairs on the "sides" of the symbol. Draw the Lewis diagram of neon.

When a pair of electrons is shared between a chlorine atom $:\ddot{\text{C}}\text{l}\cdot$ and a hydrogen atom $\text{H}\cdot$, the H atom has a share of two electrons and the Cl atom has a share of eight electrons. This arrangement is represented by the Lewis diagram of HCl, _____.

Two shared pairs constitute a double bond, represented by two lines. With this notation the Lewis diagram for formaldehyde, shown at the right, becomes _____.

Since the formal charge shows the difference between the number of electrons that an atom has in the molecule or ion and the number that the neutral atom possesses, the sum of the formal charges of all the atoms must be _____ for a molecule and equal to the net _____ on an ion.

It is possible to combine Lewis diagrams and to predict that the simplest compound of oxygen and fluorine (in which each atom has a complete octet) is _____.

Lewis diagrams do provide a bookkeeping system that shows, since only s and p orbitals are involved in the bonding, that the simplest molecule involving N and H will be _____ and that the molecule has an unshared _____ of electrons.

        H
H : C : : O :

ANSWER 13   ·B̈· ·N̈· :Ö· :F̈·

ANSWER 29   H·

ANSWER 45   H—F̈:
                   ··

ANSWER 61   +1

ANSWER 77   H—N̈—H
                   |
                   H

ANSWER 93   shapes

ITEM 15

The pairs of dots in Lewis diagrams can imply two electrons in a given orbital, in which case the two electrons must have opposite _____.

ITEM 31

Although chlorine atoms can achieve an octet by accepting one electron from an atom such as sodium, they can also achieve this octet by _____ a pair of electrons.

ITEM 47

The Lewis diagram for H_2O can be written as H : Ö : H or simplified to _____.

ITEM 63

In NH_3 the formal charge on the N atom is _____; on the H atoms it is _____. The sum is _____, as expected for a neutral molecule.

ITEM 79

A reactive compound of boron is BF_3. Combine the Lewis diagrams of B and F to show the Lewis diagram of BF_3. The formal charge on B is _____ and on F is _____.

ITEM 95

Draw Lewis diagrams for the single-bonded compounds:
ethane, C_2H_6
hydrazine, N_2H_4
hydrogen selenide, H_2Se.

B $1s^2 2s^2 2p^1$

ANSWER 14   eight

$$:\!\overset{\cdot\cdot}{\underset{\cdot\cdot}{Ne}}\!:$$

ANSWER 30 $H\!:\!\overset{\cdot\cdot}{\underset{\cdot\cdot}{Cl}}\!:$

ANSWER 46

$$\begin{array}{c} H \\ | \\ H\!-\!C\!=\!\overset{\cdot\cdot}{O}: \end{array}$$

ANSWER 62   zero
charge

ANSWER 78 $:\!\overset{\cdot\cdot}{\underset{\cdot\cdot}{F}}\!-\!\overset{\cdot\cdot}{\underset{\cdot\cdot}{O}}\!-\!\overset{\cdot\cdot}{\underset{\cdot\cdot}{F}}\!:$

ANSWER 94

NH_3 or $\begin{array}{c} H \\ | \\ :\!N\!-\!H \\ | \\ H \end{array}$

pair

Since electrons repel one another, the electrons of an atom avoid pairing in the same orbital whenever there are other available orbitals of similar energy. Thus, the normal oxygen atom has two unpaired electrons. The dots of the Lewis diagram for the oxygen atom can show this if they are arranged as _____.

ITEM 32

The Lewis diagram for Cl_2 is _____.

ITEM 48

The CO_2 molecule is described as having two double bonds. Its Lewis diagram is _____, which can be simplified to _____.

ITEM 64

In $(NH_4)^+$ the formal charge on each hydrogen atom is _____; the formal charge on the nitrogen atom is _____. The total of the formal charges is equal to _____, and this equals the charge of the ion.

ITEM 80

The incompletely filled valence shell of B in BF_3 is indicated clearly in the Lewis diagram. The boron atom needs to share _____ more electrons to fill its outer shell.

ITEM 96

Draw Lewis diagrams for the multiple-bonded compounds:
acetylene, C_2H_2
formic acid, HCOH
                   O

                   O
phosgene, ClCCl
allene, H_2CCCH_2.

ANSWER 15   spins

ANSWER 31   sharing

ANSWER 47   H—Ö—H   or   :Ö—H
                                         H

ANSWER 63   zero
                       zero
                       zero

ANSWER 79   :F̈:
                       |
                       B—F̈:
                       |
                       :F̈:
                       zero
                       zero

ANSWER 95   H   H
                       | |
                H—C—C—H
                       | |
                       H   H

                    H—N̈—N̈—H
                       | |
                       H   H

                    H—S̈e—H

ANSWER 16   :Ö· or ·Ö· etc.

(*Item 17 is on page 362.*)

ANSWER 32   :Cl̈:Cl̈:

(*Item 33 is on page 362.*)

ANSWER 48   :Ö::C::Ö:

　　　　　　　　:Ö=C=Ö:

(*Item 49 is on page 362.*)

ANSWER 64   zero
　　　　　　　　+1
　　　　　　　　+1

(*Item 65 is on page 362.*)

ANSWER 80   two

(*Item 81 is on page 362.*)

ANSWER 96   H—C≡C—H

　　　　　　　　H—C—Ö—H
　　　　　　　　　　‖
　　　　　　　　　　:Ö:

　　　　　　　　　　　:O:
　　　　　　　　　　　‖
　　　　　　　　:C̈l—C—C̈l:

　　　　　　　　H—C=C=C—H
　　　　　　　　　　|　　|
　　　　　　　　　　H　　H

(*Item 97 is on page 362.*)

9-2 BONDING IN HOMONUCLEAR DIATOMIC MOLECULES

One of the most exciting goals in chemistry is that of understanding and representing the bonding that holds atoms together in molecules. You have learned something about the energy and spatial arrangements of electrons in atoms, and you have learned a method (Lewis diagrams) for representing the involvement of pairs of electrons in bonding. Now you will learn to make more detailed diagrams, like those studied for atoms in Review 7, that indicate the spatial arrangement of the electrons in a molecule. In this section you will learn to make the diagrams for orbitals of very simple molecules and practice writing electronic configurations. This will be a review of Sections 9-2 and 9-3 of *Chemical Principles*.

It is important to remember that the treatment given here is only one of a number of approaches to the description of chemical bonds. This approach provides a useful and easily presented picture of bonding and predicts reasonably well the geometry and chemical properties of molecules whose bonding can be described on the basis of s and p orbitals.

When you are finished with this section, you should be able to write the electronic configuration of the N_2^+ ion, for example, and draw diagrams of the molecular orbitals used for bonding. If you can correctly answer Items 53 through 59, then you are ready to go on to Section 3.

ITEM 1   The electronic configuration of the hydrogen atom
                                is _____.

ITEM 11   Draw a diagram of the $1s$ orbital of helium analogous
                                to that of Item 2 for hydrogen.

ITEM 21   The electronic configuration of the lithium atom is
                                _____.

ITEM 31   At the right are shown the $2s$ and $2p$ orbitals. Label
                                the orbitals and place dots in the orbitals to represent
                                the electronic configuration of boron.

ITEM 41   The two "half-bonds" arising by overlap of two half-
                                filled p orbitals to form two half-filled π orbitals
                                constitute the bonding of atoms in B_2. The electronic
                                configuration is written as

                                    B_2: KK _____

ITEM 51   The electronic configuration of O_2 is _____.

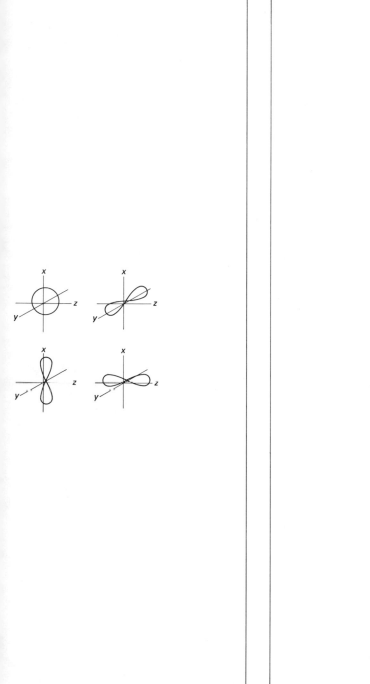

The $1s$ orbital of hydrogen can be drawn as in the diagram at the right. The symbol represents the nucleus and the dot represents the electron. This is analogous to the Lewis diagram for a hydrogen atom, which is _____, but is intended to show that the electron density cloud has the shape of a _____.

ITEM 12

If two atoms of helium are brought close together, we could imagine two molecular orbitals being produced, one bonding and the other _____. Draw outlines of the two orbitals.

ITEM 22

Draw an atomic orbital diagram for lithium. Let the symbol Li stand for the nucleus and the completely filled $1s$ shell that is not involved in bonding.

ITEM 32

The orbital diagram for atomic boron is a composite of the diagrams in Answer 31. The symbol, which usually represents the nucleus and filled shells of electrons, is omitted for clarity. Draw a diagram showing the valence orbitals of boron.

ITEM 42

The electronic configuration of the carbon atom is _____. Draw an atomic orbital diagram of carbon.

ITEM 52

The electronic configuration of atomic fluorine is _____, and the electronic configuration of F_2 is written as _____.

H •

ANSWER 1 $1s^1$

ANSWER 11

ANSWER 21 $1s^2 2s^1$

ANSWER 31

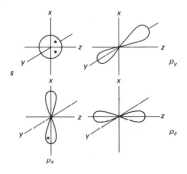

ANSWER 41 $(\sigma_s^b)^2(\sigma_s^*)^2(\pi_x^b)^1(\pi_y^b)^1$

ANSWER 51

$KK\ (\sigma_s^b)^2(\sigma_s^*)^2(\pi_x^b)^2(\pi_y^b)^2(\sigma_z^b)^2(\pi_x^*)^1(\pi_y^*)^1$

The spherical $1s$ orbitals of two hydrogen atoms can overlap. The electrons can, to some extent, share the same region in space and form a bond. This is implied by the Lewis diagram for H_2, _____, or by the orbital diagram at the right.

ITEM 13

Since two helium atoms have a total of _____ electrons, _____ of these electrons would go into the bonding orbital and _____ of these electrons would go into the antibonding orbital.

ITEM 23

If two lithium atoms are brought to within bonding distance of one another, molecular orbitals can be formed by combination of the $2s$ atomic orbitals. Draw diagrams showing the two possible molecular orbitals and insert dots corresponding to the number of electrons expected to be in each.

ITEM 33

The molecule B_2 has two sigma orbitals formed by combinations of the $2s$ orbitals. The diagrams for these, including dots for the electrons, are

σ_s^b _____ σ_s^* _____

ITEM 43

Experiments have shown that the C_2 molecule has the electronic configuration $KK\ (\sigma_s^b)^2\ (\sigma_s^*)^2\ (\pi_x^b)^2\ (\pi_y^b)^2$. Draw orbital diagrams for C_2. Show the σ^b, σ^*, and π^b orbitals and use arrows to indicate the electron spins.

ITEM 53

You already realize that no molecule of Ne_2 can exist. The reason is _____.

ANSWER 2   H·
             sphere

ANSWER 12   antibonding

ANSWER 22

ANSWER 32

ANSWER 42 $1s^2 2s^2 2p_x^1 2p_y^1$

ANSWER 52 $1s^2 2s^2 2p_x^2 2p_y^2 2p_z^1$
              $KK\ (\sigma_s^b)^2 (\sigma_s^*)^2 (\pi_x^b)^2$
              $(\pi_y^b)^2 (\sigma_z^b)^2 (\pi_x^*)^2 (\pi_y^*)^2$

ITEM 4

This type of combination of two atomic orbitals produces a *bonding molecular orbital* that has a watermelon shape. Draw a diagram indicating roughly the correct electron density of the bonding molecular orbital of H_2.

ITEM 14

The net effect of having equal numbers of electrons in bonding orbitals and in antibonding orbitals is that no bond is formed between the atoms. Therefore, a molecule of He_2 (would, would not) be expected to exist.

ITEM 24

Since the number of electrons in the _____ orbital is greater than the number of electrons in the _____ orbital, the molecule Li_2 can be expected to exist.

ITEM 34

Since the bonding electrons are canceled by the antibonding ones, these electrons play no part in holding together the B_2 molecule. The actual bonding must involve the _____ orbital electrons.

ITEM 44

The electronic configuration of atomic nitrogen is _____. Draw the orbital diagram.

ITEM 54

The electronic configuration of the ion Ne_2^+ is written as _____.

ANSWER 3   H:H

ANSWER 13   four
                two
                two

ANSWER 23

ANSWER 33

ANSWER 43

$\pi_x^b, \pi_y^b, \sigma_z^b$

ANSWER 53   that there would be equal numbers of electrons in bonding and in antibonding molecular orbitals.

ITEM 5

However, it is more convenient, especially for polyatomic molecules, to diagram bonds by showing the overlap of atomic orbitals. Draw this type of diagram for the H_2 molecule.

ITEM 15

Draw an orbital diagram for the ion He^+.

ITEM 25

The electronic configuration of Li_2 can be written $KK \, (\sigma_s^b)^2$, where KK represents the electrons in the inner $n = 1$ shells. The electronic configuration of Li_2^+ is _____.

ITEM 35

The p orbitals can be combined to form bonding and _____ molecular orbitals. p orbitals can overlap to form bonding orbitals in two ways. If the $2p_z$ orbitals overlap, a σ_z^b molecular orbital is formed, as drawn at the right. Label these orbitals.

ITEM 45

The 10 valence electrons in a molecule of N_2 will fill these molecular orbitals: _____.

ITEM 55

Write the electronic configuration of F_2^-.

$$\infty + \infty \rightarrow \infty\!\infty \longrightarrow z$$

ANSWER 4

ANSWER 14 would not
(It has not been found experimentally.)

ANSWER 24 bonding (σ_s^b)
antibonding (σ_s^*)

ANSWER 34 p (or π)

ANSWER 44 $1s^2 2s^2 2p_x^{\,1}2p_y^{\,1}2p_z^{\,1}$

ANSWER 54 $KK\ (\sigma_x^b)^2(\sigma_s^*)^2(\pi_x^b)^2$
$(\pi_y^b)^2(\sigma_z^b)^2(\pi_x^*)^2(\pi_y^*)^2(\sigma_z^*)^1$

ITEM 6

The maximum number of electrons that can occupy a molecular orbital is two. Since they occupy the same bonding orbitals, the electrons forming the H—H bond must have opposite spins; that is, the spin quantum number s of one electron is $+\frac{1}{2}$; s for the other electron must be _____.

ITEM 16

If the atomic orbitals of He and He$^+$ were combined, the number of molecular orbitals formed would be

_____.

ITEM 26

The electronic configuration of Li_2^- is _____.

ITEM 36

If the p_x orbitals overlap, an orbital given the symbol π_x^b is formed. It has approximately the shape shown at the right. This type of molecular orbital, like all others, can hold a maximum of _____ electrons.

ITEM 46

The electronic configuration of N_2 is written

_____.

ITEM 56

The electronic configuration of atomic sodium is _____. Would you expect that sodium could form Na_2 molecules?

ANSWER 5

ANSWER 15

ANSWER 25 $KK\ (\sigma_s^b)^1$

ANSWER 35 antibonding

ANSWER 45 $\sigma_s^b\quad \sigma_s^*\quad \pi_x^b\quad \pi_y^b\quad \sigma_z^b$

ANSWER 55

$KK\ (\sigma_s^b)^2(\sigma_s^*)^2(\pi_x^b)^2$
$(\pi_y^b)^2(\sigma_z^b)^2(\pi_x^*)^2(\pi_y^*)^2(\sigma_z^*)^1$

(Notice that Ne_2^+ and F_2^- are isoelectronic; that is, they contain the same number of electrons so the electronic configurations of the two are the same.)

ITEM 7

Two s atomic orbitals also can be combined so that an *antibonding orbital* is produced (as discussed in *Chemical Principles*, Section 9–2). The antibonding orbital can be shown as at the right. This is intended to indicate that the dumbbell-shaped cloud of electrons is concentrated away from the _____ of the molecule.

ITEM 17

The bonding molecular orbital formed from two s orbitals is given the symbol σ_s^b; the symbol σ_s^* is given to the _____ orbital.

ITEM 27

The electronic configuration of the beryllium atom is _____. Draw the atomic orbital diagram.

ITEM 37

In this review, the formation of a π molecular orbital by overlap of p_y orbitals is indicated as in the diagram at the right. Draw an analogous diagram for the bonding combination of p_x orbitals.

ITEM 47

Draw the orbital diagrams for N_2 and include arrows to represent electrons.

ITEM 57

The electronic configuration of the ion N_2^+ is written _____.

ANSWER 6 $-\frac{1}{2}$

ANSWER 16   two

ANSWER 26 $KK\ (\sigma_s^b)^2(\sigma_s^*)^1$

ANSWER 36   two

ANSWER 46 $KK\ (\sigma_s^b)^2(\sigma_s^*)^2(\pi_x^b)^2(\pi_y^b)^2(\sigma_z^b)^2$

ANSWER 56 $1s^2 2s^2 2p_x^2 2p_y^2 2p_z^2 3s^1$
Yes, by analogy with Li_2, Na_2 would have a σ_x^b orbital containing the two valence electrons.

411

The energy of the bonding orbital formed by combination of two s orbitals is lower than that of the antibonding orbital. Therefore when electrons are "fed into" orbitals, they will go first into the _____ orbital, which will accommodate a maximum of _____ electrons.

ITEM 18

Draw diagrams of the two molecular orbitals of He_2^+, by analogy with those of H_2, and insert dots corresponding to the number of electrons expected to be in each.

σ_s^b _____ σ_s^* _____

ITEM 28

Draw the molecular orbitals that might be expected to form if two beryllium atoms were brought close together. Label them and include the number of electrons that would have to be in each orbital.

ITEM 38

Draw a diagram that shows σ^b and π^b overlap of the two sets of three p orbitals shown at the right.

ITEM 48

In N_2 all the bonding orbitals formed by combination of the $2p$ orbitals are filled. A molecule of O_2 has two more electrons than does N_2. Since the bonding orbitals are filled, two electrons in O_2 must occupy

_____ .

ITEM 58

Draw the molecular orbitals of the N_2^+ ion. Represent the electrons with arrows.

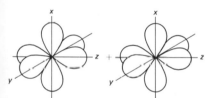

ANSWER 7   center

ANSWER 17   antibonding

ANSWER 27 $1s^2 2s^2$

ANSWER 37

ANSWER 47

ANSWER 57 $KK\ (\sigma_s^b)^2(\sigma_s^*)^2(\pi_x^b)^2(\pi_y^b)^2(\sigma_z^b)^1$

413

ITEM 9	In a molecule of H_2, the number of electrons in the bonding orbital is _____ and the number of electrons in the antibonding orbital is _____.
ITEM 19	The number of electrons in the bonding molecular orbital exceeds that in the antibonding orbital. Would you expect that the ion He_2^+ could exist?
ITEM 29	As was true for He_2, the number of electrons in the bonding and antibonding orbitals would be _____. Would you expect a molecule of Be_2 ever to be formed?
ITEM 39	Of the three bonding orbitals, π_x^b, π_y^b, and σ_z^b, the two π orbitals have the same energy and σ_z^b is of higher energy. The orbitals in order of increasing energy are $\sigma_s^b < \sigma_s^* <$ _____ = _____ < _____.
ITEM 49	The antibonding molecular orbitals formed from $2p$ atomic orbitals have the following order of energy: $\pi_x^* = \pi_y^* < \sigma_z^*$. The maximum number of electrons that can occupy each orbital is _____. Sketches are shown at the right (the dots are nuclei).
ITEM 59	The electronic configuration of the O_2^{2-} ion is _____

The structure
of molecules
414

ANSWER 8   bonding
two

ANSWER 18

σ_s^b

σ_s^*

ANSWER 28

ANSWER 38

ANSWER 48   antibonding orbitals

ANSWER 58

(These drawings show electrons with different spins in the π orbitals and an electron with either spin in the σ_z orbital.)

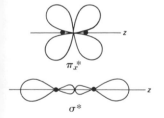

π_x^*

σ^*

415

ITEM 10 The electronic configuration of the helium atom is _____.

ITEM 20 The bonding σ_s^b molecular orbital is lower in energy than the antibonding σ_s^* orbital. Therefore, the electronic configuration of the He_2^+ molecule is written $(\sigma_s^b)^2(\sigma_s^*)^1$. The electronic configuration of H_2 is written _____.

ITEM 30 The electronic configuration of boron is _____.

ITEM 40 As you discovered in Review 7 about atomic orbitals, the repulsion between two electrons causes them to occupy two different orbitals of the same energy whenever possible. Such unpaired electrons have the same spin. Add arrows to the diagram at the right to represent the π electronic configuration of B_2.

ITEM 50 By analogy with the B_2 molecule, we would expect that the two electrons of O_2 that occupy antibonding π orbitals will have the same spin, one electron in the _____ molecular orbital and the other in the _____ orbital.

ANSWER 9   two
            zero

ANSWER 19   Yes. (It has been found
            experimentally that the bond
            is weak relative to that of H_2,
            but He_2^+ is known.)

ANSWER 29   equal (two in each)
            No.

ANSWER 39 $\pi_x^b = \pi_y^b < \sigma_z^b$

ANSWER 49   two

ANSWER 59

O_2^{2-} contains two more electrons than does O_2.
These electrons are used to fill the π_x^* and
π_y^* orbitals.
O_2^{2-}: $KK\,(\sigma_s^b)^2(\sigma_s^*)^2(\pi_x^b)^2(\pi_y^b)^2(\sigma_z^b)^2(\pi_x^*)^2(\pi_y^*)^2$

ANSWER 10 $1s^2$

(Item 11 is on page 398.)

ANSWER 20 $(\sigma_s^b)^2$

(Item 21 is on page 398.)

ANSWER 30 $1s^2 2s^2 2p_x^1$

(Item 31 is on page 398.)

ANSWER 40

(Any arrangement showing two electrons of the same spin, one in the π_x^b and the other in the π_y^b orbital, is correct.)

(Item 41 is on page 398.)

ANSWER 50 π_x^*
                     π_y^*

(Item 51 is on page 398.)

9–3 ORBITAL DIAGRAMS OF POLYATOMIC MOLECULES

The practice you have had in drawing orbital diagrams for diatomic molecules can be put to good use as we turn to more complex structures. In this section, we will look again at molecules in which the s and p electrons are used in bonding and will consider especially the relationship between molecular geometry and the molecular orbital theory of bonding. It is this structural aspect of Sections 9–4, 9–5, 9–6, and 9–7 of *Chemical Principles* that will be reviewed here.

When you have finished this review you will be able to draw diagrams that give information on the arrangement of the atoms and the most probable location of the electrons in many molecules. For example, you will be able to predict the planarity of a BH_3 molecule and the pyramid shape of NH_3. You will understand why an H_2O molecule is bent and a CO_2 molecule linear.

ITEM 1

The electronic configuration of the hydrogen atom is
_____, and the atomic orbital diagram for
hydrogen is _____.

ITEM 15

The orbital diagram of Item 14 suggests that the
angle between the two H—S bonds should be
_____ degrees.

ITEM 29

Beryllium is the first of the alkaline earth elements.
The Lewis diagrams of these elements, _____,
_____, _____, _____, _____,
and _____, suggest that they tend to form ions
by the _____ of two electrons.

ITEM 43

The composite diagram at the right shows that the
three sp^2 hybrid orbitals lie in a plane. The angle
between any two of them would be expected to be
_____.

ITEM 57

Arrange the components at the right to give an orbital diagram for methyl alcohol, CH_3OH.

ITEM 71

When only two atoms are bonded to a carbon atom,
the bonding is described by first hybridizing the
orbitals as $s, p_x, p_y, p_z \rightarrow sp, sp, p_y, p_z$. Label the orbitals
in the diagram.

Be
Mg
Ca
Sr
Ba
Ra

43

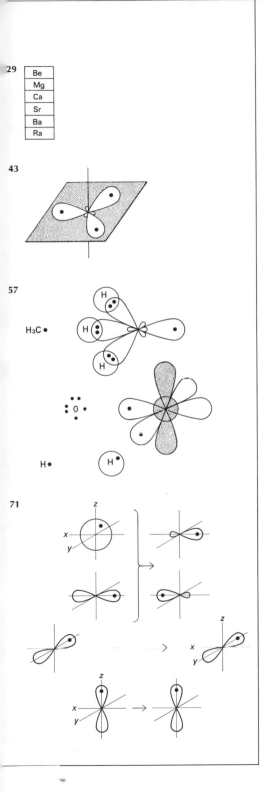

57

$H_3C \bullet$

71

The electronic configuration of the lithium atom is _____, and the atomic orbital diagram is _____.

ITEM 16

The angle between the two H—S bonds has been determined experimentally to be 92°. Thus, we see that we can roughly predict molecular shapes on the basis of _____ diagrams, something we cannot do with _____ diagrams.

ITEM 30

In addition to forming ionic compounds, some alkaline earth metals form compounds, such as beryllium hydride, which are not ionic but have two _____ bonds.

ITEM 44

The molecule BH_3 can exist at high temperatures. The sharing of the three outer boron electrons with the electrons of the three hydrogen atoms can be represented by the orbital diagram _____

ITEM 58

Although the bonding in H_2O can be described in terms of s, p_x, p_y, and p_z orbitals, an alternative description using four sp^3 hybrid orbitals for the six valence electrons of the oxygen atom is possible. Draw such an orbital diagram.

ITEM 72

Bonding in an acetylene molecule, H—C≡C—H, can be described by using the orbital diagrams of Item 71. Draw an orbital diagram for H—C≡C—H.

BeH$_2$

ANSWER 1   1s

H •

ANSWER 15   90

ANSWER 29

Be: Mg: Ca: Sr: Ba: Ra:
loss (or transfer)

ANSWER 43   360/3 = 120°

ANSWER 57

ANSWER 71

425

ITEM 3

A molecule of lithium hydride, LiH, considered as a covalent molecule, can be represented by the overlap of the two atomic orbitals as _____.

ITEM 17

The orbital diagram of the H_2O molecule is _____.

ITEM 31

If some energy were added to a beryllium atom, the process at the right could occur. The electronic configuration of the excited state would be _____, and _____ electrons would be available for bonding.

ITEM 45

The orbital diagram for the molecule BF_3 is _____.

ITEM 59

The angle predicted for the H_2O molecule by the sp^3 orbital description is _____. The angle that was predicted on the basis of s, p_x, p_y, and p_z orbitals was _____.

ITEM 73

In the diagram for Answer 72, the triple bond between the carbon atoms is described as involving one _____ bond and two _____ bonds.

2s   *2s*   *2p*

ANSWER 2 $1s^2 2s$

ANSWER 16   orbital
Lewis

ANSWER 30   covalent

ANSWER 44

ANSWER 58

ANSWER 72

ITEM 4

This combination of two s orbitals gives rise to a *sigma bond*. The bonding orbital in LiH is represented by the symbol _____.

ITEM 18

On the basis of the orbital diagram of the H_2O molecule, the H—O—H angle is predicted to be _____. (In fact, it is 105°. The difference can be attributed to repulsion between the hydrogens and to hybridization—a term that will be discussed shortly.)

ITEM 32

For the description of the two bonds in BeH_2, which are found experimentally to be equivalent, it is assumed that the s and p orbitals mix or *hybridize*, as indicated at the right. Each new sp hybrid orbital contains _____ electron(s).

ITEM 46

On the basis of the diagram of Item 45, BF_3 is predicted to be a _____ molecule with angles between the B—F bonds of _____ degrees.

ITEM 60

The experimentally observed angle is 105°. Electron repulsion in so small a molecule is probably responsible for spreading out the electrons by hybridization of the s and p orbitals of oxygen to form _____ orbitals.

ITEM 74

Since two sp hybrid orbitals project linearly in opposite directions, the molecule acetylene must be _____ in shape.

Be 2p
2s
Be
→
Be (sp)
(sp) Be

ANSWER 17

ANSWER 31 $1s^2 2s^1 2p^1$
two

ANSWER 45

ANSWER 59   109°28'
90°

ANSWER 73   sigma
pi

ITEM 5

In LiH there are _____ electrons of _____ spin in the bonding orbital and _____ electrons in the antibonding $\sigma_s{}^*$ orbital.

ITEM 19

The electronic configuration of the nitrogen atom is _____. The Lewis diagram is _____.

ITEM 33

It is known that the compound BeH_2 has two equivalent covalent bonds. Yet the electronic configuration $1s^22s^2$ does not suggest covalent bonding. If one electron is *promoted* to a $2p$ orbital to give the configuration _____ and then the s and p orbitals are hybridized, the diagram at the right is obtained.

ITEM 47

The ground state electronic configuration of carbon is _____.

ITEM 61

The ground state electronic configuration of silicon is _____. The orbital diagram for SiH_4 is _____.

ITEM 75

The Lewis diagram for the hydrogen cyanide molecule, HCN, is _____.

one
(*sp*) orbital

another
(*sp*) orbital

ANSWER 4 σ_s^b

ANSWER 18   90°

ANSWER 32   one

ANSWER 46   planar (or flat)
              120
              (This   structure   has   been
                  found experimentally.)

ANSWER 60 sp^3

ANSWER 74   linear

ITEM 6

The electronic configuration of the fluorine atom is _____. Draw an orbital diagram of the fluorine atom and shade with pencil those orbitals that are filled with two electrons and not available for bonding. Place dots in orbitals with single electrons.

ITEM 20

The orbital diagram for the nitrogen atom is _____.

ITEM 34

The two sp hybrid orbitals are arranged linearly as drawn at the right. Like other atomic orbitals, these hybrid orbitals can be combined with orbitals of other atoms to produce two kinds of molecular orbitals: _____ and _____.

ITEM 48

To explain the four equivalent bonds that occur in such molecules as CH_4, we say that one electron must be _____ from the $2s$ orbital to the $2p_z$ to give the configuration _____.

ITEM 62

When a carbon atom is bonded to three other atoms, three sp^2 orbitals, rather than four sp^3 orbitals, are used to form three sigma bonds. The sp^2 orbitals in carbon, as in boron, lie in a _____ and project at angles of _____ from one another.

ITEM 76

Draw an orbital diagram for HCN.

(one dashed
to clarify drawing)

ANSWER 5   two
opposite
no

ANSWER 19 $1s^2 2s^2 2p_x^1 2p_y^1 2p_z^1$

$:\overset{\cdot}{\underset{\cdot}{N}}\cdot$

ANSWER 33 $1s^2 2s^1 2p^1$

ANSWER 47 $1s^2 2s^2 2p_x^1 2p_y^1$

ANSWER 61 $1s^2 2s^2 2p^6 3s^2 3p_x^1 3p_y^1$

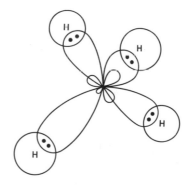

ANSWER 75 $H\!-\!C\!\equiv\!N:$

ITEM 7

A hydrogen atom and a fluorine atom each have one orbital containing an electron that is available for bonding. Combination of the s orbital of hydrogen and the p orbital of fluorine produces a bonding and a(n) _____ molecular orbital.

ITEM 21

The Lewis diagram for NH_3 is _____, and the orbital diagram is _____.

ITEM 35

In this section we will treat only molecules in their ground state. This means that for the molecules considered only bonding molecular orbitals will be needed. The bonding orbital diagram for BeH_2 is _____, and the shape of the molecule is predicted to be _____.

ITEM 49

The four orbitals $2s$, $2p_x$, $2p_y$, and $2p_z$ can be mixed, or _____, to give four equivalent orbitals.

ITEM 63

If one s orbital and two p orbitals of the carbon configuration $1s^2 2s^1 2p_x^1 2p_y^1 2p_z^1$ are hybridized to form three sp^2 orbitals, one electron remains in a _____ orbital.

ITEM 77

The bonding in a molecule of carbon dioxide, CO_2, also can be described in terms of sp, sp, p_y, and p_z orbitals on the carbon atom. Draw a Lewis and an orbital diagram for CO_2.

ANSWER 6 $1s^2 2s^2 2p_x^2 2p_y^2 2p_z^1$

ANSWER 20

ANSWER 34   bonding
antibonding

ANSWER 48   promoted
$1s^2 2s^1 2p_x^1 2p_y^1 2p_z^1$

ANSWER 62   plane
120°

ANSWER 76

Draw an orbital diagram for hydrogen fluoride, HF, showing the overlap of the s and p orbitals to form a bond.

ITEM 22

The NH_3 molecule is predicted to have a pyramidal rather than a planar structure. This has been verified experimentally. The angle between any two N—H bonds, however, is 107°, rather than the predicted value of _____.

ITEM 36

It has been found experimentally that BeH_2 is linear, as is the molecule $BeCl_2$. The orbital diagram for $BeCl_2$ is _____.

ITEM 50

The new sp^3 hybrid orbitals have the same general shape as sp or sp^2 orbitals; that is, they can be represented by the drawing _____.

ITEM 64

The p orbital is perpendicular to the plane of the three sp^2 orbitals. As in the C_2 and N_2 molecules, the two lobes of the p orbital can overlap with the two lobes of a p orbital of another atom to form a _____ bond.

ITEM 78

Each double bond of the CO_2 molecule is described as consisting of one _____ and one _____ bond.

ANSWER 7   antibonding

ANSWER 21

$$
\begin{array}{c}
\text{H} \\
\ddot{} \\
:\text{N}:\text{H} \\
\ddot{} \\
\text{H}
\end{array}
$$

ANSWER 35

linear

ANSWER 49   hybridized

ANSWER 63   *p*

ANSWER 77   :Ö=C=Ö:

ITEM 9

The number of electrons in the σ^b molecular orbital that forms the bond in HF is _____. The number of electrons in the antibonding σ^* orbital is _____.

ITEM 23

In Section 9–2 you learned that p orbitals can overlap to form bonding orbitals in two ways. Label the orbitals at the right.

ITEM 37

Unlike $BeCl_2$, $CaCl_2$ is essentially ionically bonded. The bonding in $CaCl_2$ results from a _____ of electrons rather than a _____ of electrons.

ITEM 51

The four sp^3 hybrid orbitals project at angles of 109°28′, which can be drawn as at the right. Draw sp^3 orbitals along these directions.

ITEM 65

The Lewis diagram for ethylene, C_2H_4, is _____.

ITEM 79

On the basis of the orbital diagram, the shape of the CO_2 molecule is predicted to be _____.

ANSWER 8

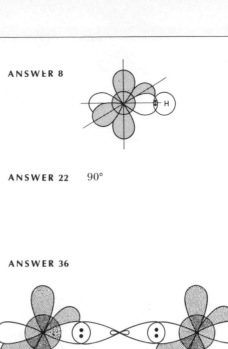

ANSWER 22   90°

ANSWER 36

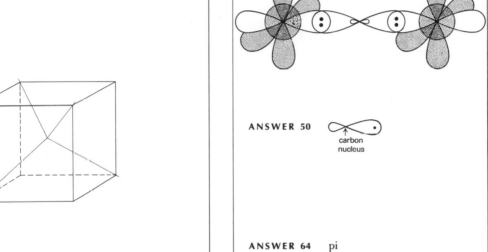

ANSWER 50

carbon
nucleus

ANSWER 64   pi

ANSWER 78   sigma
              pi

439

The Lewis diagram of the chlorine atom is
_____, and the orbital diagram (use shading
for the filled orbitals) is _____.

Draw diagrams for all the orbitals formed by combinations of the s and p orbitals of two nitrogen atoms
in N_2 and use dots to represent the electrons.

The covalent compound magnesium hydride, MgH_2,
has the Lewis diagram _____ and the orbital
diagram _____.

In the carbon atom there are _____ valence
electrons. If the bonding can be accounted for by
sp^3 hybrid orbitals, there will be _____ bonds at
angles of 109°28′.

The orbital diagram for ethylene (at the right) shows
that the carbon atoms are joined by one _____
bond and one _____ bond.

Recall, by contrast, that the molecule H_2O is bent, as
predicted by the orbital diagram for H_2O, which is
_____.

ANSWER 9   two
            zero

ANSWER 23
            $\sigma_z{}^b$

            $\pi_x{}^b$

ANSWER 37   transfer
            sharing

ANSWER 51

ANSWER 65

ANSWER 79   linear

ITEM 11   The orbital diagram of HCl is _____.

ITEM 25   Since there is an equal number of electrons in the σ_s^b and the σ_s* orbitals, the s electrons (do, do not) contribute to the bonding of N_2.

ITEM 39   The predicted angle between the two Mg—H bonds is _____ degrees.

ITEM 53   Draw an orbital diagram for a molecule of methane, CH_4.

ITEM 67   The three sigma bonds of each carbon atom in ethylene result from combinations of hybrid orbitals that are described as _____ hybrids. The pi (π) bond is formed from _____ orbitals.

ITEM 81   Shortcomings of the simple atomic orbital method were indicated by its prediction for NH_3. An H—N—H angle of 90° was predicted if p orbitals were used for bonding. Since the actual H—N—H angle (107°) is closer to the one found in a tetrahedral molecule such as CH_4, it is possible that the bonding actually involves _____ orbitals.

ANSWER 10   :C̈l·

ANSWER 24

ANSWER 38   H : Mg : H

ANSWER 52   four
four

ANSWER 66   sigma
pi

ANSWER 80

ITEM 12

The electronic configuration of sulfur and the Lewis diagram for the sulfur atom are _____.

ITEM 26

The description of the bonding in the N_2 molecule is that the nitrogen atoms are bonded by one _____ bond and two _____ bonds.

ITEM 40

The ground state electronic configuration of boron is _____.

ITEM 54

The solidly shaded figure at the right is a tetrahedron. Instead of saying that the angles in CH_4 are _____, we can say that the CH_4 molecule is tetrahedral.

ITEM 68

The Lewis diagram for formaldehyde, H_2CO, is _____.

ITEM 82

Draw an orbital diagram for NH_3 and show bonding by sp^3 orbitals.

ANSWER 11

ANSWER 25   do not

ANSWER 39   180

ANSWER 53

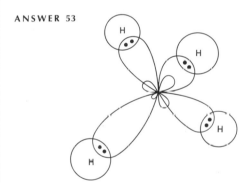

ANSWER 67   *sp²*
                 p

ANSWER 81   *sp³* or hybrid

ITEM 13

Draw an orbital diagram for the valence electrons of sulfur.

ITEM 27

The Lewis diagram for N_2 shows that there are three covalent bonds, but it does not show the distinction between the two types of covalent bonding, that is, between _____ bonds and _____ bonds, that orbital diagrams reveal.

ITEM 41

Since boron forms three equivalent, covalent bonds in compounds such as boron trifluoride, BF_3, one of the $2s$ electrons must be promoted to the $2p_y$ or $2p_z$ orbital, thus giving the configuration _____.

ITEM 55

The Lewis diagram for ethane, C_2H_6, is _____.

ITEM 69

Draw an orbital diagram for the formaldehyde molecule.

ITEM 83

The ammonium ion, NH_4^+, is formed when H^+ is added to NH_3. The four N—H bonds in NH_4^+ are completely equivalent, so the bonding can be described on the basis of _____ orbitals of the nitrogen atom.

ANSWER 12 $1s^2 2s^2 2p^6 3s^2 3p_x{}^2 3p_y{}^1 3p_z{}^1$

$:\overset{\cdot}{\underset{\cdot}{S}}\cdot$

ANSWER 26 sigma $(\sigma_z{}^b)$
pi (π^b)

ANSWER 40 $1s^2 2s^2 2p_x{}^1$

ANSWER 54 109°28′

ANSWER 68
H
  \
   C=O
  /   ¨¨
H

ANSWER 82

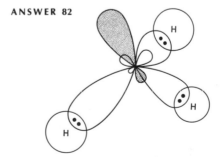

ITEM 14

Draw an orbital diagram for the molecule H_2S.

ITEM 28

The ground state electronic configuration of the beryllium atom is _____.

ITEM 42

Again, hybridization, as indicated at the right, is necessary to explain the fact that the three bonds (in BF_3, for example) are _____.

ITEM 56

Add orbitals and atom symbols to the line sketch at the right to produce an orbital diagram for ethane.

ITEM 70

If a π bond is to form as a result of the overlap of p orbitals, in the manner shown at the right, the axes of the two p orbitals that each contain one electron must lie in the same _____.

ANSWER 13

ANSWER 27   sigma
                  pi

ANSWER 41 $1s^2 2s^1 2p_x^1 2p_y^1$
                  or $1s^2 2s^1 2p_x^1 2p_z^1$

ANSWER 55

```
     H  H                    H  H
     ..  ..                  |  |
H : C : C : H    or    H — C — C — H
     ..  ..                  |  |
     H  H                    H  H
```

ANSWER 69

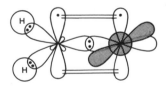

ANSWER 83 sp^3

ANSWER 14

(*Item 15 is on page 422.*)

ANSWER 28 $1s^2 2s^2$

(*Item 29 is on page 422.*)

ANSWER 42   equivalent

(*Item 43 is on page 422.*)

ANSWER 56

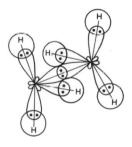

(*Item 57 is on page 422.*)

ANSWER 70   plane

(*Item 71 is on page 422.*)

REVIEW 10 *d* ORBITALS IN BONDING

Although the participation of d orbitals in bonding is no different in principle than the participation of s and p orbitals, it has been convenient to leave our discussion of d orbitals until we could use them in studying the bonding of complex ions. In this review we will consider first the use of d orbitals in the bonding of nonmetals and then their participation in bonding in complex ions of the transition metals. As in Review 9, the emphasis is on the geometry of molecules; therefore, we will consider only localized molecular orbital bonding as discussed in Section 10–4 of *Chemical Principles*. This review is intended as a stepping stone to your study of the ligand field treatment of complex ions.

When you have finished the review you will be able to describe the bonding of molecules or ions in terms of the hybrid orbitals of the central atom once the formula and geometry are given. And if you know the number of unpaired electrons in a complex ion, you will be able to predict whether the ion is an inner- or an outer-orbital complex.

To work through this review you must be familiar with the material of Reviews 7, 8, and 9. Furthermore, it is necessary to know the names and geometry of the five d orbitals. Since p orbitals are identical except for direction, there was little need to distinguish between them. The participation of d orbitals in hybridization depends entirely on their geometry. So you should remember that the d_{z^2} orbital is localized along the z axis, the $d_{x^2-y^2}$ orbital is localized along the x and y axes, and the d_{xy}, the d_{yz}, and the d_{xz} orbitals are localized between the x and y, y and z, and x and z axes, respectively.

d_{z^2} $d_{x^2-y^2}$

d_{xy} d_{yz} d_{zx}

Beryllium has the electronic configuration $1s^2 2s^2$. In $BeCl_2$ and other covalent compounds of beryllium, the angle between bonds is _____ degrees.

ITEM 14

These orbitals are designated sp^3d or $sp^3d_{z^2}$ because the only d orbital that has the necessary orientation in space for trigonal bipyramidal hybridization is the d_{z^2}. Draw the sp^3d orbitals in the diagram at the right. (Assume that the shape of each sp^3d orbital is the same as that of an sp orbital.)

ITEM 27

In the compound SF_4 (sulfur tetrafluoride), sulfur uses $sp^3d_{z^2}$ orbitals for bonding. The number of these orbitals is _____, and the number of sulfur electrons that must be placed in them is _____.

ITEM 40

In a Ti—F bond in TiF_6^{2-} the electrons come originally from the _____. The number of electrons in each bonding σ^b orbital is _____, and the number in each antibonding σ^* orbital is _____.

ITEM 53

The configuration of an outer-orbital complex of Cr^{2+}, including the bonding electrons of the ligands, would be _____. There will remain _____ unpaired electrons in $3d$ orbitals.

ITEM 66

The electronic configuration of an octahedral inner-orbital complex of Co^{3+} (including the bonding ligand electrons) is _____. There are _____ unpaired electrons in an inner-orbital complex of Co^{3+} and it is _____ magnetic.

ITEM 79

In a complex transition metal ion the bonding electrons are supplied by the _____ molecules or ions. The d electrons are not involved in the bonding and, therefore, are described as _____.

ITEM 2

We account for a bond angle of 180° by postulating *sp* hybridization of orbitals. The *sp* orbitals in beryllium result from the hybridization of _____ and _____ orbitals. Draw an orbital diagram of the molecule BeH_2.

ITEM 15

The bonding in PCl_5, then, can be described as overlap of half-filled _____ orbitals of phosphorus with the half-filled *p* orbitals of chlorine atoms.

ITEM 28

Draw an orbital diagram for SF_4 and show only the bonding orbital of each fluorine atom. (The nonbonding electrons lie in the plane that is the base of the bipyramid.)

ITEM 41

Draw an orbital diagram for *one bond* of TiF_6^{2-}.

ITEM 54

Experimental studies have shown that $Cr(H_2O)_6^{2+}$ has four unpaired electrons. It is therefore an _____er-orbital complex.

ITEM 67

Another type of hybrid orbital is the dsp^2. These four orbitals lie in the *xy* plane at right angles to one another. The atomic orbitals with the best orientation in space for dsp^2 hybridization are the following: $d_{x^2-y^2}$, _____, _____, _____.

ANSWER 1   180

ANSWER 14

ANSWER 27   five
six

ANSWER 40   fluoride ion
two
zero

ANSWER 53

$KL\ 3s^23p^63d^44(sp^3d^2)^{12}$
or $KL\ 3s^23p^63d_{xy}{}^13d_{yz}{}^13d_{xz}{}^13d_{z^2}{}^14(sp^3d^2)^{12}$
four

ANSWER 66

$KL\ 3s^23p^63d^6(d^2sp^3)^{12}$
or $KL\ 3s^23p^63d_{xy}{}^23d_{yz}{}^23d_{xz}{}^2(d^2sp^3)^{12}$
no
dia

ANSWER 79   ligand
nonbonding

ITEM 3

Boron has the electronic configuration $1s^2 2s^2 2p_x^1$. The The B—H bonds in BH_3 lie in a plane; the angle between any two of the bonds is _____ degrees.

ITEM 16

Draw an orbital diagram for PCl_5 (phosphorus pentachloride).

ITEM 29

When a sulfur atom is bonded to six other atoms, the geometry of the molecule is octahedral. Therefore, we assume that sulfur uses _____ orbitals for the bonding.

ITEM 42

Draw an orbital diagram for Ti^{4+} with the six ligand fluoride ions. Show only the bonding p orbital of each fluoride.

ITEM 55

The manganese(II) cation has the electronic configuration $KL\ 3s^2 3p^6 3d^5$. An octahedral inner-orbital complex of Mn^{2+} has the electronic configuration (including the bonding ligand electrons) _____.

ITEM 68

Draw a diagram showing the geometry of dsp^2 hybrid orbitals. Assume that the shape of each hybrid orbital is the same as an sp orbital.

ANSWER 2   the 2*s*
one of the 2*p* (or 2*p_x*)

ANSWER 15 sp^3d (or $sp^3d_{z^2}$)

ANSWER 28

ANSWER 41

ANSWER 54   out

ANSWER 67   *s*
p_x
p_y

ITEM 4

The trigonal geometry of BH_3 is considered to be the result of hybridization of three atomic orbitals, $2s$, _____, and _____, to produce new ones known as _____ orbitals.

ITEM 17

The molecule PCl_5 can be considered as being produced by the addition of one phosphorus atom $\cdot \overset{\cdot}{P} :$ to five chlorine atoms $\cdot \overset{\cdot\cdot}{\underset{\cdot\cdot}{Cl}} :$. Each bond is formed by the overlap of a chlorine p orbital containing _____ electron(s) with a phosphorus _____ orbital containing _____ electron(s).

ITEM 30

Draw an orbital diagram for SF_6 and show only the bonding orbital of each fluorine atom.

ITEM 43

The ion Ti^{3+} has the electronic configuration KL $3s^2 3p^6 3d^1$. Ti^{3+} reacts with water to yield the octahedral complex ion $Ti(H_2O)_6^{3+}$ [hexaaquotitanium(III) cation]. Since the geometry is octahedral, the titanium orbitals used for bonding are considered to be _____ hybrids that are formed from the following orbitals: _____.

ITEM 56

In an inner-orbital complex of Mn^{2+}, the number of unpaired electrons is _____.

ITEM 69

Nickel has the electronic configuration KL $3s^2 3p^6 4s^2 3d^8$; Ni^{2+} has the configuration _____.

$$\dot{P}: +\,5\cdot\ddot{\underset{..}{Cl}}: \quad \rightarrow \quad :\ddot{\underset{..}{Cl}}-\underset{\underset{:\ddot{\underset{..}{Cl}}:}{|}}{\overset{\overset{:\ddot{\underset{..}{Cl}}:}{|}}{P}}-\ddot{\underset{..}{Cl}}: \\ :\ddot{\underset{..}{Cl}}: $$

ANSWER 3   120

ANSWER 16

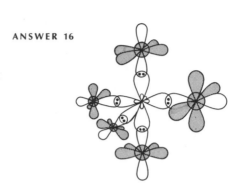

ANSWER 29 sp^3d^2

ANSWER 42

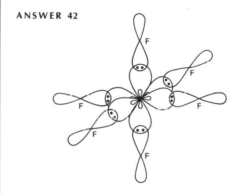

ANSWER 55

$KL\ 3s^2 3p^6 3d^5 (d^2 sp^3)^{12}$
    or $KL\ 3s^2 3p^6 3d_{xy}^2 3d_{yz}^2 3d_{xz}^1 (d^2 sp^3)^{12}$

ANSWER 68

ITEM 5

The electronic configuration of carbon is $1s^2 2s^2 2p_x^1 2p_y^1$. The geometry of CH_4 and other compounds in which carbon is bonded to four atoms is described as _____; the angle between bonds is about _____.

ITEM 18

The ion PCl_4^+ can be considered as being formed by the bonding of one phosphorus atom, three chlorine atoms, and one chloronium ion Cl^+. Both electrons of one of the bonds in PCl_4^+ are contributed by phosphorus. Expressed in Lewis diagrams, this reaction is written _____.

ITEM 31

Bromine has the electronic configuration $1s^2 2s^2 2p^6 3s^2 3p^6 4s^2 3d^{10} 4p^5$. If one electron from the $4s$ and one from the $4p$ orbital are promoted to the $4d_{z^2}$ and $4d_{x^2-y^2}$ orbitals and hybridization occurs, new orbitals will be produced, _____ in number and designated _____. (Note that the $3d$ orbitals are filled and not used in hybridization.)

ITEM 44

Each bond in $Ti(H_2O)_6^{3+}$ is formed by overlap of a titanium d^2sp^3 orbital with a filled sp^3 orbital of a ligand water molecule. The number of d^2sp^3 hybrids is _____, and the total number of electrons from water molecules used in bonding is _____.

ITEM 57

An outer-orbital octahedral complex of Mn^{2+} has the electronic configuration (including the bonding electrons of the ligands) _____. There are _____ unpaired electrons.

ITEM 70

The ion Ni^{2+} reacts with cyanide ion to yield the square planar complex $Ni(CN)_4^{2-}$ [tetracyanonickelate(II)] ion which is diamagnetic. Write the electronic configuration of the Ni^{2+} ion in the complex (including the bonding electrons from the ligand cyano groups).

ANSWER 4 $2p_x$
            $2p_y$
            sp^2

ANSWER 17   one
            sp^3d
            one

ANSWER 30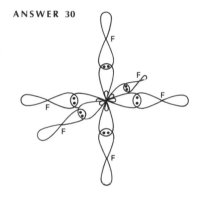

ANSWER 43 d^2sp^3
            $3d_{z^2}, 3d_{x^2-y^2}, 4s,$
            $4p_x, 4p_y, 4p_z$

ANSWER 56   one

ANSWER 69 $KL\ 3s^2 3p^6 3d^8$

465

To account for the tetrahedral geometry of carbon compounds, we assume that hybridization of the _____, _____, _____, and _____ orbitals occurs. The hybrid orbitals are designated _____.

The ion PCl_6^- [hexachlorophosphate(V)] can be thought of as the result of the combination of one phosphorus atom with five chlorine atoms and _____.

A molecule of BrF_5 is square pyramidal, yet sp^3d^2 hybridization is used. Draw the orbital diagram and show only the bonding p orbitals for fluorine.

Thus, the one $3d$ electron from Ti^{3+} must be in one of the d orbitals not used in bonding ($3d_{xy}$, $3d_{yz}$, or $3d_{xz}$) and is a *nonbonding* electron. The number of electrons in Ti^{3+} that have unpaired spins is _____. The number of unpaired electrons in $Ti(H_2O)_6^{3+}$ is _____.

The Mn^{3+} ion has the electronic configuration KL $3s^23p^63d^4$. An octahedral inner-orbital complex of Mn^{3+} has the $3d$ electrons of Mn^{3+} arranged as _____. There are _____ unpaired electrons.

The ion Ni^{2+} forms an octahedral complex with ammonia, the $Ni(NH_3)_6^{2+}$ [hexaamminenickel(II)] cation that has two unpaired electrons. Write the electronic configuration of the Ni^{2+} ion including the bonding electrons from the NH_3 molecules.

Ti^{3+}: $KL\ 3s^23p^63d$

ANSWER 5 tetrahedral
109° (109°28′)

ANSWER 18

$$\cdot\overset{..}{\underset{..}{P}}: + 3\cdot\overset{..}{\underset{..}{Cl}}: + \overset{..}{\underset{..}{Cl}}:\oplus \rightarrow :\overset{..}{\underset{..}{Cl}}-\overset{\overset{\textstyle:\overset{..}{Cl}:}{|}}{\underset{\underset{\textstyle:\overset{..}{Cl}:}{|}}{P\oplus}}-\overset{..}{\underset{..}{Cl}}:$$

ANSWER 31 six
sp^3d^2

ANSWER 44 six
12

ANSWER 57

$KL\ 3s^23p^63d^54(sp^3d^2)^{12}$
  or $KL\ 3s^23p^63d_{xy}{}^13d_{yz}{}^1$
    $3d_{xz}{}^13d_{z^2}{}^13d_{x^2-y^2}{}^14(sp^3d^2)^{12}$
five

ANSWER 70

$KL\ 3s^23p^63d^8(dsp^2)^8$ as
  $KL\ 3s^23p^63d_{xy}{}^23d_{yz}{}^23d_{xz}{}^23d_{z^2}{}^2(d_{x^2-y^2}sp^2)^8$

ITEM 7

Bonding in many compounds of nitrogen ($1s^2 2s^2 2p_x^1$ $2p_y^1 2p_z^1$) can be described in terms of sp^3 hybrid orbitals. The number of nitrogen electrons distributed in the four sp^3 orbitals is _____.

ITEM 20

The bonds in PCl_6^- are directed toward the apices of an octahedron. To account for this geometry, the theory assumes hybridization of the $3s$, $3p_x$, $3p_y$, $3p_z$, $3d_{z^2}$, and $3d_{x^2-y^2}$ orbitals to form sp^3d^2 orbitals. They are _____ in number and will accommodate the bonding electrons in PCl_6^-, _____ electrons from P and _____ from Cl.

ITEM 33

Although the bonding in BrF_4^- [tetrafluorobromate (III)] involves sp^3d^2 hybridization, the Br—F bonds are directed toward the corners of a square. Draw the orbital diagram and show only the p bonding orbitals for fluorine.

ITEM 46

Chromium has the electronic configuration KL $3s^2 3p^6 4s^2 3d^4$. The electron configuration of Cr^{3+} is _____, in which there are _____ unpaired electrons.

ITEM 59

An octahedral outer-orbital complex of Mn^{3+} has _____ unpaired electrons.

ITEM 72

The square planar complexes of ions such as Ni(II) that contain _____ electrons in the outermost d orbitals are considered to involve _____ orbitals in formation of sigma bonds to ligands.

ANSWER 6 $2s$
$2p_x$
$2p_y$
$2p_z$
sp^3

ANSWER 19 one chloride ion $[:\overset{..}{\underset{..}{Cl}}:]^-$

ANSWER 32

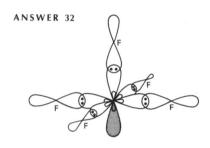

ANSWER 45 one
one

ANSWER 58 $3d_{xy}^2 3d_{yz}^1 3d_{xz}^1$
two

ANSWER 71

Ni^{2+} as the free ion has two unpaired electrons, so the configuration remains unchanged; an outer-orbital complex is formed.

$KL\ 3s^2 3p^6 3d^8 4(sp^3d^2)^{12}$
or $KL\ 3s^2 3p^6 3d_{xy}^2 3d_{yz}^2$
$3d_{xz}^2 3d_{z^2}^1 3d_{x^2-y^2}^1 4(sp^3d^2)^{12}$

ITEM 8

Draw the sp^3 orbital diagram for NH_3 and shade the orbital that contains two electrons from the nitrogen atom. Because these electrons are not involved in bond formation, they are called *nonbonding*.

ITEM 21

The sp^3d^2 hybrid orbitals are directed toward the apices of a regular octahedron. Draw the sp^3d^2 orbitals in the diagram at the right.

ITEM 34

Titanium has the electronic configuration $1s^2 2s^2 2p^6 3s^2 3p^6 4s^2 3d^2$ or, in abbreviated form, $KL\ 3s^2 3p^6 4s^2 3d^2$, where K is a filled $n = 1$ shell and L is a filled $n = 2$ shell. The ion Ti^{4+} has the electronic configuration _____.

ITEM 47

Chromic ion, Cr^{3+}, reacts with water to yield the octahedral complex ion $Cr(H_2O)_6^{3+}$ [hexaaquochromium(III) cation]. As in $Ti(H_2O)_6^{3+}$, the bonding electrons are supplied by _____, and the bonding involves _____ orbitals of Cr^{3+} that result from hybridization of the following orbitals: _____.

ITEM 60

The $Mn(CN)_6^{3-}$ ion [hexacyanomanganese(III)] has two unpaired electrons. The ion is therefore an _____er-orbital complex.

ITEM 73

Many complexes of silver(I), such as $Ag(NH_3)_2^+$ [diamminesilver(I)], have a linear structure; thus, silver can be considered to use _____ hybrid orbitals for binding the ligands.

ANSWER 7   five

ANSWER 20   six
                 five
                 seven

ANSWER 33

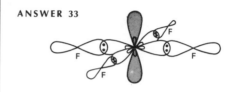

ANSWER 46 $KL\ 3s^2 3p^6 3d^3$
                 three

ANSWER 59   four (the four in the free
                 Mn^{3+} ion)

ANSWER 72   eight
                 dsp^2

If a proton, H^+, is donated to NH_3, the nonbonding sp^3 electrons become bonding by overlap of the sp^3 orbital with the _____ of the hydrogen ion. The shape of the NH_4^+ ion is _____.

In bonds to four other atoms, phosphorus uses _____ hybrid orbitals and the bonds are directed toward the apices of a _____.

In Ti^{4+} the $3d$, $4s$, and $4p$ orbitals are empty and can be used for bonding to atoms or ions (*ligands*) that have nonbonding electron pairs available, such as Cl^-, NH_3, and H_2O. If the $3d_{z^2}$, $3d_{x^2-y^2}$, $4s$, $4p_x$, $4p_y$, and $4p_z$ orbitals of Ti^{4+} are hybridized, six d^2sp^3 orbitals are formed. They are directed toward the apices of _____.

The configuration of the Cr^{3+} ion in $Cr(H_2O)_6^{3+}$, including the electrons from water, is KL $3s^23p^63d^3$ $(d^2sp^3)^{12}$. It is called an inner-orbital complex because _____.

The cyanide ion has the Lewis diagram $^\ominus:C\!\equiv\!N:$. Draw an orbital diagram for cyanide assuming that both carbon and nitrogen use sp hybrids for bonding.

A silver atom has the electronic configuration KLM $4s^24p^65s^14d^{10}$. Write the electronic configuration for Ag^+ in $Ag(NH_3)_2^+$ (including the bonding electrons of the ammonia molecules).

ANSWER 8

ANSWER 21

ANSWER 34 $KL\ 3s^23p^6$

ANSWER 47 water molecules
d^2sp^3
$3d_{z^2},\ 3d_{x^2-y^2},\ 4s,$
$\qquad 4p_x,\ 4p_y,\ 4p_z$

ANSWER 60 inn

ANSWER 73 sp

ITEM 10

Phosphorus has the electronic configuration $1s^2 2s^2 2p^6 3s^2 3p_x^1 3p_y^1 3p_z^1$. Like nitrogen, phosphorus can use _____ hybrid orbitals in bonding to four other atoms.

ITEM 23

In bonds to five other atoms, phosphorus uses _____ hybrid orbitals and the bonds are directed toward the apices of a _____.

ITEM 36

The designation d^2sp^3 indicates that the d orbitals included in hybridization have a lower principal quantum number, n, than do the s and p orbitals. They are *inner-orbital* hybrids. *Outer-orbital* hybrids of the same geometry are known as _____ orbitals.

ITEM 49

The electronic configuration of Cr^{2+} is _____. Since the number of d electrons is _____, each in a separate $3d$ orbital, the d_{z^2} and $d_{x^2-y^2}$ orbitals are no longer both available for incorporation into a d^2sp^3 hybrid that can overlap with ligand orbitals unless there is a change in the configuration.

ITEM 62

When cyanide ion is a ligand in complex ions such as $Mn(CN)_6^{3-}$, the formation of bonds involves overlap of the _____ orbitals of carbon with the _____ orbitals of Mn^{3+}.

ITEM 75

According to the localized molecular orbital view of bonding, the hybridization of bonding orbitals of the central ion of a tetrahedral complex is _____.
Or when phosphorus is bonded to four other atoms in a tetrahedral molecule, the hybridization is _____.

ANSWER 9   1s orbital
                 tetrahedral

ANSWER 22 sp^3
                 tetrahedron

ANSWER 35   an octahedron

ANSWER 48   the d orbitals involved in hybridization have a lower principal quantum number than the s and p orbitals

ANSWER 61

ANSWER 74 $KLM\ 4s^24p^64d^{10}5(sp)^4$

ITEM 11	The ion PCl_4^+ [tetrachlorophosphonium or tetra-chlorophosphorus(V) cation] is tetrahedral. Therefore, according to the localized molecular orbital theory, each bond is the result of overlap of a chlorine orbital with a(n) ――――― orbital of phosphorus.
ITEM 24	When phosphorus is bonded to six other atoms, the ――――― bonding orbitals are directed toward the apices of ―――――.
ITEM 37	In outer-orbital hybrids, the principal quantum number of the d orbitals is ――――― n for the s and p orbitals. An example is BrF_5 (Item 32) in which the $4s$, $4p_x$, ―――――, ―――――, ―――――, and ――――― orbitals of bromine are hybridized.
ITEM 50	If $Cr(H_2O)_6^{2+}$ is an inner-orbital complex ion, one electron originally in a $3d_{z^2}$ or $3d_{x^2-y^2}$ orbital will have to be paired with another electron in a ―――――, ―――――, or ――――― orbital. These d electrons are nonbonding.
ITEM 63	The electronic configuration of Fe^{3+} is $KL\,3s^23p^63d^5$. The octahedral complex ion $Fe(CN)_6^{3-}$ [hexacyanoferrate(III)] has one unpaired electron. The configuration of the Fe^{3+} in the complex (including the ligand bonding electrons) is ―――――.
ITEM 76	When phosphorus is bonded to five other atoms, the hybridization is known as ―――――. Draw a diagram showing the geometry of these orbitals.

ANSWER 10 sp^3

ANSWER 23 sp^3d (or $sp^3d_{z^2}$)
            trigonal bipyramid

ANSWER 36 sp^3d^2

ANSWER 49

$KL\ 3s^23p^63d^4$
    or $KL\ 3s^23p^63d_{xy}{}^13d_{yz}{}^13d_{xz}{}^13d_{z^2}{}^1$
four

ANSWER 62 sp
            d^2sp^3

ANSWER 75 sp^3
            sp^3

ITEM 12

Unlike nitrogen, phosphorus can be bonded to five other atoms, as in PCl_5, in which the P—Cl bonds are directed toward the apices of a triangle-base (trigonal) bipyramid. To account for five bonds, we assume participation of the _____ orbitals.

ITEM 25

Draw an orbital diagram for PCl_6^-. For the chlorine atoms, you need show only the bonding orbitals.

ITEM 38

The ion Ti^{4+} reacts with fluoride ions to form the TiF_6^{2-} ion [hexafluorotitanium(IV)]. The fluoride ions are located at the apices of an octahedron with the Ti^{4+} ion at the center. Therefore, each bond can be described as the overlap of a p orbital of a fluoride ion with a _____ orbital of Ti^{4+}.

ITEM 51

The configuration of an inner-orbital complex of Cr^{2+}, including the ligand bonding electrons, is _____. There are _____ unpaired electrons.

ITEM 64

Cobalt has the electronic configuration KL $3s^2 3p^6 4s^2 3d^7$. The ion Co^{3+} has _____ paired $3d$ electrons and _____ unpaired electrons. An outer-orbital octahedral complex of Co^{3+} has _____ unpaired electrons and _____ nonbonding $3d$ electrons.

ITEM 77

When phosphorus is bonded to six other atoms, the hybridization is known as _____, and the shape of the molecule is _____.

Ti⁴⁺: $KL\ 3s^23p^6$

ANSWER 11 sp^3

ANSWER 24 sp^3d^2 or $(sp^3d_{z^2}^1d_{x^2-y^2}^1)$
an octahedron

ANSWER 37   the same as
$4p_y$
$4p_z$
$4d_{z^2}$
$4d_{x^2-y^2}$

ANSWER 50 $3d_{xy}$
$3d_{yz}$
$3d_{xz}$

ANSWER 63

$KL\ 3s^23p^63d^5(d^2sp^3)^{12}$ as
$\quad KL\ 3s^23p^63d_{xy}^23d_{yz}^23d_{xz}^1(d^2sp^3)^{12}$
(The outer-orbital configuration would have five unpaired electrons, one in each $3d$ orbital.)

ANSWER 76 sp^3d (or $sp^3d_{z^2}$)

Phosphorus has $3d$ orbitals that are relatively close in energy to the $3s$ and $3p$ orbitals containing the valence electrons. Calculations show that hybridization of the $3s$, $3p_x$, $3p_y$, $3p_z$, and $3d_{z^2}$ orbitals produces new orbitals, _____ in number, directed toward the apices of a trigonal bipyramid.

Sulfur has the electronic configuration $1s^2 2s^2 2p^6 3s^2$ $3p_x^2 3p_y^1 3p_z^1$. The bond angle in SCl_2 indicates that the sulfur is using primarily sp^3 hybrid orbitals. Draw an orbital diagram for Cl—S—Cl and shade the orbitals filled with nonbonding electrons.

This overlap results in two sigma orbitals, one bonding and the other _____.

If $Cr(H_2O)_6^{2+}$ is an outer-orbital complex, the following orbitals will be incorporated into the sp^3d^2 hybrids: _____.

A substance having unpaired electrons is *paramagnetic;* it is attracted into a magnetic field. A *diamagnetic* substance is repelled by a magnetic field; a diamagnetic complex ion has _____ unpaired electrons.

When a transition metal is bonded octahedrally to six ligand ions or molecules, the hybridization is _____. Draw an orbital diagram for the octahedral complex of a transition metal ion with NH_3 (excluding the d orbitals).

ANSWER 12 *d*

ANSWER 25

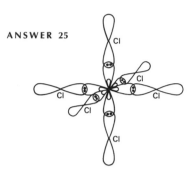

ANSWER 38 d^2sp^3

ANSWER 51

$KL\ 3s^23p^63d^4(d^2sp^3)^{12}$
   or $KL\ 3s^23p^63d_{xy}^2 3d_{yz}^1 3d_{rz}^1(d^2sp^3)^{12}$
two

ANSWER 64

two $(KL\ 3s^23p^63d_{xy}^2 3d_{yz}^1 3d_{xz}^1 3d_{z^2}^1 3d_{x^2-y^2}^1)$
four
four
six

ANSWER 77 sp^3d^2
           octahedral

d Orbitals
in bonding
482

ANSWER 13   five

(Item 14 is on page 456.)

ANSWER 26

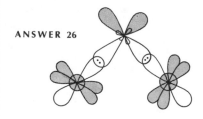

(Item 27 is on page 456.)

ANSWER 39   antibonding

(Item 40 is on page 456.)

ANSWER 52 $4s$, $4p_x$, $4p_y$,
$4p_z$, $4d_{z^2}$, $4d_{x^2-y^2}$

(Item 53 is on page 456.)

ANSWER 65   no

(Item 66 is on page 456.)

ANSWER 78 d^2sp^3 or sp^3d^2

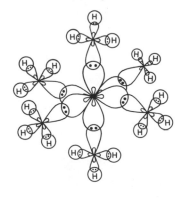

(Item 79 is on page 456.)

483

REVIEW 11 AN INTRODUCTION TO ORGANIC COMPOUNDS

Organic chemistry is the chemistry of carbon compounds. To introduce you to the marvelous number and variety of them, this review will work through the structure and names of the simplest, most common organic compounds. You need not learn all the names, but you should be able to write the structure of most of them, once you are given the name.

The names presented in this review are generally those assigned in accordance with the rules agreed upon by the International Union of Pure and Applied Chemistry (IUPAC). They are not as interesting as the common names, but they have the advantage of being logical and systematic. To interpret systematic names, you really only need to know how to count (preferably in Greek as well as in English): The name will indicate the structure. The common name is usually no help in deducing the structure. For example, the name tricyclo$[3.3.2.0^{2,8}]$ deca-3,6,9-triene, once you have deciphered it, clearly says the molecule is

The name by which it is actually known to organic chemists, bullvalene, provides food for thought, but little clue to the structure of the molecule.

11–1 HYDROCARBONS

This section is devoted to hydrocarbons of all kinds, but mainly small ones, and is a review of parts of Sections 11–2, 11–4, and 11–5 of *Chemical Principles*. Before you try this section, you should know the material of Reviews 5 and 9; in particular, you should be able to draw Lewis diagrams. When an item asks for a Lewis diagram, you should include all the valence electrons, either as lines if they are bonded or as dots if nonbonded. If an item asks for a diagram or a structural formula, the nonbonded electrons or single bonds need not be shown if you understand that they are present. Double bonds and triple bonds always should be shown.

To complete items involving double bonds, you should know that if two groups of atoms (such as the CHBrCl groups in the following example) are connected by a single bond, the two groups can rotate relative to one another. In two-dimensional representation, the structural formulas below are equally valid representations of the *same molecule*.

    H H   H Cl
    | | | |
Cl—C—C—Cl   Cl—C—C—Br
    | | | |
    Br Br   Br H

    H Br
    | |
Cl—C—C—H
    | |
    Br Cl

However, if the groups (such as CHCl in the following example) are connected by a double bond, no rotation around that bond can occur. Therefore, the formulas that follow represent two distinctly different compounds.

$$
\begin{array}{ccc}
\text{H} & & \text{H} \\
\diagdown & & \diagup \\
& \text{C}=\text{C} & \\
\diagup & & \diagdown \\
\text{Cl} & & \text{Cl}
\end{array}
\qquad
\begin{array}{ccc}
\text{H} & & \text{Cl} \\
\diagdown & & \diagup \\
& \text{C}=\text{C} & \\
\diagup & & \diagdown \\
\text{Cl} & & \text{H}
\end{array}
$$

The formula on the left shows the two hydrogens in what is called a cis conformation: they are on the same "side" of the double bond (as distinct from being on the same carbon). In the formula on the right, the two hydrogen atoms are trans, that is, on different sides of the double bond.

Remember that your answer need not be exactly the same as the one given on the answer page, but you should satisfy yourself that your answer is equivalent. If you can figuratively turn your diagram around or rotate a single bond to obtain our diagram, the answers are equivalent. For example, the formulas below represent the same molecule.

$$
\begin{array}{cc}
\text{H} & \\
| & \\
\text{H}-\text{C}-\text{H} \quad \text{H} & \\
\diagdown \quad \diagup & \\
\text{C}=\text{C} & \\
\diagup \quad \diagdown & \\
\text{H} \qquad \text{H} &
\end{array}
\qquad
\begin{array}{cc}
& \text{H} \\
& | \\
\text{H} \quad \text{H}-\text{C}-\text{H} \\
\diagdown \quad \diagup \\
\text{C}=\text{C} \\
\diagup \quad \diagdown \\
\text{H} \qquad \text{H}
\end{array}
$$

$$
\begin{array}{cc}
\text{H} \qquad \text{H} \\
\diagdown \quad \diagup \\
\text{C}=\text{C} \\
\diagup \quad \diagdown \\
\text{H} \quad \text{H}-\text{C}-\text{H} \\
| \\
\text{H}
\end{array}
$$

ITEM 1

Hydrocarbons are compounds containing only hydrogen and _____. The simplest has the formula CH and the name *methyne*. Draw a Lewis diagram for the electrically neutral methyne molecule.

ITEM 15

Usually, the suffix "ene" is indicative of a compound with a double bond, an *olefin*. In the systematic nomenclature this is always true, as in the name *ethene*. The names *ethylene* and *ethene* refer to the same molecule, for which the Lewis diagram is _____.

ITEM 29

Give the systematic names and structural formulas of the six saturated and unsaturated three-carbon hydrocarbons.

ITEM 43

The common names, systematic names, and structural formulas of the two isomeric butanes are _____.

ITEM 57

If six hydrogen atoms are removed from butane, from carbons 1, 2, 3, and 4, a *triene* could be produced. The Lewis diagram of *butatriene* is _____.

ITEM 71

Double bonds that have the structure C=C—C=C are called *conjugated*. An example is 1,3-butadiene. Draw Lewis diagrams for the *cis-* and *trans-*1,3-pentadienes, which also have conjugated double bonds.

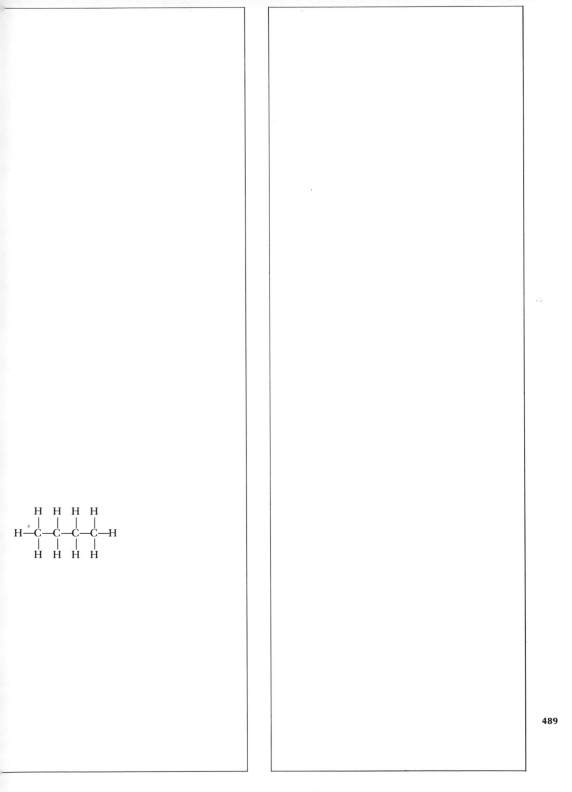

489

ITEM 2

You will never find CH in a bottle—it is far too reactive. But it does have a name, which is _____.

ITEM 16

Draw an orbital diagram for ethylene.

ITEM 30

Consider the removal of one hydrogen atom from a propane molecule. The six hydrogen atoms at the ends of the chain are all equivalent. Removal of any one of them would leave a *propyl* radical with the Lewis diagram _____.

ITEM 44

There are two isomeric four-carbon cycloalkanes, too. The Lewis diagram for cyclobutane is _____, and the Lewis diagram for methylcyclopropane is _____.

ITEM 58

Isomers of the butadienes are the two possible *butynes.* Write the names and Lewis diagrams of the two butyne molecules.

ITEM 72

Two other hydrocarbons with conjugated double bonds are 1,3-cyclohexadiene and 1,3,5-hexatriene. Draw their Lewis diagrams.

H H H
H—C—C—C—H
H H H

ANSWER 1 carbon

·C—H

ANSWER 15

$$H_2C=CH_2$$ (drawn as)

H   H
 \\   /
  C=C
 /   \\
H   H

ANSWER 29

$CH_3CH_2CH_3$ $H_2C=CHCH_3$

propane   propene

$H_2C\!-\!-\!-\!CH_2$ $HC\!\!=\!\!=\!\!CH$
      \\   /   \\   /
      CH_2 CH_2

cyclopropane   cyclopropene

$H_2C=C=CH_2$ $HC\equiv CCH_3$

propadiene   propyne

ANSWER 43

n-butane,

butane

H H H H
| | | |
H—C—C—C—C—H
| | | |
H H H H

isobutane

2-methylpropane

          H
          |
       H—C—H
       H | H
       | | |
    H—C—C—C—H
       | | |
       H H H

ANSWER 57

H   H
 \\   /
  C=C=C=C
 /   \\
H   H

ANSWER 71

trans

cis

491

The hydrocarbon CH_2 is also extremely reactive. It is known as *methylene,* and the neutral molecule has the Lewis diagram _____.

ITEM 17

A double bond is one kind of *unsaturation;* a triple bond is another. Triple bonds are denoted by the suffix "yne" in the name of a compound. Ethyne has the Lewis diagram _____.

ITEM 31

Removal of a hydrogen atom from the central carbon of the propane chain yields another radical, different from the propyl radical. It has the name *isopropyl* and the Lewis diagram _____.

ITEM 45

Four carbons in a molecule also allow the existence of another cyclic alkane, *bicyclobutane,* in which there are two rings. The Lewis diagram is shown at the right. Is it an isomer of cyclobutane?

ITEM 59

The Lewis diagram for 3-*buten*-1-*yne* is _____ and for *butadiyne* is _____.

ITEM 73

An extreme example — so extreme that it belongs to another class of compounds — is 1,3,5-cyclohexatriene, better known as *benzene.* A Lewis diagram for benzene is _____.

H H H
| | |
H—C—C—C—H
| | |
H H H

H   H
 \   /
H—C — C
   | \ |
   C — C—H
  / |
 H   H

ANSWER 2   methyne

ANSWER 16

ANSWER 30

H H H   H H H
| | | | | |
H—C—C—C· or ·C—C—C—H   etc.
| | | | | |
H H H   H H H

(They are equivalent because you need only to turn one to have the other.)

ANSWER 44

```
        H H                      H
        | |                      |
     H—C—C—H                  H—C—H  H
        | |                      |      |
     H—C—C—H                  H—C —— C—H
        | |                        \   /
        H H                         C
                                   /  \
                                  H    H
```

(The methyl group can be attached to any of the three equivalent carbons.)

ANSWER 58

```
        H H                      H       H
        | |                      |       |
 H—C≡C—C—C—H               H—C—C≡C—C—H
        | |                      |       |
        H H                      H       H

 1-butyne (or ethylacetylene)    2-butyne (or dimethylacety-
                                 lene)
```

ANSWER 72

```
         H
         |
      H  C                        H          H
      | ||                         \        /
   H—C   C—H              H          C=C
      |   |                \        /      \
   H—C   C—H                C=C            H
      | ||                 /    \
      H  C                H      H
         |                       trans
         H

                              H         H
                               \       /
                         H       C=C
                          \     /      \
                           C=C          H
                          /   \        /
                         H     H  H—C=C
                                   /      \
                                  H        H
                                     cis
```

493

Neutral CH_3 is called the *methyl radical;* a radical is an atom or molecule with one unpaired electron. The Lewis diagram for the methyl radical is _____.

ITEM 18

You may realize already that the common name for H—C≡C—H is *acetylene*, which is quite different from the systematic name, _____.

ITEM 32

Draw Lewis diagrams for the isopropyl carbonium ion and the isopropyl carbanion.

ITEM 46

Two different radicals can be formed by the removal of one hydrogen atom from a *n*-butane molecule. The Lewis diagrams are _____.

ITEM 60

And finally, there are two cyclic dienes. *Methylene-cyclopropene* has the Lewis diagram _____, and 1,3-*cyclobutadiene* has the Lewis diagram _____.

ITEM 74

Neither of the two Lewis diagrams given in Answer 73 is a good representation of benzene because the electrons in a benzene molecule are distributed equally among the carbons of the ring. One way to show this in a diagram is at the right. Draw a similar diagram for 1,2-dimethylbenzene.

An introduction to organic compounds
494

H H H H
| | | |
H—C—C—C—C—H
| | | |
H H H H

ANSWER 3

H   H
| |
:C   or   ·C—H
   \ |
    H

ANSWER 17   H—C≡C—H

ANSWER 31

H H H
| | |
H—C—C—C—H
| |
H   H

ANSWER 45   No, because bicyclobutane has two fewer hydrogen atoms than does cyclobutane.

ANSWER 59

H H
| |
H—C≡C—C=C—H

H—C≡C—C≡C—H

ANSWER 73

or

ITEM 5

The methyl radical is also very reactive. If it reacts with a hydrogen atom, a molecule having the Lewis diagram _____ will be formed. You would expect its name to begin with the letters _____.

ITEM 19

Draw an orbital diagram for acetylene.

ITEM 33

Removal of any hydrogen atom from the cyclopropane molecule yields one radical. It has the name _____ and the Lewis diagram _____.

ITEM 47

Similarly, two different radicals can result from the removal of a hydrogen atom from isobutane. The Lewis diagrams are _____.

ITEM 61

1,2-Cyclobutadiene is impossible because the C=C=C structure is always linear (180°) and cannot form a square or nearly square molecule such as cyclobutane, in which you would expect the C—C—C bond angle to be about _____ degrees.

ITEM 75

The compound 1,2-dimethylbenzene is often named *ortho*-dimethylbenzene, usually written *o*-dimethylbenzene. *meta*-Dimethylbenzene is the 1,3-dimethylbenzene isomer. Draw a diagram representing *m*-dimethylbenzene.

```
    H   H   H
    |   |   |
H—C—C—C—H
    |   |   |
    H   |   H
   H—C—H
        |
        H
```

497

ANSWER 4

```
    H
    |
  ·C—H
    |
    H
```

ANSWER 18   ethyne

ANSWER 32

```
    H   H   H
    |   |   |
H—C—C—C—H
    |   ⊕   |
    H       H
```

```
    H       H
    |   ⊖   |
H—C—C:—C—H
    |   |   |
    H   H   H
```

ANSWER 46

```
    H   H   H   H
    |   |   |   |
H—C—C—C—C·
    |   |   |   |
    H   H   H   H
```
(The electron can be on either end carbon, for *butyl* or *n-butyl*).

```
    H   H   H   H
    |   |   |   |
H—C—C·—C—C—H
    |       |   |
    H       H   H
```
(The electron can be on either central carbon for *sec-butyl*, said "secondary-butyl.")

ANSWER 60

```
    H       H
     \     /
       C
       ‖
       C                H       H
                         \     /
   C═══C                  C—C
  /       \               ‖   ‖
 H         H              C—C
                         /     \
                        H       H
```

ANSWER 74

```
        H   H
        |   |
    H   C   C   C—H
     \ / \ / \ / |
      C   ⊙   C  H
      |       |
      C       C  H
     / \ / \ / \ /
    H   C   C   C
        |   |   \ H
        H   H
```

CH$_4$ has the name *methane*. The names and formulas, then, of the four possible neutral hydrocarbons containing one carbon are as follows: _____.

A saturated hydrocarbon has an IUPAC name ending in _____, an olefin has a name ending in _____, and a compound with a triple bond has a name ending in _____. The suffix indicating a radical is _____.

A general name (other than paraffin) for a saturated hydrocarbon is *alkane*. The radical derived from an alkane is named *alkyl*. By analogy with the names you have learned, you know that an *alkene* has a _____ and an *alkyne* has a _____.

Consider the removal of two hydrogen atoms from butane (at the right) to form a double bond. If hydrogens are removed, one each from carbons 1 and 2 (or 3 and 4), an alkene named *1-butene* would result. (The carbons that are doubly bonded are given the lowest possible numbers.) The Lewis diagram is _____.

Alkanes containing five carbons are known collectively as *pentanes*. Draw Lewis diagrams for the three noncyclic pentanes. (Remember that, regardless of how the molecule is drawn on paper, branching, by definition, does not occur on an end carbon.)

The 1,4-substituted benzene compounds are known as *para*-disubstituted compounds. For example, *p*-diethylbenzene can be drawn as _____.

ANSWER 5

H—C—H with H above and H below (methane structure)

H | H—C—H | H

meth

ANSWER 19

ANSWER 33   cyclopropyl

```
    H   H
     \ /
      C
     / \
H—C———C—H
      |
      H
```

(The electron can be on any of the carbons.)

ANSWER 47

```
    H  H
H—C—C—C—H
    H  |  H
      H—C—H
         |
         H
```

(The hydrogen can be taken from any CH₃ group for *iso-butyl.*)

```
    H     H
H—C—C—C—H
    H  |  H
      H—C—H
         |
         H
```

(*t-butyl,* said "tertiary-butyl")

ANSWER 61   90

ANSWER 75

```
        H     H
   H    C     C—H
    C   ‖     H
   C         C
    C   ◯    C
   H    C     C  H
        C     C
        H  H—C—H  H
              H
```

H H H H
| | | |
H—C—C—C—C—H
| | | |
H H H H
1 2 3 4

499

ITEM 7

If a hydrogen atom, H·, is lost from a methane molecule, the resulting radical has the Lewis diagram _____ and the name _____. If a hydrogen ion, H⁺, is removed from methane, the resulting ion has the name *methide* and the Lewis diagram _____.

ITEM 21

The names and structural formulas (written in the form H_3CCH_3) of the hydrocarbon molecules containing two carbons (including the one important radical) are _____.

ITEM 35

The only *cycloalkane* mentioned so far has been _____, and the only *cycloalkene* mentioned has been _____.

ITEM 49

If two hydrogen atoms are removed, one each from carbons 2 and 3, 2-*butene* is produced, but two isomers are possible. In one, the hydrogen atoms are on the same side of the double bond and the methyl groups on the other. This is *cis*-2-*butene*, for which the Lewis diagram is _____.

ITEM 63

The systematic name for the compound at the right is _____.

ITEM 77

Let *R* stand for any alkyl radical and draw diagrams for *o*-, *m*-, and *p*-dialkylbenzenes. Label them as *ortho*, *meta*, or *para*.

H
|
H—C—H   H—C—H
      \   /
  H—C—C—H
     | |
     H   H
  1   2   3   4

H
|
H—C—H
H   H |
| | |
H—C—C—C—H
     | |
     H   H
H—C—H
|
H

ANSWER 6   methyne, CH
                methylene, CH_2
                methyl, CH_3
                methane, CH_4

ANSWER 20   ane
                ene
                yne
                yl

ANSWER 34   double bond
                triple bond

ANSWER 48
H   H
 \   /
  C═C
 /   \
H   H—C—H
                |
            H—C—H
                |
                H

ANSWER 62
H   H   H   H   H
| | | | |
H—C—C—C—C—C—H
| | | | |
H   H   H   H   H
(*n*-pentane)

H   H   H   H
| | | |
H—C—C—C—C—H
| | | |
H | H   H
    |
H—C—H
    |
    H
(isopentane)

        H
        |
    H—C—H
        |
    H   H
    | |
H—C—C—C—H
    | |
    H   H
        |
    H—C—H
        |
        H
(neopentane)

ANSWER 76

501

If a hydride ion, $H:^-$, is removed from methane, the resulting ion is called the *methyl carbonium ion*. It has the Lewis diagram _____.

ITEM 22

Ethyl carbonium ion has the Lewis diagram _____. Ethide, $CH_3CH_2^-$, is the corresponding carbanion, which is defined as _____.

ITEM 36

The letters indicating a four-carbon compound are "but." The Lewis diagram for the straight-chain *butane* molecule is _____. It is commonly known as *n-butane* (normal-butane).

ITEM 50

If two hydrogen atoms are removed from carbons 2 and 3 so the hydrogen atoms are on opposite sides of the double bond, the resulting molecule is known as *trans-2-butene*. Draw the Lewis diagram.

ITEM 64

The systematic name for the isomer shown at the right is 2,2-*dimethylpropane*, in which the 2 refers to the number of the carbon atom of the chain and "dimethyl" refers to the two methyl groups. The systematic name for

$$CH_3-CH-CH_2CH_3$$
$$|$$
$$CH_3$$

is _____.

ITEM 78

If a hydrogen atom is removed from a benzene molecule, the resulting radical is called *phenyl*. Draw the Lewis diagram for diphenylmethane.

Left column structures:

$$H-\overset{\overset{\displaystyle H}{|}}{\underset{\underset{\displaystyle H}{|}}{C}}-H \quad \underset{1}{} \quad \underset{2}{}\quad \underset{3}{}\quad \underset{4}{}$$

H—C—H (position 1), H—C—C—H with H H, H—C—H (positions 2 3 4)

1 2 3 4

(second structure below, a cyclohexane-type framework)

ANSWER 7

$$H-\overset{\overset{\displaystyle H}{|}}{\underset{\underset{\displaystyle H}{|}}{C}}\cdot$$

methyl

$$H-\overset{\overset{\displaystyle H}{|}}{\underset{\underset{\displaystyle H}{|}}{C}}:^{-}$$

ANSWER 21

ethane, H_3CCH_3
ethene or ethylene, $H_2C{=}CH_2$
ethyne or acetylene, $H-C{\equiv}C-H$
ethyl, H_3CCH_2

ANSWER 35 cyclopropane
cyclopropene

ANSWER 49

$$H-\overset{\overset{\displaystyle H}{|}}{C}-H \quad H-\overset{\overset{\displaystyle H}{|}}{C}-H$$
$$\overset{}{\underset{\underset{\displaystyle H \qquad H}{}}{C{=}C}}$$

ANSWER 63 pentane

ANSWER 77

ortho   meta   para

503

ITEM 9

The name *carbonium ion* indicates that a carbon atom of the ion carries a positive charge. The name *carbanion* indicates that a carbon atom has a _____, as in the methide ion.

ITEM 23

The three-carbon compounds have names that begin with the letters "prop." The Lewis diagram for propane, C_3H_8, is _____.

ITEM 37

Another four-carbon alkane is possible, one in which the carbons are not linked in a single chain but in which the carbons are branched. Draw the Lewis diagram for *isobutane*, the branched-chain compound.

ITEM 51

Draw the Lewis diagram for cyclobutene.

ITEM 65

Draw the Lewis diagrams for the two 2-*pentenes* and label them cis and trans.

ITEM 79

Draw a diagram for diphenylacetylene.

ANSWER 8

H
|
H—C+
|
H

ANSWER 22

H H
| |
H—C—C+
| |
H H

an ion having a negative charge on a carbon atom

ANSWER 36

H H H H
| | | |
H—C—C—C—C—H
| | | |
H H H H

ANSWER 50

H
|
H—C—H   H
        \\   /
         C=C
        /   \\
      H   H—C—H
                |
                H

ANSWER 64   2-methylbutane

ANSWER 78

ITEM 10

Methyl carbonium ion has the Lewis diagram _____. Methide, the methyl carbanion, has the Lewis diagram _____.

ITEM 24

Propane is a "straight-chain" paraffin, but three carbons also can be arranged in a ring. This cyclic molecule is known as *cyclopropane*. It has the Lewis diagram _____.

ITEM 38

The two butanes are *structural isomers* of one another. Structural isomers are molecules having the same number and kind of atoms but different arrangements of atoms. Each of the isomeric butanes has _____ carbon atoms and _____ hydrogen atoms, but they are arranged in different ways.

ITEM 52

The olefin *methylenecyclopropane* is named as a cyclopropane in which two hydrogen atoms on the same carbon are replaced by CH_2, which is called the _____ group.

ITEM 66

The six-carbon chains are *hexanes*, the seven carbon chains are *heptanes*. Draw the structural formula for the alkane 3,3,5-trimethylheptane.

ITEM 80

Benzene and certain other planar, cyclic, conjugated compounds have characteristic chemical properties that distinguish them from other compounds. These benzene or benzenoid compounds are called *aromatic*. 1,3,5-Hexatriene (is, is not) aromatic.

ANSWER 9 negative charge

ANSWER 23

```
      H   H   H
      |   |   |
  H—C—C—C—H
      |   |   |
      H   H   H
```

ANSWER 37

```
      H   H   H
      |   |   |
  H—C—C—C—H
      |   |   |
      H   C   H
         / \
        H | H
          H
```

ANSWER 51

```
  H       H
   \      |
    C—C—H
    ‖
    C—C—H
   /      |
  H       H
```

ANSWER 65

```
      H           H  H
      |           |  |
  H—C—H       C—C—H
      |           |  |
      C=C       H  H
     /     \
    H       H
```

cis-2-pentene

```
      H
      |
  H—C—H       H
      |           |
      C=C       H  H
     /     \      |  |
    H       C—C—H
              |  |
              H  H
```

trans-2-pentene

ANSWER 79

```
        H       H               H       H
        |       |               |       |
        C—C                   C—C
       /    \                 /    \
  H—C      C—C ≡ C—C      C—H
       \    /                 \    /
        C—C                   C—C
        |       |               |       |
        H       H               H       H
```

ITEM 11

The suffix "ane" indicates a *paraffin*, or *saturated* hydrocarbon: a hydrocarbon that has no double or triple bonds or other electrons available for bonding. Every carbon atom in a saturated hydrocarbon is bonded to _____ other atoms.

ITEM 25

If one double bond is present in a three-carbon, straight-chain hydrocarbon, the compound is named *propene* or *propylene*. It has the Lewis diagram _____.

ITEM 39

The butane isomers are clearly different compounds, differing in boiling point, melting point, and all other properties. The Lewis diagram of *n*-butane is _____ and of its isomer is _____.

ITEM 53

Draw the Lewis diagrams for the two isomeric methylcyclopropenes. (Two carbon atoms in cyclopropene are equivalent, but different from the third.)

ITEM 67

Write the structural formulas of the compounds (a) 3-ethyl-2-hexene and (b) 3-methyl-1,5-hexadiene.

ITEM 81

Compounds such as the ones in Items 1–72 are called *aliphatic*, as distinguished from aromatic. Aliphatic compounds do not contain _____.

	n	iso
bp	0°C	−12°C
mp	−138°C	−159°C

ANSWER 10

ANSWER 24

ANSWER 38   four
ten

ANSWER 52   methylene

ANSWER 66

ANSWER 80   is not
(It is not cyclic.)

ITEM 12

In methane the H—C—H bond angle is 109°28', and the carbon atom uses _____ orbitals for bonding. Two-dimensional drawings cannot show the actual bond angles in saturated hydrocarbons, but we know that nearly all the bond angles (C—C—C, C—C—H, and H—C—H) will be about _____.

ITEM 26

The cyclic olefin, *cyclopropene*, has the Lewis diagram _____.

ITEM 40

The branched-chain butane has the common name *isobutane*, but the systematic name is 2-*methylpropane*. Thus it is considered a propane in which the central carbon is bonded to a _____.

ITEM 54

Consider now the removal of four hydrogen atoms from butane to produce two double bonds. Can this be done to isobutane without changing the carbon atom arrangement?

ITEM 68

Eight carbon chains are *octanes*, nine carbon chains are *nonanes*, and ten carbon chains are *decanes*. Name the hexamethyl compound at the right. Number the chain to give the methyl groups the lowest possible numbers.

ITEM 82

Which of the following compounds are aromatic: cyclohexene, butylbenzene, diphenylmethane, naphthalene (shown at the right).

ANSWER 11   four

ANSWER 25

H—C—H   H (or   C=C   etc.)

(structures showing H—C—H, C=C, H—C—H)

ANSWER 39

H—C—C—C—C—H   H—C—C—C—H
(with H atoms)   H—C—H

ANSWER 53

3-methylcyclopropene   1-methylcyclopropene

ANSWER 67

(a) CH₃—CH₂—CH₂—C=C with CH₂ / CH₃ and H / CH₃

or CH₃—CH₂—CH₂—C=C with CH₂ / CH₃ and H

(b) C=CH—CH₂—CH—C=C

ANSWER 81   benzene
             or benzenoid rings

CH₃
CH₃CHCH₃
1   2   3

H—C—C—C—H
(with H—C—H below)

CH₃   CH₃   CH₃
CH₃—CH₂—CH₂—C—C—CH₂—C—CH₃
CH₃   CH₃   CH₃

511

The saturated hydrocarbon containing two carbon atoms is named *ethane*. Draw the Lewis diagram for ethane.

If two double bonds are present in a compound, it is called a *diene* or *diolefin*. The Lewis diagram for propadiene is _____.

In the IUPAC system an alkane is given the name corresponding to the longest single carbon chain, and the branches are identified by name and by the number of the carbon to which they are attached. The central carbon of propane is numbered _____, no matter which end of the chain is numbered 1.

From *n*-butane, however, four hydrogens can be removed, one each from carbons 1 and 3, and two from carbon 2. The resulting 1,2-*butadiene* has the Lewis diagram _____.

The structural formula of 1,4-decadiyne is _____ and of cyclooctene is _____.

H H H H
| | | |
H—C—C—C—C—H
| | | |
H H H H

ANSWER 12 sp^3
109°

ANSWER 26

ANSWER 40   methyl radical
(or methyl group)

ANSWER 54   No.

ANSWER 68   2,2,4,4,5,5-hexamethyloctane

ANSWER 82   butylbenzene,
diphenylmethane,
naphthalene

ITEM 14

The suffix "yl" designates a radical. If one hydrogen atom is removed from ethane, the resulting radical will be named _____ and will have the Lewis diagram _____.

ITEM 28

The systematic name for the three-carbon hydrocarbon with a triple bond is _____. It also can be named as an acetylene in which one hydrogen is replaced by a methyl group: The common name is *methylacetylene*. Draw the Lewis diagram for this compound.

ITEM 42

In the compound at the right, the longest single chain contains _____ carbon atoms. The name therefore *cannot* correspond to any propane. The systematic name must be _____.

ITEM 56

Or, if hydrogens are removed, one each from carbons 1, 2, 3, and 4, the resulting 1,3-*butadiene* has the Lewis diagram _____.

ITEM 70

The straight-chain radicals having five, six, seven, eight, nine, and ten carbon atoms are known as _____, _____, _____, _____, _____, and _____.

H H H
H—C—C—C—H
    | |
    H   H
H—C—H
    |
    H

H H H H
H—C—C—C—C—H
    | | | |
    H H H H

ANSWER 13

H H
| |
H—C—C—H
| |
H H

ANSWER 27

H   H
\   /
C═C═C
/   \
H   H

ANSWER 41 2

ANSWER 55

                    H
                    |
H   C—H
\ |
C═C═C H
/ |
H   H

ANSWER 69

HC≡C—CH₂—C≡C—CH₂CH₂CH₂CH₂CH₃

ANSWER 14   ethyl

$$H-\underset{\underset{H}{|}}{\overset{\overset{H}{|}}{C}}-\underset{\underset{H}{|}}{\overset{\overset{H}{|}}{C}}\cdot$$

(Any H can be removed because they are all equivalent.)

(Item 15 is on page 488.)

ANSWER 28   propyne

$$H-\underset{\underset{H}{|}}{\overset{\overset{H}{|}}{C}}-C\equiv C-H$$

(Item 29 is on page 488.)

ANSWER 42   four
butane

(Item 43 is on page 488.)

ANSWER 56

(Item 57 is on page 488.)

ANSWER 70   pentyl, hexyl, heptyl, octyl, nonyl, and decyl

(Item 71 is on page 488.)

11-2 THE FUNCTIONAL GROUPS

Alkanes are unreactive compounds: Drastic conditions are required to break the sigma bonds between the carbon and hydrogen atoms. The pi bonds of alkenes and alkynes are broken more easily, so these compounds are more reactive; addition of atoms to double and triple bonds is a common reaction. However, the presence of halogen, oxygen, nitrogen, sulfur, or phosphorus atoms in a molecule greatly extends the possibilities for reaction. In part, this is because of their nonbonded valence electrons.

In this section, which is a review of parts of Section 11–3 of *Chemical Principles*, again you will draw Lewis diagrams to emphasize the presence of nonbonded electrons. In doing so, you will learn the names and structures of simple organic compounds containing the most common reactive atoms or groups of atoms, the *functional groups*. When you have finished this section, you will be able to recognize names and draw structural diagrams for halides, alcohols, aldehydes, ketones, acids, ethers, esters, and amines.

ITEM 1

Although alkanes are extremely unreactive compounds, they will react with chlorine gas in sunlight to produce *chloroalkanes*. For example, from methane, one product is *chloromethane* (also called monochloromethane and methyl chloride); it has the Lewis diagram _____.

ITEM 16

Alcohols containing two *hydroxyl* (OH) groups are called *diols* or *glycols*. Draw the Lewis diagram for 1,2-ethanediol, better known as ethylene glycol.

ITEM 31

The compound at the right is another example of an enol. Its systematic name is _____. Like its isomer, $CH_3CH=CHOH$, this enol rapidly rearranges to a carbonyl compound.

ITEM 46

The simplest carboxylic acid is *formic acid*. Since its systematic name is *methanoic acid*, it must contain _____ carbon atom(s). The Lewis diagram is _____

ITEM 61

The reaction of a carboxylic acid with an alcohol in the presence of an inorganic acid leads to the formation of an *ester*. For example,

$$\begin{array}{ccc} H & & O \\ | & & \| \\ H-C-O-H & + & H-O-C-H \\ | & & \\ H & & \end{array}$$

$$\rightarrow \begin{array}{cc} H & O \\ | & \| \\ H-C-O-C-H & + \underline{\qquad}. \\ | & \\ H & \end{array}$$

ITEM 76

Draw structural formulas for the following organic compounds: 2-methyl-4-chloro-1-butene, methyl alcohol, and acetone.

Carboxyl group

ITEM 2

The other products are *dichloromethane* (methylene chloride), *trichloromethane* (chloroform), and *tetra-chloromethane* (carbon tetrachloride). Draw Lewis diagrams for these compounds.

ITEM 17

Draw the structural formulas for 1,4-butanediol and 1-pentene-3,5-diol.

ITEM 32

The proton transfer reaction shown at the right leads to a *ketone*, a general name for a compound containing a carbonyl as a nonterminal carbon rather than at the end of the chain, as it is in a(n) _____.

ITEM 47

Acetic acid has the systematic name *ethanoic* acid, but its IUPAC name is rarely used. The Lewis diagram of acetic acid is _____.

ITEM 62

All esters contain the partial structure

$$C\!-\!O\!-\!\overset{\displaystyle O}{\overset{\|}{C}}$$

of which the C$=$O group is derived from an acid and the other carbon (and the other oxygen) is derived from an _____.

ITEM 77

Draw structural formulas for the following: phenol, *p*-dibromobenzene, formaldehyde.

H—C—H (with H on top)
|
C=C (OH below left C, H on bottom right)
→ H—C—C—C—H (with H top on each end C, H O H below)

ANSWER 1

    H
   |
H—C—H
   |
  :Cl:

ANSWER 16

H   H
| |
H—C   C—H   or   H—C—C—O—H etc.
| |
:O: :O:
| |
H   H

ANSWER 31   1-propen-2-ol

ANSWER 46   one

H
 \
  C—O—H
 ||
 :O:

ANSWER 61 H_2O

ANSWER 76

    H   H Cl
    | | |
H—C=C—C—C—H
       | |
       H H

    H—C—H
      |
      H

    H
    |
H—C—O—H
    |
    H

    H O H
    | || |
H—C—C—C—H
    | |
    H   H

Organic halogen compounds are named systematically by a prefix designating the number and positions of the halogen atoms followed by the appropriate hydrocarbon name. As an example, the compound shown at the right is named 1,2,2,4-*tetrachlorobutane*. Draw a similar diagram for 1,1,2-trifluoropropane.

ITEM 18

The term "alcohol" is used for aliphatic hydroxyl compounds. The term for compounds containing a hydroxyl group directly bonded to a benzene ring is *phenol*. The parent compound is *phenol* itself, which is shown at the right. 2-Methylphenol can be drawn as _____.

ITEM 33

Since a ketone carbonyl group cannot be at the end of a chain, the simplest ketone is *propanone*, usually called *acetone* (shown at the right). The carbonyl group is bonded to two _____.

ITEM 48

The systematic names of acids are those of the corresponding hydrocarbons with the final "e" replaced by "oic" and the word "acid" added. The carboxyl carbon is counted as number 1. Thus, the three-carbon acid at the right is named _____.

ITEM 63

An ester is named after the alcohol and acid from which it is derived. The ester at the right is named methyl formate (or methyl methanoate) and is derived from _____ alcohol and _____ acid.

ITEM 78

Draw structural formulas for the following: 2-pentanone, acetic acid, 3-bromocyclohexanone.

```
Cl  H  Cl  Cl
 |   |   |   |
H—C—C—C—C—H
 |   |   |   |
 H   H  Cl  H
 4   3   2   1
```

```
        H
        |
       :O:
        |
   H    C    H
    \  / \  /
     C    C
     ‖    |
     C    C
    / \  / \
   H   C    H
        |
        H
```

```
 H       H
 |       |
H—C—C—C—H
 |   ‖   |
 H   O   H
```

```
 H   H
 |   |
H—C—C—C—O—H
 |   |   ‖
 H   H   O
 3   2   1
```

```
 H
 |
H—C—O—C—H
 |       ‖
 H      :O:
```

ANSWER 2

```
     H                    H                    :Cl:
     |                    |                     |
:Cl—C—Cl:        :Cl—C—Cl:        :Cl—C—Cl:
     |                    |                     |
     H                   :Cl:                  :Cl:
```

ANSWER 17

```
    H  H  H  H
    |  |  |  |
H—O—C—C—C—C—O—H
    |  |  |  |
    H  H  H  H
```

```
         H  H  H
         |  |  |
H—C≡C—C—C—C—O—H
         |  |  |
         H  O  H  H
            |
            H
```

ANSWER 32   aldehyde

ANSWER 47

```
        H
        |
     H—C
        \
     H    C—O—H
           ‖
          :O:
```

ANSWER 62   alcohol

ANSWER 77

```
      H        H
       \      /
        C—C
      //      \
  H—C          C—O—H
      \\      /
        C—C
       /      \
      H        H
```

```
      H        H
       \      /
        C—C
      //      \
 Br—C          C—Br
      \\      /
        C—C
       /      \
      H        H
```

```
H—C—H
    ‖
    O
```

525

ITEM 4

Some common names consist of the hydrocarbon radical name followed by the halide name with a prefix "di" or "tri" indicating two or three halide atoms. The compound at the right is named *n-hexyl fluoride*. The systematic name is _____.

ITEM 19

Draw diagrams for 2-ethylphenol and 2-phenylethanol. (When a number is not given, it is assumed to be 1, as in 2-phenyl-1-ethanol.)

ITEM 34

A ketone is named systematically by considering the longest chain carrying the ketone group to be the parent hydrocarbon. The carbonyl carbon is given the lowest possible number and the "e" of the hydrocarbon name is replaced by _____.

ITEM 49

The acid that has the systematic name propenoic acid has the Lewis diagram _____.

ITEM 64

The name of the ester thus includes the name of an acid in which the suffix "ic" of the acid name is replaced by "ate" in the ester name. The Lewis diagram of ethyl formate is _____.

ITEM 79

Draw structural formulas for the following: benzoic acid, ethyl acetate, trimethylamine.

H—C—C—C—C—C—C—F

with H H H H H H above and H H H H H H below the carbon chain

$CH_3CH_2CCH_2CH_3$
with O (double bonded) below the third carbon

3-pentanone

ANSWER 3

H—C—C—C—H

with H F F above and H H F below

ANSWER 18

ANSWER 33   methyl groups

ANSWER 48   propanoic acid
(The common name is propionic.)

ANSWER 63   methyl (methanol)
formic (methanoic)

ANSWER 78

H—C—C—C—C—C—H

with H H H H above and H O H H H below

H—C—C—O—H

with H above and H O below

527

ITEM 5

The haloalkane $CH_3CH_2CH_2Br$ has the systematic name _____ and the common name _____.

ITEM 20

Write names and structural formulas for the one-carbon and two-carbon alcohols and diols.

ITEM 35

In the case of propanone, the number is redundant. The common name of propanone is _____.

ITEM 50

Many times the formula for an acid is written without showing the double bond. For example, CH_3COOH is equivalent to the formula shown at the right. The common name of this acid is _____, and the systematic name is _____.

ITEM 65

The Lewis diagrams for methyl formate and for methyl acetate are _____.

ITEM 80

Draw structural formulas for 3,3-difluoroheptanal, ether (i.e., diethyl ether), isopropyl formate, and 3-phenylpropanoic acid.

CH_3CCH_3

$$H-\overset{\overset{\displaystyle H}{|}}{\underset{\underset{\displaystyle H}{|}}{C}}-\overset{\overset{\displaystyle }{}}{\underset{\underset{\displaystyle O}{\|}}{C}}-O-H$$

ANSWER 4   1-fluorohexane

ANSWER 19

ANSWER 34   one

ANSWER 49

ANSWER 64

ANSWER 79

529

ITEM 6

There are two structural isomers of monoiodopropane. Write the common names and formulas for both.

ITEM 21

Alcohols do not ionize in water: They do not have the basic properties of NaOH in water nor the acidic properties of HOCl in water. However, phenols are acidic in water and, therefore, capable of donating a _____ to _____.

ITEM 36

The Lewis diagram of 2-pentanone is _____. The common name is methyl n-propyl ketone.

ITEM 51

Acids in which the carboxyl group is bonded directly to a benzene ring are known as *benzoic acids*. The parent acid, benzoic acid, has the structural formula _____.

ITEM 66

Draw diagrams for methyl benzoate and phenyl acetate.

ANSWER 5 1-bromopropane
n-propyl bromide

ANSWER 20

methanol, methyl alcohol H_3COH
methanediol $H_2\underset{\underset{\textstyle OH}{|}}{C}OH$

ethanol, ethyl alcohol CH_3CH_2OH
1,2-ethanediol, ethylene glycol
  $HOCH_2CH_2OH$
1,1-ethanediol $HO\underset{\underset{\textstyle OH}{|}}{C}HCH_3$

ANSWER 35 acetone

ANSWER 50 acetic
ethanoic

ANSWER 65

ANSWER 80

531

(Turn to page 552.)

ITEM 7	How many isomers are possible for dibromopropane? Give the systematic names.
ITEM 22	The characteristic structure of a phenol is _____. Draw a diagram for *meta*-chlorophenol.
ITEM 37	The structural formula of 2,4-dimethyl-3-pentanone is _____. The common name is diisopropyl ketone.
ITEM 52	Draw a diagram to represent 2,4,6-tribromobenzoic acid.
ITEM 67	The ester derived from isopropyl alcohol and *o*-chlorobenzoic acid has the name *isopropyl o-chlorobenzoate* and the structural formula _____.

ANSWER 6 *n*-propyl iodide

H—C—C—C—I with H H H top and H H H bottom

iso-propyl iodide

H—C—C—C—H with H H H top and H I H bottom

ANSWER 21 proton (or hydrogen ion)
H_2O

ANSWER 36

H—C—C—C—C—C—H with H / H H top and H :O: H H H bottom

ANSWER 51

or

ANSWER 66

533

ITEM 8   Draw diagrams to represent the compounds 1,1-dichloro-2-methyl-1-propene and *cis*-2,3-dibromo-2-butene.

ITEM 23   Consider the diagram at the right. The name of this compound would be _____. This kind of alcohol, in which the OH group is attached to a doubly bonded carbon, is known as an *enol*.

ITEM 38   The common names of ketones, as you have seen, usually indicate structure. For example, ethyl phenyl ketone has the structural formula at the right. Methyl *o*-bromophenyl ketone has the structural formula _____.

ITEM 53   Write structural formulas for phenol, benzaldehyde, and benzoic acid.

ITEM 68   Write partial structures characteristic of the following types of compounds: alcohols, _____; aldehydes, _____; ketones, _____; esters, _____; acids, _____.

H   H
 \ /
  C=C
 / \
H   H
H—C—H   OH
   |
   H

H   H
 C—C   H H
 /   \ | |
H—C   C—C—C—C—C—H
 \   /   ‖ | |
  C—C   O H H
 H   H

ANSWER 7

four
1,1-dibromopropane $(CH_3CH_2CHBr_2)$
1,2-dibromopropane $(CH_3CHBrCH_2Br)$
1,3-dibromopropane $(CH_2BrCH_2CH_2Br)$
2,2-dibromopropane $(CH_3CBr_2CH_3)$

ANSWER 22   a hydroxyl group bonded directly to a benzene ring

ANSWER 37

ANSWER 52

ANSWER 67

535

ITEM 9   Draw a diagram for 3,4-diiodo-1-pentyne.

ITEM 24   Enols are rare species because they are extremely un-
                                stable. They rearrange to give a *carbonyl* compound
                                (containing a C=O group), as shown at the right. A
                                proton is transferred from _____ of the enol to
                                carbon atom 2, which was doubly bonded in the enol.

ITEM 39   The Lewis diagrams of *cis-* and *trans*-3-penten-2-one
                                are _____.

ITEM 54   Write structural formulas for methyl alcohol, formal-
                                dehyde, and formic acid.

ITEM 69   An important class of organic nitrogen compounds
                                is *amines:* These are derivatives of ammonia in which
                                one or more hydrogen atoms of NH_3 are replaced
                                by aliphatic or aromatic radicals. *Methylamine* is
                                shown at the right. The Lewis diagram for *ethylamine*
                                is _____.

ANSWER 8

ANSWER 23   *cis*-1-propenol
or *cis*-1-propen-1-ol

ANSWER 38

ANSWER 53

ANSWER 68   C—O—H
H—C=O
C—C—C

537

ITEM 10

Under proper conditions, 2-bromopropane (iso-propyl bromide) can be converted to an alcohol that has the Lewis diagram shown at the right and the common name *isopropyl alcohol*. The reaction is a displacement of Br by _____.

ITEM 25

This proton transfer reaction is instantaneous, so any enol made in a reaction will be transformed almost completely to a compound containing a C=O group, known as the _____ group. (Phenols are special cases and do not undergo this reaction.)

ITEM 40

The structural formula of acetone is _____.

ITEM 55

Write structural formulas for ethanol, acetaldehyde, and acetic acid.

ITEM 70

Propylamine has the Lewis diagram _____. (If isopropyl is not specified, the *n*-propyl derivative is meant.)

```
      H  H  H
      |  |  |
  H—C—C—C—H
      |  |  |
      H :O: H
         |
         H
```

ANSWER 9

```
      H  H  H
      |  |  |
  H—C≡C—C—C—C—H
         |  |  |
         I  I  H
```

ANSWER 24   the OH group

ANSWER 39

cis

trans

ANSWER 54

```
      H
      |
  H—C—O—H
      |
      H
```

```
  H     H
    \  /
     C
     ‖
     O
```

```
  H     OH
    \  /
     C
     ‖
     O
```

ANSWER 69

```
      H  H
      |  |   ..
  H—C—C—N—H
      |  |  |
      H  H  H
```

539

The systematic name of isopropyl alcohol is 2-*propanol*, in which the 2 designates _____ and the suffix "ol" designates the _____ group.

All *aldehydes* contain the partial structure H—C≡O, a hydrogen bonded to a _____ group. The simplest aldehyde (in which the rest of the structure is only a H atom) has the Lewis diagram _____.

Both ketones and aldehydes contain a _____. The difference between ketones and aldehydes is _____.

The reaction of two alcohol molecules in concentrated sulfuric acid produces an *ether*. For example, from two molecules of ethyl alcohol, one molecule of *diethyl ether* and one molecule of _____ are produced, as shown at the right.

Dimethylamine is a derivative of NH_3 in which two hydrogen atoms are replaced by _____. The Lewis diagram is _____.

ANSWER 10   OH

ANSWER 25   carbonyl

ANSWER 40

$$H-\underset{\underset{H}{|}}{\overset{\overset{H}{|}}{C}}-\underset{\underset{O}{||}}{C}-\underset{\underset{H}{|}}{\overset{\overset{H}{|}}{C}}-H$$

ANSWER 55

$$H-\underset{\underset{H}{|}}{\overset{\overset{H}{|}}{C}}-\underset{\underset{H}{|}}{\overset{\overset{H}{|}}{C}}-O-H$$

$$H-\underset{\underset{H}{|}}{\overset{\overset{H}{|}}{C}}-\underset{\underset{O}{||}}{C}\overset{H}{\diagdown}$$

$$H-\underset{\underset{H}{|}}{\overset{\overset{H}{|}}{C}}-\underset{\underset{O}{||}}{C}-OH$$

ANSWER 70

$$H-\underset{\underset{H}{|}}{\overset{\overset{H}{|}}{C}}-\underset{\underset{H}{|}}{\overset{\overset{H}{|}}{C}}-\underset{\underset{H}{|}}{\overset{\overset{H}{|}}{C}}-\overset{..}{N}-H$$

$$H-\underset{\underset{H}{|}}{\overset{\overset{H}{|}}{C}}-\underset{\underset{H}{|}}{\overset{\overset{H}{|}}{C}}-O-H + H-O-\underset{\underset{H}{|}}{\overset{\overset{H}{|}}{C}}-\underset{\underset{H}{|}}{\overset{\overset{H}{|}}{C}}-H \rightarrow$$

$$H-\underset{\underset{H}{|}}{\overset{\overset{H}{|}}{C}}-\underset{\underset{H}{|}}{\overset{\overset{H}{|}}{C}}-O-\underset{\underset{H}{|}}{\overset{\overset{H}{|}}{C}}-\underset{\underset{H}{|}}{\overset{\overset{H}{|}}{C}}-H + ?$$

ITEM 12

Methanol, or *methyl alcohol* as it is commonly known, has the Lewis diagram _____, and *ethanol*, or *ethyl alcohol*, has the Lewis diagram _____.

ITEM 27

The one-carbon aldehyde is usually called *formaldehyde*, although the systematic name is *methanal*. *Acetaldehyde*, or *ethanal*, has one carbonyl group and a methyl group. Draw the Lewis diagram.

ITEM 42

Draw structural formulas for cyclohexanone and cyclohexanol.

ITEM 57

Ether molecules contain an oxygen atom bonded to two carbon atoms. Diethyl ether has the Lewis diagram shown at the right. Dimethyl ether has the Lewis diagram _____.

ITEM 72

Triethylamine has the Lewis diagram _____.

H—C—H
$\|$
:O:

Formaldehyde

$$\begin{array}{ccccc} H & H & & H & H \\ | & | & \ddot{} & | & | \\ H-C-C-\ddot{O} & & C-C-H \\ | & | & \ddot{} & | & | \\ H & H & & H & H \end{array}$$

ANSWER 11 the number of the carbon to which a group is attached OH (hydroxyl)

ANSWER 26 carbonyl

H—C—H
$\|$
:O:

ANSWER 41 carbonyl group (C=O)

in the position of the carbonyl. In aldehydes the carbonyl carbon is at the end of the chain; in ketones it is not.

ANSWER 56 H_2O

ANSWER 71 Methyl groups (CH_3)

$$\begin{array}{ccc} H & & H \\ | & \ddot{} & | \\ H-C-N-C-H \\ | & | & | \\ H & H & H \end{array}$$

ITEM 13   2-Pentanol has the structural formula _____, and 3-heptanol has the structural formula _____.

ITEM 28   An aldehyde carbon must always be at the end of a chain, and it is understood to be carbon 1. The name is then that of the corresponding hydrocarbon with the final "e" replaced by "al." The compound at the right is named _____.

ITEM 43   Draw structural formulas for formaldehyde and acetaldehyde.

ITEM 58   The names of simple ethers consist of the names of the two radical groups attached to the oxygen followed by the word "ether." The Lewis diagram for methyl ethyl ether is _____.

ITEM 73   Draw a diagram for cyclopentylamine.

CH$_3$CH$_2$CH
$\overset{\|}{\text{O}}$

ANSWER 12

H
|
H—C—O̤—H
|
H

H H
| |
H—C—C—O̤—H
| |
H H

ANSWER 27

H
|
H—C—C—H
| ‖
H :O:

ANSWER 42

ANSWER 57

H   H
| |
H—C—O̤—C—H
| |
H   H

ANSWER 72

H H   H H
| | | |
H—C—C—N̤—C—C—H
| | | | |
H H C H H
      / \
     H C H
       / | \
      H H H

545

Draw the Lewis diagrams for *trans*-2-buten-1-ol and *cis*-2-buten-1-ol.

The Lewis diagram for butanal is ————————, and the Lewis diagram for 3-butenal is ——————.

Aldehydes in which the HC═O group is bonded directly to a benzene ring are known as *benzaldehydes*. Benzaldehyde, the parent compound, is shown at the right. Draw the structural formula for *para*-methyl-benzaldehyde.

Write structural formulas for diphenyl ether and *n*-propyl cyclobutyl ether.

Amines in which the nitrogen atom is bonded directly to a benzene ring are called *anilines*. The parent compound is shown at the right. Draw a diagram for *N*-methylaniline; the *N* indicates that the methyl is bonded to the nitrogen atom.

ANSWER 13

H H H H H
H—C—C—C—C—C—H
H O H H H
|
H

H
|
O
H H H H H H
H—C—C—C—C—C—C—C—H
H H H H H H H

ANSWER 28   propanal
(1-Propanal is redundant. The common name is propionaldehyde.)

ANSWER 43

O
‖
H—C—H

H   H
| /
H—C—C
| ‖
H   O

ANSWER 58

H   H H
H—C—O—C—C—H
H   H H

ANSWER 73

H   H   H
H—C—C   H
C—N—H
H—C—C   H
H   H   H

ITEM 15	Draw Lewis diagrams for 3-chloro-1-octanol and 2-methyl-2-propanol (usually known as *t*-butyl alcohol).
ITEM 30	The Lewis diagram for 3,4-dibromopentanal is _____.
ITEM 45	Aldehydes react with oxygen to form *carboxylic acids* that contain the partial structure H—O—C=O. As the name suggests, most carboxylic acids can donate _____ to water molecules.
ITEM 60	All ketones contain the partial structure

$$\overset{\displaystyle O}{\underset{\displaystyle C-C-C}{\|}}$$

and all aldehydes contain the partial structure _____. All ethers contain the partial structure _____.

ITEM 75	The prefix "amino" indicates an NH_2 group, as in *p*-aminophenol. Draw a diagram for this phenol.

ANSWER 14

```
    H
    |
H—C        H
    |   \  /
    H    C=C
         /    \
        H      H—C—Ö—H
                   |
                   H
        trans
```

```
     H           H
     |           |
 H—C         C—Ö—H
     |   \  / ··
     H    C=C
         /    \
        H      H
        |      |
        H      H
           cis
```

ANSWER 29

```
           H  H  H
           |  |  |
H—C—C—C—C—H
      ‖   |  |  |
     :O:  H  H  H
```

(The common name is butyr-aldehyde.)

```
           H
           |
H—C—C—C=C—H
      ‖   |  |  |
     :O:  H  H  H
```

ANSWER 44

ANSWER 59

ANSWER 74

549

ANSWER 15

H—O̤—C—C—C—C—C—C—C—C—H

with H H :C̈l: H H H H H on top and H H H H H H H H on bottom

$$H-\overset{..}{\underset{..}{O}}-\overset{\overset{H}{|}}{\underset{\underset{H}{|}}{C}}-\overset{\overset{H}{|}}{\underset{\underset{H}{|}}{C}}-\overset{\overset{:\overset{..}{C}l:}{|}}{\underset{\underset{H}{|}}{C}}-\overset{\overset{H}{|}}{\underset{\underset{H}{|}}{C}}-\overset{\overset{H}{|}}{\underset{\underset{H}{|}}{C}}-\overset{\overset{H}{|}}{\underset{\underset{H}{|}}{C}}-\overset{\overset{H}{|}}{\underset{\underset{H}{|}}{C}}-\overset{\overset{H}{|}}{\underset{\underset{H}{|}}{C}}-H$$

H
|
H—C—H
H
|
H—C—C—Ö—H
H
|
H—C—H
|
H

(Item 16 is on page 520.)

ANSWER 30

$$H-\overset{\overset{H}{|}}{\underset{\underset{H}{|}}{C}}-\overset{\overset{H}{|}}{\underset{\underset{:\overset{..}{B}r:}{|}}{C}}-\overset{\overset{:\overset{..}{B}r:}{|}}{\underset{\underset{H}{|}}{C}}-\overset{\overset{H}{|}}{\underset{\underset{H}{|}}{C}}-\overset{}{\underset{\underset{:\overset{..}{O}:}{||}}{C}}-H$$

(Item 31 is on page 520.)

ANSWER 45   protons (or hydrogen ions)

(Item 46 is on page 520.)

ANSWER 60   H—C=O
                C—O—C

(Item 61 is on page 520.)

ANSWER 75

(Item 76 is on page 520.)

Beyond the bare-bones knowledge of organic compounds that you now have, lie the fascinating questions of what compounds and reactions are already known, which remain to be discovered, how reactions occur, and ultimately, why do they occur?

REVIEW 12 COLLIGATIVE PROPERTIES OF SOLUTIONS

The study of solutions is important because most chemical reactions occur in solution and because many methods of purification of compounds depend on the properties of their solutions. This review will present calculation methods involving the colligative properties of solutions, the properties that depend on *how many* particles of solute are present in solution, but not *what* these solute particles are. The material treated in this review corresponds to Section 14–10 of *Chemical Principles*.

The four colligative properties we will examine are the lowering of the vapor pressure (Section 12–2), elevation of the boiling point (Section 12–3), depression of the freezing point (Section 12–4), and osmotic pressure (Section 12–5) that accompany solution formation. Although the calculations in this review are concerned primarily with the determination of molecular weights, this knowledge of solutions will serve as a base for further exploration of their properties.

12-1 MOLE FRACTION AND MOLALITY

To do calculations involving the colligative properties of solutions, you should be able to describe the relative amounts of solute and solvent in terms not only of molarity but also of mole fraction and molality. In this section you will learn the definitions of these terms and how to perform calculations involving them. Then you will be in a position to study colligative properties of solutions, the subject of the following sections.

If you can do correctly Items 35 through 42 at the end of this section, you are already prepared for Section 12-2.

ITEM 1

The total number of moles in a solution containing 2.0 moles of alcohol and 3.0 moles of water is _____.

ITEM 8

Note that in Item 7 the sum of the mole fractions is one. Prove that this is true for any binary (two-component) solution containing n_A moles of A and n_B moles of B.

ITEM 15

In a solution containing 0.50 mole of water and 0.030 mole of alcohol, we would consider _____ to be the solute; its mole fraction would be $X_A =$ _____.

ITEM 22

A 0.36-*molal* KCl solution has _____ mole(s) of KCl in 1000 g of solvent.

ITEM 29

To perform calculations involving molality, you must remember, and make use of, its definition, which is _____.

ITEM 36

A sample of solution containing 0.037 mole of solute in 1000 g of water has the molality _____. The number of moles of water present is _____; the mole fraction of solute, X_A, is _____.

ITEM 2

What fraction of the total moles in the solution at the right is alcohol?

ITEM 9

In a solution of A and B, if $X_A = 0.12$, then X_B must be $1.00 -$ _____ $=$ _____.

ITEM 16

If 0.0010 mole of H_2SO_4 is dissolved in 55 moles of water, the mole fraction of H_2SO_4 is $X_A =$ _____.

ITEM 23

In a solution consisting of 0.062 mole of HCl and 450 g of alcohol, the number of moles of solute per gram of alcohol is _____; the molality, m, is _____.

ITEM 30

To make mole fraction calculations you must remember that

$$X_{solute} = \frac{\text{moles of solute present}}{\text{total number of moles present}}$$

and that, for very dilute solutions, this becomes $X_{solute} =$ _____.

ITEM 37

What is the mole fraction of solute in a solution containing 0.00241 mole of solute and 1.96 moles of solvent?

2.0 moles alcohol
+
3.0 moles water

0.00241 mole of solute
1.96 moles of solvent

ANSWER 1   5.0

ANSWER 8 $X_A + X_B = \dfrac{n_A}{n_A + n_B} + \dfrac{n_B}{n_A + n_B}$

$$= \dfrac{n_A + n_B}{n_A + n_B} = 1$$

ANSWER 15   alcohol

$$\dfrac{0.030}{0.53} = 0.057$$

ANSWER 22   0.36

ANSWER 29   the number of moles of solute per 1000 g of solvent

ANSWER 36 $m = 0.037$

$$\dfrac{1000 \text{ g}}{18 \text{ g mole}^{-1}} = 55.6 \text{ moles}$$

$$\dfrac{0.037 \text{ mole}}{55.6 \text{ moles}} = 0.00067$$

ITEM 3

What fraction of the total number of moles in the solution at the right is water?

ITEM 10

Calculate the mole fractions of the three components in a solution containing 4.73 moles of water, 1.40 moles of alcohol, and 3.21 moles of acetic acid.

ITEM 17

For very dilute solutions, such as that in Item 16, n_A is much smaller than _____. In such a case, the expression for X_A can be simplified to $X_A \simeq$ _____.

ITEM 24

Molality is defined as _____.

ITEM 31

Calculate the mole fraction and the molality of KBr in a solution made by dissolving 1.0×10^{-3} mole of KBr in 200 g of water.

ITEM 38

To calculate the molality of the solution in Item 37, we need to know the molecular weight of the solvent ($MW_B = 98$). Then the weight of solvent present is _____; the moles of solute per 1000 g solvent is _____.

0.12 mole water
+
0.79 mole alcohol

$$X_A = \frac{n_A}{n_A + n_B}$$

0.00241 mole of solute
1.96 moles of solvent
(*MW* of solvent = 98)

ANSWER 2 $\dfrac{2.0}{5.0} = 0.40$

ANSWER 9   0.12
0.88

ANSWER 16 $\dfrac{0.0010}{55} = 1.8 \times 10^{-5}$

ANSWER 23 $\dfrac{0.062 \text{ mole}}{450 \text{ g}}$

$= 1.4 \times 10^{-4} \text{ mole g}^{-1}$

$10^3 \times 1\,4 \times 10^{-4} = 0.14$

ANSWER 30 $\dfrac{\text{moles of solute}}{\text{moles of solvent}}$

ANSWER 37

$$X_A = \frac{0.00241 \text{ mole}}{1.96 \text{ moles}} = 0.00123$$

ITEM 4

In this solution the fraction of moles contributed by water is $0.12/0.91 = 0.13$. We say that the *mole fraction* of water is 0.13. The mole fraction of alcohol in the same solution is _____.

ITEM 11

The sum of the mole fractions in Answer 10 is _____. The sum of the mole fractions of all substances in any solution must equal _____.

ITEM 18

Calculate X_A for a solution of 0.020 g of sulfuric acid, H_2SO_4, in 50 g of benzene, C_6H_6. (See the periodic table inside the front cover for atomic weights.)

ITEM 25

Note the difference between "molality" and the term used in solution stoichiometry, that is, "molarity." The latter is defined as _____.

ITEM 32

The number of moles of solute is often designated by n_A. If we consider solutions that contain 1000 g of solvent, we see from the definition of molality that the symbol n_A and the symbol _____ will both represent the number of moles of _____ present.

ITEM 39

For calculations of both m and X_A, it is necessary to know the number of _____ of solute.

ANSWER 3 $\quad \dfrac{0.12}{0.91} = 0.13$

ANSWER 10 $\quad X_{\text{water}} = \dfrac{4.73}{9.34} = 0.506$

$$X_{\text{alcohol}} = \dfrac{1.40}{9.34} = 0.150$$

$$X_{\text{acetic acid}} = \dfrac{3.21}{9.34} = 0.344$$

ANSWER 17 $\quad n_B$

$$\dfrac{n_A}{n_B}$$

ANSWER 24 $\quad$ the number of moles of solute per 1000 g of solvent

ANSWER 31

$$X_{\text{KBr}} = \dfrac{1.0 \times 10^{-3}\ \text{mole}}{200\ \text{g}/(18\ \text{g mole}^{-1})} = 9.1 \times 10^{-5}$$

$$m_{\text{KBr}} = \left(\dfrac{1.0 \times 10^{-3}\ \text{mole}}{200\ \text{g}} \right) 1000$$

$$= 5.0 \times 10^{-3}\ \text{mole}\ (1000\ \text{g})^{-1}$$

ANSWER 38

$$(1.96\ \text{moles})(98\ \text{g mole}^{-1}) = 192\ \text{g}$$

$$m = \left(\dfrac{0.00241\ \text{mole}}{192\ \text{g}} \right)(1000)$$

$$= 0.0126$$

ITEM 5

The mole fraction of a substance in any mixture is defined as the number of moles of that substance divided by the total _____ in the mixture.

ITEM 12
.

In a solution containing a small amount of substance A and a large amount of substance B, the first (A) is often called the *solute* and the second (B) is called the _____. Such a solution is a *dilute* solution of substance A in substance B.

ITEM 19

The number of moles of water in the solution at the right is _____; the mole fraction of KCl is _____.

ITEM 26

What would you do to prepare a 0.15-molal aqueous solution of acetic acid from a 0.15-mole sample of acetic acid?

ITEM 33

For dilute solutions $X_A = n_A/n_B$. We shall now see that X_A can be simply related to m, the molality. Let MW_B be the molecular weight of the solvent. For a solution containing 1000 g of solvent, $n_B =$ _____.

ITEM 40

Moreover, for calculations of m we also need to know the weight of _____ and, for calculations of X_A, the _____ of solvent.

0.020 mole KCl
+
1000 g H₂O

ANSWER 4 $\dfrac{0.79}{0.91} = 0.87$

ANSWER 11   1.000
one

ANSWER 18

$$n_B = \frac{50 \text{ g}}{78 \text{ g mole}^{-1}} = 0.64 \text{ mole}$$

$$n_A = \frac{0.020 \text{ g}}{98 \text{ g mole}^{-1}} = 0.00020 \text{ mole}$$

$$X_A = \frac{0.00020 \text{ mole}}{0.64 \text{ mole}} = 0.00031$$

ANSWER 25   the number of moles of solute per liter of solution

ANSWER 32 m
solute

ANSWER 39   moles

If n_A moles of substance A and n_B moles of substance B form a solution, the mole fractions X_A and X_B are given by the relationships $X_A =$ ——————— and $X_B =$ ———————.

ITEM 13

If n_B represents the number of moles of solvent and n_A the number of moles of solute in a solution, then the mole fraction of solvent is $X_B =$ ———————; the mole fraction of solute is $X_A =$ ———————.

ITEM 20

The relative amounts of solute and solvent can also be expressed by the *molality, m,* which is defined as the number of moles of solute per 1000 g of solvent. In a solution containing 0.020 mole of KCl and 1000 g of H_2O, the molal concentration of KCl is ———————.

ITEM 27

What weight of ethyl alcohol, C_2H_5OH, would you add to 1000 g of water to prepare a 0.50-molal solution?

ITEM 34

If a dilute solution is assumed, substitution for n_A and n_B in terms of the molality and the molecular weight of solvent gives $X_A = n_A/n_B =$ ———————.

ITEM 41

Calculate the mole fraction and the molality of HBr in a solution of 0.49 g of HBr in 60 g of acetic acid, CH_3COOH.

ANSWER 5 number of moles

ANSWER 12 solvent

ANSWER 19

$$\frac{1000 \text{ g}}{18 \text{ g mole}^{-1}} = 55.6 \text{ moles}$$

$$X_A = \frac{0.020 \text{ mole}}{55.6 \text{ mole}} = 3.6 \times 10^{-4}$$

ANSWER 26 Dissolve the acetic acid in 1000 g of water.

ANSWER 33 $1000/MW_B$

ANSWER 40 solvent
number of moles

ITEM 7

The mole fractions of a solution containing 1.34 moles of A and 0.260 mole of B are $X_A =$ _____ and $X_B =$ _____ .

ITEM 14

The colligative properties of solutions are usually dealt with in terms of the amount of solute relative to the total amount of solution. Calculations involving these properties, therefore, use the variable X_A, which is the _____ of _____ .

ITEM 21

In a solution containing 0.27 mole of solute and 325 g of solvent, the number of moles of solute per gram of solvent is _____ ; the molality, moles per 1000 g, is $m =$ _____ .

ITEM 28

To make a 0.50-molal solution of ethyl alcohol by adding alcohol to 250 g of water, you would not add 23 g, as in Item 28, but only _____ $\times$ 23 g = _____ g.

ITEM 35

According to the relation $X_A = (MW_B/1000)m$, which is valid for _____ solutions, the molality of the solution and the mole fraction of solute are proportional to one another; the proportionality factor depends only on the molecular weight of the _____ .

ITEM 42

Show again that, for dilute solutions, the values of m and X_A are proportional to one another (a proportionality that will be used in the following section): $X_A = n_A/n_B =$ _____ .

ANSWER 6
$$\frac{n_A}{n_A + n_B}$$

$$\frac{n_B}{n_A + n_B}$$

ANSWER 13
$$\frac{n_B}{n_A + n_B}$$

$$\frac{n_A}{n_A + n_B}$$

ANSWER 20   0.020

ANSWER 27

0.50 mole (46.1 g mole^{-1}) = 23 g

ANSWER 34 $\dfrac{m}{1000/MW_B} = \left(\dfrac{MW_B}{1000}\right)m$

ANSWER 41

$$\text{moles HBr} = \frac{0.49 \text{ g}}{81 \text{ g mole}^{-1}} = 0.0060$$

$$\text{moles acetic acid} = \frac{60 \text{ g}}{60 \text{ g mole}^{-1}} = 1.0$$

$$X_{HBr} = \left(\frac{0.0060 \text{ mole}}{1.0 \text{ mole}}\right) = 0.0060$$

$$m_{HBr} = \left(\frac{0.0060 \text{ mole}}{60 \text{ g}}\right)1000 = 0.10$$

ANSWER 7 $\dfrac{1.34}{1.60} = 0.838$

$\dfrac{0.260}{1.60} = 0.162$

(*Item 8 is on page 556.*)

ANSWER 14   mole fraction
solute

(*Item 15 is on page 556.*)

ANSWER 21 $\dfrac{0.27 \text{ mole}}{325 \text{ g}} = 0.00083$

$(1000)(0.00083) = 0.83$

(*Item 22 is on page 556.*)

ANSWER 28 $\left(\dfrac{250}{1000}\right)$

5.8 g

(*Item 29 is on page 556.*)

ANSWER 35   dilute
solvent

(*Item 36 is on page 556.*)

ANSWER 42 $X_A = n_A/n_B$

$= \dfrac{m}{1000/MW_B} = \left(\dfrac{MW_B}{1000}\right)m$

571

12–2 VAPOR PRESSURE LOWERING

Now that the background material relating the mole fraction of solute to molality has been developed, we can consider four properties of solutions that depend on these quantities. The treatment here is limited, first, to binary solutions (i.e., to a single solute dissolved in a solvent). Second, we will examine only binary solutions in which the solute is relatively non-volatile and the solute molecules show little tendency to associate, or dissociate, when dissolved in the solvent.

The principal application of the theory developed in this review is the determination of the molecular weight of the solute. When you have finished this section, you will be able to calculate the molecular weight of a compound from data on its concentration in a solution and the decrease in vapor pressure of the solution from that of the pure solvent. Items 21 and 22 will test your skill in doing this.

It is assumed in this review that you are familiar with the concept of vapor pressure and its relationship to the boiling point and freezing point of a pure liquid. We will begin by considering the effect that the addition of solute to a solvent has on the vapor pressure of the solvent. You will find that the resulting decrease in the vapor pressure of the solvent is one of the colligative properties of the solution.

ITEM 1

First let us examine a solution in which the solute is nonvolatile (i.e., the solute has a negligible vapor pressure). As the solute is added to the solvent, the solvent vapor pressure, P_B, decreases, as shown at the right. Because this relationship is linear, with $P_B = 0$ when $X_B = 0$, we can write $P_B \propto$ _____ or $P_B = $ (const) _____.

ITEM 5

For dilute solutions it is usually more convenient to consider the amount of solute present and to have an expression involving X_A, the _____ of solute.

ITEM 9

The relationship at the right was shown in Section 12–1 to be a good approximation for dilute solutions. Thus, $\Delta P = P_B^0 X_A$ can be written $\Delta P = ($_____$)m$.

ITEM 13

When 1.76 g of a solute is dissolved in 1000 g of CCl_4, the lowering of the vapor pressure is 0.58 torr at 20°C. The solution must have a molality of _____; therefore, 1.76 g of solute must be equivalent to _____ mole(s).

ITEM 17

Since 0.165 mole of the solute weighs 13.7 g, the weight per mole (i.e., the _____ weight) is _____ g.

ITEM 21

Calculate the molecular weight of compound Y if a 6.9-g sample dissolved in 150 g of benzene lowers the vapor pressure of benzene at 50°C by 9.8 torr.

ITEM 25

The value of the constant is best obtained experimentally from measurements of ΔP for solutions of known _____, but the value of the constant can also be calculated from the _____ and _____ of the pure solvent.

P_B (solvent v.p.)

X_B (mole fraction of solvent)

1.0   0.9   0.8

$$X_A \simeq \frac{n_A}{n_B} = \frac{m}{1000/MW_B}$$

$$\simeq \left(\frac{MW_B}{1000}\right)m$$

For CCl_4:
$\Delta P = (14.0)m$ at $20°C$

For C_6H_6 at $50°C$: $\Delta P = 21.2m$
(for ΔP in units of torr)

ITEM 2

A pure solvent (containing no solute) has a value of X_B equal to _____ and a vapor pressure denoted by P_B^0. Application of the equation $P_B = (const)X_B$ to the pure solvent shows that $(const) = $ _____.

ITEM 6

Since the mole fractions X_A and X_B are related by $X_A + X_B = 1$, then $X_B = $ _____. If this relation is substituted in $P_B = P_B^0 X_B$, we obtain $P_B = $ _____.

ITEM 10

You can see from the expression

$$\Delta P = (MW_B P_B^0 / 1000)m$$

that ΔP is _____ to m and that the proportionality factor depends only on properties of the

_____.

ITEM 14

Since 1.76 g of solute in Item 13 is 0.041 mole, there are _____ g per mole.

ITEM 18

The value of the proportionality constant $(MW_B P_B^0 / 1000)$ for the solvent acetone at 20°C is 10.7 torr for a 1-molal solution. Calculate the molecular weight of compound D if a 3.54-g sample lowers the vapor pressure of 100 g of acetone by 2.83 torr.

ITEM 22

At 50°C, the vapor pressure of water is 92.5 torr. Calculate the molecular weight of compound Z if a 7.84-g sample dissolved in 50.0 g of water lowers the vapor pressure to 89.6 torr.

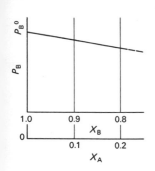

ANSWER 1 X_B
X_B

ANSWER 5 mole fraction

ANSWER 9 $\dfrac{MW_B P_B^0}{1000}$

ANSWER 13

$$m = \frac{0.58 \text{ torr}}{14.0 \text{ torr for 1-molal solution}} = 0.041$$

0.041

ANSWER 17 molecular

$$\frac{13.7 \text{ g}}{0.165 \text{ mole}} = 83$$

ANSWER 21

6.9 g in 150 g benzene $= 46$ g in 1000 g
$\Delta P = 21.2m$

$$m = \frac{9.8 \text{ torr}}{21.2 \text{ torr per 1-molal solution}} = 0.46$$

$$MW_Y = \frac{46 \text{ g}}{0.46 \text{ mole}} = 100 \text{ g mole}^{-1}$$

ANSWER 25 molality
molecular weight
vapor pressure

Solutions whose vapor pressure behavior con-forms to the graph at the right (i.e., to the equation _____) obey Raoult's law.

ITEM 7

Addition of solute lowers the vapor pressure of the solvent by the amount $\Delta P = P_B^0 - P_B$. Since $P_B = (P_B^0 - P_B^0 X_A)$, we have $\Delta P = P_B^0 -$ _____ $=$ _____.

ITEM 11

For carbon tetrachloride at 20°C, for example, the value of $(MW_B P_B^0/1000)$ is 14.0 torr per 1.00-molal solution. It follows that the vapor pressure lowering when a 1.00-molal solution is made by using CCl_4 as solvent with any _____ will be _____.

ITEM 15

In the solution at the right there is _____ g of solute per gram of CCl_4, or _____ g of solute per 1000 g of CCl_4.

ITEM 19

The proportionality constant between ΔP and m can be determined experimentally by measuring ΔP for a solution of known molality. The value of the constant can be calculated also if the molecular weight and _____ of the pure solvent are known.

ITEM 23

To obtain the molecular weight of a nonvolatile material you need (1) the _____ of solute in a known weight of solvent and (2) the number of _____ of solute in the same weight of solvent.

$$X_B$$

1.0   0.9   0.8

$$X_A$$

0.1   0.2

$$\Delta P = \left(\frac{MW_B P_B^0}{1000}\right) m$$

1.04 g solute
+
76.0 g CCl$_4$ (at 20°C)

$$\Delta P_{CCl_4} = (14.0) m \text{ at } 20°C$$

$$\Delta P = \left(\frac{MW_B P_B^0}{1000}\right) m$$

ANSWER 2   one (1.0)
$$P_B^0$$

ANSWER 6

$$1 - X_A$$
$$P_B = P_B^0 (1 - X_A) = P_B^0 - P_B^0 X_A$$

ANSWER 10   directly proportional
solvent

ANSWER 14 $\dfrac{1.76 \text{ g}}{0.041 \text{ mole}} = 43 \text{ g mole}^{-1}$

ANSWER 18

3.54 g(100 g of solvent)$^{-1}$
   $= 35.4$ g(1000 g solvent)$^{-1}$

$$m = \frac{\Delta P}{(MW_B P_B^0 / 1000)}$$

$$= \frac{2.83 \text{ torr}}{10.7 \text{ torr per 1-molal solution}}$$

$$= 0.264$$

$$MW_D = \frac{35.4 \text{ g}}{0.264 \text{ mole}} = 134 \text{ g mole}^{-1}$$

ANSWER 22

7.84 g in 50.0 g H$_2$O $= 157$ g in 1000 g

$$m = \frac{\Delta P}{MW_B P_B^0 / 1000} = \frac{1000 \text{ g} \times 2.9 \text{ torr}}{18.0 \text{ g mole}^{-1} \times 92.5 \text{ torr}}$$

$$= 1.74$$

$$MW_Z = \frac{157 \text{ g}}{1.74 \text{ mole}} = 90 \text{ g mole}^{-1}$$

ITEM 4

Raoult's law, which is a reasonably good approximation for dilute solutions, states that the vapor pressure of the solvent varies directly with the _____ of the solvent.

ITEM 8

For dilute solutions obeying _____ law, the lowering of the vapor pressure of the solvent is proportional to the mole fraction of _____.

ITEM 12

Similarly, any solution consisting of a solute in CCl_4 at 20°C that gives a vapor pressure lowering of 14.0 torr must have m equal to _____; that is, it contains _____ mole of solute for every 1000 g of CCl_4.

ITEM 16

For the solution of Item 15, $\Delta P = 2.31$ torr. Thus, there is _____ mole of solute per 1000 g CCl_4; that is, 13.7 g solute is _____ mole.

ITEM 20

The vapor pressure of pure benzene, C_6H_6, at 50°C is 271.3 torr. What is the value of the proportionality constant between ΔP and m at 50°C?

ITEM 24

The number of moles of solute in 1000 g of solvent (i.e., the _____) can be obtained from the relation $\Delta P = (const)m$ once the value of the constant is known.

$$P_B = P_B^0 X_A$$

$$\Delta P = 14.0m$$
(for ΔP in units of torr)

13.7 g solute
per 1000 g CCl$_4$
(at 20°C)

$\Delta P_{CCl_4} = (14.0)m$ (at 20°C)

ANSWER 3 $P_B = (\text{const})X_B$ or $P_B = P_B^0 X_B$

ANSWER 7 $(P_B^0 - P_B^0 X_A)$
$P_B^0 X_A$

ANSWER 11   solute
14.0 torr

ANSWER 15 $\dfrac{1.04 \text{ g}}{76.0 \text{ g}} = 0.0137$

$0.0137(1000) = 13.7$

ANSWER 19   vapor pressure

ANSWER 23   weight
moles

ANSWER 4   mole fraction

(Item 5 is on page 574.)

ANSWER 8   Raoult's
solute

(Item 9 is on page 574.)

ANSWER 12   1.00
1.00

(Item 13 is on page 574.)

ANSWER 16

per 1000 g solvent: $\dfrac{2.31 \text{ torr}}{14.0 \text{ torr}} = 0.165$

0.165

(Item 17 is on page 574.)

ANSWER 20

$\dfrac{MW_B P_B^0}{1000} = \dfrac{78.1 \text{ g mole}^{-1} \times 271.3 \text{ torr}}{1000 \text{ g}}$

$= 21.2$ torr per 1-molal solution

(Item 21 is on page 574.)

ANSWER 24   molality

(Item 25 is on page 574.)

12-3 BOILING POINT ELEVATION

We have noted that the lowering of the vapor pressure, ΔP, of a particular solvent at a given temperature depends on the relative numbers of moles of solute and solvent present, hence, on the molality of the solution. You have seen how this colligative property of a solution can be used to determine the molecular weight of the solute.

Other colligative properties of solutions often can be measured more conveniently, and these also can be used to determine molecular weights. The relationships of these properties to the molality of the solutions can be deduced from the effect of the solute on the vapor pressure of the solvent. The next colligative property to be studied is the raising, or elevation, of the boiling point that accompanies the addition of a nonvolatile solute to a solvent.

Typical of the problems you should be able to solve at the end of the review is this: "A solution of 46.8 g of a solute in 1000 g water has a ΔT_b value of 0.38°. The freezing point depression constant for water is 0.51. Calculate the molecular weight of the solute."

ITEM 1

The vapor pressure of a liquid, as shown at the right, always _____ as the temperature rises.

ITEM 4

The two vapor pressure curves in the accompanying figure represent pure solvent and dilute solution containing a nonvolatile solute. Label the curves *solvent* and *solution*.

ITEM 7

The difference in temperature between the boiling point of the solution and the boiling point of the pure _____ is known as the *boiling point elevation*.

ITEM 10

Since, for dilute solutions, ΔT_b and ΔP are proportional to one another, we can write $\Delta T_b \propto$ _____ or _____ = _____.

ITEM 13

As was true of the proportionality constant between ΔP and m, the constant k_b depends on the nature of the _____ but is not influenced by the nature of the _____.

ITEM 16

The k_b values for various solvents at the right can be regarded as indicating the boiling point _____ for 1-molal solutions of nonvolatile solutes in these solvents. (Theoretically, k_b is $RT^2 MW_B / 1000 \Delta H_{vap}$, where R is the gas constant, T is the boiling point, MW_B is the molecular weight of the solvent, and ΔH_{vap} is the molar heat of vaporization. The constant k_b is nearly always determined experimentally.)

ITEM 19

The molal boiling point elevation constant for carbon tetrachloride is 5.03. If a solution containing 0.929 g of compound L dissolved in 89.3 g of carbon tetrachloride has a boiling point elevation of 0.460 deg, what is the molecular weight of L?

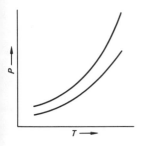

Solvent	k_b
Water	0.5
Benzene	2.5
Chloroform	3.7
Ethyl alcohol	1.2

ITEM 2

The boiling point of a liquid is the temperature at which the vapor pressure is equal to the external pressure. Thus, the boiling point can be located in the figure at the right as the temperature at which the dashed line, representing the external pressure, and the solid curve, representing the _____ of the liquid, intersect.

ITEM 5

Redraw these two curves, label the axes, and locate on the temperature axis the boiling points of the pure solvent and of the solution.

ITEM 8

The vapor pressure lowering and the boiling point elevation of dilute solutions are relatively small. Therefore, for comparisons of the vapor pressure curves for solvents and dilute solutions, the curves near the boiling point can be approximated, as shown, by straight parallel lines. Label these lines and the boiling points on the diagram at the right.

ITEM 11

Furthermore, in Section 12–2 we saw that ΔP is proportional to m, the _____. From this and the preceding discussion (Items 9 and 10), it follows that $\Delta T_b \propto$ _____.

ITEM 14

The constant k_b can be determined for a solvent by measuring ΔT_b for a solution of known _____.

ITEM 17

Since k_b for water is 0.51, an aqueous solution that boils 1.37°C higher than pure water must have a molality of _____.

ITEM 20

Chloroform, $CHCl_3$, has a boiling point of 61.3°C. A solution of 1.68 g of methylcyclohexane, C_7H_{14}, in 30.0 g of $CHCl_3$ has a boiling point of 63.4°C. What is the boiling point elevation constant of chloroform?

external pressure

$\Delta T_b = k_b m$

$\Delta T_b = 0.51\,m$
for aqueous solutions

ANSWER 1   increases

ANSWER 4

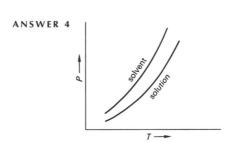

ANSWER 7   solvent

ANSWER 10 ΔP
$$\Delta T_b = (\text{const})\Delta P$$

ANSWER 13   solvent
solute

ANSWER 16   elevation

ANSWER 19

$$\frac{0.929\ \text{g}}{89.3\ \text{g solvent}} = 10.4\ \text{g}\ (1000\ \text{g})^{-1}$$

$$m = \frac{\Delta T_b}{k_b} = \frac{0.460\ \text{deg}}{5.03\ \text{deg}} = 0.0915$$

$$MW_L = \frac{10.4\ \text{g}}{0.0915\ \text{mole}} = 114\ \text{g mole}^{-1}$$

589

ITEM 3

As you know from Section 12–2, the addition of a nonvolatile solute to a solvent _____ the vapor pressure of the solvent.

ITEM 6

Since the vapor pressure curve for the solution lies below and to the right of the curve for the pure solvent, the boiling point of the solution is _____ than that of the pure solvent.

ITEM 9

It follows, as the figure at the right suggests, that the boiling point elevation, ΔT_b, and the vapor pressure lowering, ΔP, are _____ to one another. ($\Delta T_b = \Delta P \tan \alpha$; $\tan \alpha$ is a constant if the vapor pressure lines are parallel.)

ITEM 12

With the introduction of the proportionality constant, k_b, the relationship between the boiling point elevation and the molality of a solution can be written as the equation _____ = _____ .

ITEM 15

The molality of the solution at the right is _____ . The boiling point elevation allows us to calculate k_b for benzene (using the equation $\Delta T_b = k_b m$): $k_b =$ _____ .

ITEM 18

A solution of 46.8 g of solute in 1000 g of water has a ΔT_b value of 0.38 deg. The molality of the solution is _____ . In 1000 g of water there are _____ g or _____ mole(s) of solute. Thus, the weight per mole, or molecular weight, can be calculated to be _____ .

ΔT_b

external pressure

solvent

solution

ΔP

α

bp solv   bp soln

$T \longrightarrow$

29 g naphthalene ($C_{10}H_8$)
+
1000 g benzene (C_6H_6)

boiling point 0.58°C higher
than that of pure benzene

$\Delta T_b = 0.51\,m$
for aqueous solutions

ANSWER 2   vapor pressure

ANSWER 5

external pressure

$T \longrightarrow$ bp solv   bp soln

ANSWER 8

solvent

solution

$T \longrightarrow$ bp solv   bp soln

ANSWER 11   molality
m

ANSWER 14   molality

ANSWER 17

$$m = \frac{1.37 \text{ deg}}{0.51 \text{ deg per 1-molal solution}} = 2.7$$

ANSWER 20

$$\Delta T_b = k_b m = 63.4 - 61.3 = 2.1°C$$

$$m = \left[\frac{1.68 \text{ g}/(98.2 \text{ g mole}^{-1})}{30.0 \text{ g}} \right] 1000 = 0.570$$

$$k_b = \frac{2.1 \text{ deg}}{0.570\,m} = 3.7 \text{ deg per 1-molal solution}$$

ANSWER 3   lowers (or decreases)

(Item 4 is on page 586.)

ANSWER 6   higher

(Item 7 is on page 586.)

ANSWER 9   directly proportional

(Item 10 is on page 586.)

ANSWER 12 $\Delta T_b = k_b m$

(Item 13 is on page 586.)

ANSWER 15

$$\text{moles } C_{10}H_8 = \frac{29 \text{ g}}{128 \text{ g mole}^{-1}} = 0.23$$

$$k_b = \frac{\Delta T_b}{m} = \frac{0.58 \text{ deg}}{0.23 m}$$

$$= 2.5 \text{ deg per 1-molal solution}$$

(Item 16 is on page 586.)

ANSWER 18

$$\frac{0.38 \text{ deg}}{0.51 \text{ deg for 1-molal solution}} = 0.75 m$$

46.8 g

0.75 mole

$$\frac{46.8 \text{ g}}{0.75 \text{ mole}} = 62 \text{ g mole}^{-1}$$

(Item 19 is on page 586.)

12-4 FREEZING POINT DEPRESSION

A third colligative property is the lowering, or depression, of the freezing point that generally accompanies solution formation. Freezing point depressions usually can be measured more easily than either vapor pressure lowerings or boiling point elevations and are often used to determine the molecular weight of a newly synthesized or newly isolated compound. Like the boiling point elevation, the freezing point depression is related to the molality of the solution, and this relationship can be deduced from the effect of the solute on the vapor pressure of the solvent.

Items 16 through 20 provide a test of your knowledge of this section.

ITEM 1

In the diagram at the right, curve AD represents the increase in the vapor pressure of the liquid phase with increase in temperature. Curve BA represents the increase in the vapor pressure of the _____ phase with increase in temperature.

ITEM 4

Addition of a nonvolatile solute to a liquid lowers the vapor pressure in accordance with Raoult's law, but in general, the solute has no effect on the vapor pressure of the solid phase. Label the vapor pressure curves at the right *solid solvent*, *liquid solvent*, and *liquid solution*. (This assumes that all the solute remains in solution.)

ITEM 7

The difference in temperature between the freezing point of the solution and the _____ is known as the *freezing point depression*, T_f, that accompanies solution formation.

ITEM 10

From trigonometry you will remember that for the right triangle

$a = b \tan \alpha$. In the diagram at the right, then, the line $GH = T_f \tan \alpha$ and the line $(\Delta P + GH) = \Delta T_f \tan \gamma$. Therefore, $\Delta P = (\Delta P + GH) - GH =$ _____.

ITEM 13

The constant k_f for a solvent can be calculated from the freezing point and the heat of fusion, but its value is nearly always determined experimentally. The freezing point of benzene is 5.48°C. If a solution of 0.448 g of naphthalene, $C_{10}H_8$, in 9.82 g of benzene freezes at 3.66°C, what is k_f for benzene?

ITEM 16

The freezing point of pure benzene is 5.5°C, and the value of k_f for benzene is 5.1. A 0.19-molal solution of a nonvolatile solute in benzene will have $\Delta T_f =$ _____ and will start to freeze at _____ °C.

ITEM 19

A solvent often used for determining the molecular weight of organic compounds is camphor, which has a k_f of 40.0. If 0.015 g of compound Q dissolved in 1.00 g of camphor causes a freezing point depression of 5.3 deg, compound Q has a molecular weight of _____.

ITEM 2

A *triple point* of a substance is defined as a temperature at which three phases are in equilibrium. In the diagram at the right, solid, liquid, and vapor phases are in equilibrium at point _____. At this temperature the vapor pressure of the liquid is equal to the vapor pressure of the _____.

ITEM 5

The diagram in Answer 4 shows that the temperature at which the solution is in equilibrium with the solid is _____ than the temperature at which the solvent is in equilibrium with the solid.

ITEM 8

Label the curves on the expanded portion from previous figures. Locate the freezing points of the solvent and the solution on the temperature axis.

ITEM 11

Since α and γ are constants, the term $(\tan \gamma - \tan \alpha)$ is a constant, and we can write $\Delta T_f \propto \Delta P$. Recalling that ΔP is proportional to m, the _____ of the solution, we write the proportionality relation $\Delta T_f \propto$

_____.

ITEM 14

The freezing point depression constant for water is 1.86 deg per 1-molal solution. A 1.00-molal solution will have a freezing point of _____°C. A 0.176-molal solution will begin to freeze at _____°C.

ITEM 17

A solution is made to contain 3.69 g of an unknown material in 28.8 g of benzene. The weight of solute per gram of benzene is _____, and the weight per 1000 g of benzene is _____.

ITEM 20

The freezing point of phenol, C_6H_5OH, is 40.5°C, and its freezing point depression constant is 7.27 deg per 1-molal solution. When 0.0820 g of a deep blue hydrocarbon is dissolved in 1.00 g of phenol, the freezing point of the solution is 35.8°C. What is the molecular weight of the hydrocarbon?

$\Delta T_f = k_f m$

ANSWER 1   solid

ANSWER 4

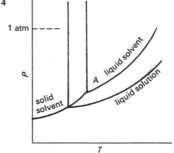

ANSWER 7   freezing point
of the solvent

ANSWER 10 $\Delta T_f \tan \gamma - \Delta T_f \tan \alpha$
or $\Delta T_f(\tan \gamma - \tan \alpha)$

ANSWER 13

$$\frac{0.448 \text{ g}}{9.82 \text{ g benzene}} = 45.6 \text{ g per } 1000 \text{ g}$$

$$\frac{45.6 \text{ g}}{128 \text{ g mole}^{-1}} = 0.356 \text{ mole}$$

$$k_f = \frac{\Delta T_f}{m} = \frac{1.82 \text{ deg}}{0.356 \text{ mole}}$$

$$= 5.11 \text{ deg per 1-molal solution}$$

ANSWER 16

(5.1 deg per 1-molal solution)(0.19 molal)
$= 0.97$ deg
$5.5°C - 1.0°C = 4.5$

ANSWER 19

0.015 g $(1.00$ g$)^{-1} = 15$ g $(1000$ g solvent$)^{-1}$
$\Delta T_f = k_f m$

$$m = \frac{5.3 \text{ deg}}{40 \text{ deg per 1-molal solution}} = 0.133$$

$$MW_Q = \frac{15 \text{ g}}{0.133 \text{ mole}} = 110 \text{ g mole}^{-1}$$

599

ITEM 3

At the right, the line representing the temperatures and pressures at which liquid and solid are in equilibrium is labeled _____. The *freezing point* (or *melting point*) is defined as the temperature at which liquid and solid are in equilibrium at a pressure of 1 atm. Since the liquid–solid equilibrium is only slightly pressure dependent, the freezing point is at almost exactly the same temperature as the _____.

ITEM 6

In other words, the freezing point (and the triple point) of a solution is _____ than that of the pure solvent.

ITEM 9

In a small portion of the diagram the vapor pressure curves can be approximated by straight lines and the solvent–vapor line can be assumed to be parallel to the _____ line.

ITEM 12

If the freezing point depression constant, k_f, is now introduced, an equation similar to that written for ΔT_b is obtained; that is, $\Delta T_f =$ _____.

ITEM 15

A 0.26-molal solution of sucrose in water, for which $k_f = 1.86$, will have a value of ΔT_f of _____ deg. The solution will begin to freeze at _____°C.

ITEM 18

The solution in Item 17 begins to freeze at 2.8°C. With the information at the right, we see that the molality is _____ and, since there are 128 g of solute per 1000 g of benzene, that the molecular weight of the solute is _____.

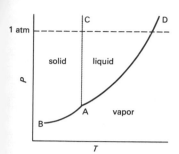

1 atm

C ———————— D

solid | liquid

P

A vapor

B

T

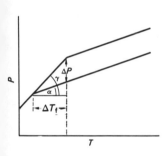

P

γ ΔP

α

|← ΔTf →|

T

Freezing point of pure benzene = 5.5 °C
k_f for benzene = 5.1

ANSWER 2   A
            solid

ANSWER 5   lower

ANSWER 8

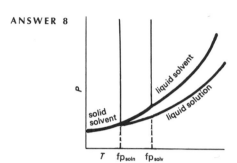

P

solid
solvent

liquid solvent

liquid solution

T   fp$_{soln}$ fp$_{solv}$

ANSWER 11   molality
             m

ANSWER 14

−1.86
$\Delta T = k_f m$
  = (1.86° per 1-molal solution) (0.176 mole)
  = 0.327 °C
0.00 °C − 0.327 °C = −0.327

ANSWER 17 $\dfrac{3.69}{28.8} = 0.128$ g

             0.128(1000) = 128 g

ANSWER 20

$T_f = k_f m$
$m = (40.5 − 35.8)/7.27$
  = 0.65 mole in 1000 g solvent
wt in 1000 g solvent
  = (0.0820/1.00)(1000) = 82.0 g

$MW = \dfrac{82.0 \text{ g}}{0.65 \text{ mole}} = 126$

601

ANSWER 3   AC
              triple point

(Item 4 is on page 596.)

ANSWER 6   lower

(Item 7 is on page 596.)

ANSWER 9   solution–vapor

(Item 10 is on page 596.)

ANSWER 12 $k_f m$

(Item 13 is on page 596.)

ANSWER 15

$0.26 m(1.86$ deg per 1-molal solution$) = 0.48$
$0.00°C - 0.48°C = -0.48$

(Item 16 is on page 596.)

ANSWER 18

$$\frac{5.5 \text{ deg} - 2.8 \text{ deg}}{5.1 \text{ deg per 1-molal solution}} = 0.53 \text{ molal}$$

$$\frac{128 \text{ g}}{0.53 \text{ mole}} = 240 \text{ g mole}^{-1}$$

(Item 19 is on page 596.)

12-5 OSMOTIC PRESSURE

The final property of a solution that depends on the number of solute molecules present, and therefore is a colligative property, is the osmotic pressure obtained when the solution is separated from the pure solvent by a semipermeable membrane. (A *semipermeable membrane* allows the solvent to pass through but prevents the passage of the solute.)

Osmotic pressure can be exhibited by arranging an apparatus as in the upper figure below and allowing the system to come to equilibrium. Solvent flows from the pure solvent compartment into the solution compartment until a certain pressure, shown by the column of liquid, builds up and prevents further flow of solvent. This pressure is called the *osmotic pressure*. The osmotic pressure can be illustrated also with an apparatus shown in the right-hand figure. In this apparatus a pressure can be applied to the solution until a sensitive flow indicator shows that no solvent is flowing. Again the additional pressure that must be applied to the solution to prevent the pure solvent from flowing into the solution is the osmotic pressure.

ITEM 1

Osmosis is defined as the spontaneous flow of solvent into a solution, or from a more dilute to a more concentrated solution, that occurs when the two liquids are separated from each other by a _____ membrane.

ITEM 5

The proportionality relationship π _____ can be written between π and m.

ITEM 9

The osmotic pressure of a 1.00-molal aqueous solution at 0°C is 22.4 atm. Then the general osmotic pressure equation for dilute aqueous solutions at 0°C is $\pi =$ _____.

ITEM 13

Both experimental data and theoretical calculations show that, for very dilute solutions, the proportionality constant between π and n_A/V has the value RT for any solvent. Thus, we can write the equation _____.

ITEM 17

To prevent solvent from flowing through a membrane and into the solution described in Item 16, we would have to apply pressure on the solution until the excess pressure is _____ atm.

ITEM 21

If the weight of solute per liter of solution in the preceding items is 8.32 g, the molecular weight must be _____.

ITEM 25

The sensitivity of osmotic pressure is particularly helpful when high molecular weights are determined because a large weight of solute corresponds to a relatively small number of _____ of solute.

$\pi = 28.3$ torr
$n_A/V = 0.00152$ mole liter^{-1}

ITEM 2

A perfect semipermeable membrane allows
_____ to pass through it but does not permit
passage of a _____.

ITEM 6

If this proportionality were converted to an equality
by the introduction of a constant, the value of the
constant would depend only on the properties of
the _____.

ITEM 10

The equation $\pi = (\text{const})m$ can be used in the same
way as were the equations $\Delta P =$ _____, $\Delta T_b =$
_____, and $\Delta T_f =$ _____.

ITEM 14

The constant R is identical to the gas constant that
appears in the ideal gas equation $PV = nRT$. Rearranged to this form, the osmotic pressure relationship is _____.

ITEM 18

In applying the equation $\pi V = n_A RT$ you must be
careful to have the same units of pressure and
volume on both sides of the equation. Therefore, the
pressure units of π and the volume units of V must
be the same as those implied by the value of
_____ used in the equation.

ITEM 22

At 27°C, 0.00647 g of a deep blue hydrocarbon is
dissolved in enough cyclohexane, C_6H_{12}, to give 10.0
ml of solution. The osmotic pressure of the solution
is 94.3 torr. What is the molecular weight of the blue
compound?

ITEM 26

Of the four colligative properties of solutions,
_____, _____, _____, and
_____, osmotic pressure measurements are
used most to determine the molecular weights of
high molecular weight materials.

ANSWER 1   semipermeable

ANSWER 5 $\propto m$

ANSWER 9 $(22.4)m$ atm

ANSWER 13 $\pi = RTn_A/V$

ANSWER 17   24.4

ANSWER 21 $\dfrac{8.32 \text{ g}}{0.00152 \text{ mole}} = 5470$

ANSWER 25   moles

ITEM 3

Osmotic pressure is defined as the excess pressure that must be applied to a ——————— to prevent osmosis when the two liquids are separated by ———————.

ITEM 7

The value of the constant in the relationship $\pi = (\text{const})m$ can be determined by measuring the ——————— for a solution of known ———————.

ITEM 11

An interesting looking osmotic pressure equation is found for *very* dilute solutions if we use n_A/V (where n_A is the moles of solute and V is the volume of solution) rather than the ———————, which we have been using, to express the concentration of solute.

ITEM 15

Or, since n_A/V in units of moles per liter of solution is the same as M, the ———————, the equation can be written ———————.

ITEM 19

A solution of a newly synthesized material produces an osmotic pressure of 28.3 torr when separated by a membrane from pure solvent at 25°C. The value of π in atmospheres is ———————, and the number of moles of solute per liter of solution is ———————.

ITEM 23

Calculate the osmotic pressure of a 1.00×10^{-3}-molar aqueous solution at 25°C against pure water.

ANSWER 2   solvent
              solute

ANSWER 6   solvent

ANSWER 10 $(\text{const})m$ or $(MW_B P_B^0/1000)m$
              $k_b m$
              $k_f m$

ANSWER 14 $\pi V = n_A RT$

ANSWER 18 R

ANSWER 22

$\pi V = n_A RT$

$\pi = 94.3 \text{ torr}/760 \text{ torr atm}^{-1} = 0.124 \text{ atm}$

$n_A = \dfrac{0.124 \ (0.010)}{0.0820 \ (300)} = 5.04 \times 10^{-5} \text{ mole in 10 ml}$

wt in 10.0 ml of solution $= 6.47 \times 10^{-3}$ g

$MW = \dfrac{6.47 \times 10^{-3} \text{ g}}{5.04 \times 10^{-5} \text{ mole}} = 128$

ANSWER 26   vapor pressure lowering
              boiling point elevation
              freezing point depression
              osmotic pressure

ITEM 4
As with the three colligative properties already discussed, the _____, the _____, and the _____, the osmotic pressure, π, is, for dilute solutions, proportional to the _____ of the solution.

ITEM 8
When this constant is known for the solvent, it is possible to measure the _____ of a solution and then calculate its _____ to determine the molecular weight of the solute.

ITEM 12
In very dilute solutions, n_A/V is proportional to m. The relationship $\pi \propto m$ can be converted to

_____.

ITEM 16
Since R has the value 0.0820 liter atm deg^{-1} mole^{-1}, the osmotic pressure of a solution containing 1.00 mole in 1000 ml of solution at 25°C is _____.

ITEM 20
The result of the experiment of Item 19 would permit the calculation of the molecular weight if, in addition to knowing that there is 0.00152 mole liter^{-1}, you knew the _____ of solute per liter.

ITEM 24
The osmotic pressure of a 1.00×10^{-3}-molal solution is approximately equal to the osmotic pressure of a 1.00×10^{-3}-molar solution and is therefore easily measureable. However, the freezing point depression would be _____, and the boiling point elevation would be _____. Since they are so small, these quantities could be measured only with considerable difficulty.

ANSWER 3   solution
a semipermeable membrane

ANSWER 7   osmotic pressure
molality

ANSWER 11   molality (m)

ANSWER 15   molarity
$\pi = MRT$ (or $\pi = M_A RT$)

ANSWER 19

$$\frac{28.3 \text{ torr}}{760 \text{ torr atm}^{-1}} = 0.0372 \text{ atm}$$

$$n_A = \pi V / RT$$

$$= \frac{0.0372 \text{ atm } (1.000 \text{ liter})}{(0.0820 \text{ liter atm deg}^{-1} \text{mole}^{-1})(298 \text{ deg})}$$

$$= 0.00152 \text{ mole}$$

For water:
$k_f = 1.86\,°C$ per 1-molal solution
$k_b = 0.51\,°C$ per 1-molal solution

ANSWER 23

$\pi = n_A RT / V$ or $\pi = MRT$
$\quad = 0.0010 \text{ mole liter}^{-1}$
$\qquad (0.082 \text{ liter atm deg}^{-1} \text{ mole}^{-1})(298 \text{ deg})$
$\quad = 0.0244 \text{ atm or } 18.5 \text{ torr}$

ANSWER 4   vapor pressure lowering
boiling point elevation
freezing point depression
molality

(Item 5 is on page 606.)

ANSWER 8   osmotic pressure (π)
molality (m)

(Item 9 is on page 606.)

ANSWER 12 $\pi \propto n_A/V$

(Item 13 is on page 606.)

ANSWER 16

$\pi = n_A RT/V$ or $\pi = MRT$

$$= \frac{1.00 \text{ mole}}{1.00 \text{ liter}} (0.0820 \text{ liter atm deg}^{-1} \text{ mole}^{-1})(298 \text{ deg})$$

$= 24.4$ atm

(Item 17 is on page 606.)

ANSWER 20   weight (number of grams)

(Item 21 is on page 606.)

ANSWER 24 $1.86 \times 0.00100 = 0.00186\,°C$
$0.51 \times 0.00100 = 0.00051\,°C$

(Item 25 is on page 606.)

615

EQUILIBRIUM CALCULATIONS FOR
HOMOGENEOUS GAS REACTIONS

Whenever a chemist desires to prepare a compound, he wants to use a reaction that "goes
to completion," but chemical reactions proceed
only until they reach a state of equilibrium.
When the equilibrium state is reached, the
system can contain mostly products, mostly
reactants, or any intermediate proportion of
products and reactants.

The position of equilibrium in a chemical
system can sometimes be deduced from an
expression relating the concentrations of all
reagents to a constant for the reaction. For example, if $N_2O_4(g)$ is introduced into a container, dissociation to $NO_2(g)$ occurs according
to the reaction equation $N_2O_4(g) \rightleftharpoons 2NO_2(g)$.
After some definite fraction of N_2O_4 has been
converted to NO_2, the concentrations of the
two reagents will remain constant, and equilibrium is established. The concentrations of
the reagents at equilibrium are related by an
expression that has, for this example, the form
$K = [NO_2]^2/[N_2O_4]$, where K is the equilibrium
constant for this reaction. (If you have read
Chapter 15 of *Chemical Principles*, you know that
this is an approximation that is valid for ideal
behavior in much the same way that the expression $PV = nRT$ is really valid only for ideal
gases.)

This review deals with the equilibria established by gases in a container having a fixed
volume and temperature. (See Sections 15–1
and 15–2 of *Chemical Principles*.) It is assumed
that you know how to write the expression for

the equilibrium constant for the reaction if the equation for the reaction is given and that you are able to solve quadratic equations of the form $ax^2 + bx + c = 0$.

A typical problem that you will learn to solve is the following: "Calculate the equilibrium concentrations when 0.60 mole of PCl_5 and 0.020 mole of PCl_3 are allowed to come to equilibrium, according to the reaction $PCl_5(g) \rightleftharpoons PCl_3(g) + Cl_2(g)$ in a 4.7-liter container at 250°C. The equilibrium constant at this temperature is 0.042." When you have finished this review you will be able to solve without difficulty this problem and those of Items 75 through 78.

ITEM 1

At 250°C phosphorus pentachloride dissociates according to the equation at the right. If 1.00 mole of PCl_5 were introduced into a container at 250°C, at a later time there would be (less, more) than 1.00 mole PCl_5 in the container.

ITEM 16

A reaction cell originally contained 1.50 moles of H_2 and 1.50 moles of O_2. After the cell was heated, it contained 0.34 mole of H_2O. Fill in the following table.

	Initially	Used up	Remaining
Moles H_2	1.50		
Moles O_2	1.50		

ITEM 31

The value for the equilibrium constant for the reaction $H_2(g) + I_2(g) \rightleftharpoons 2HI(g)$ at 426°C is 54. In one experiment the equilibrium concentrations of I_2 and HI were $[I_2] = 1.3 \times 10^{-3}$ and $[HI] = 1.6 \times 10^{-2}$. Calculate the equilibrium concentration of H_2.

ITEM 46

Solution of this quadratic equation gives a value of x of 0.016. Tabulate the number of moles and the concentrations at equilibrium.

	N_2O_4	NO_2
Moles	_____	_____
Conc., moles liter^{-1}	_____	_____

ITEM 61

Solution of the quadratic equation yields $x = 0.07$ mole. The number of moles at equilibrium of $H_2 = $ _____, of $I_2 = $ _____, and of HI = _____. Use these values to check the solution of the problem by calculating the value of the equilibrium constant from them.

$PCl_5(g) \rightleftharpoons PCl_3(g) + Cl_2(g)$

1.50 moles H_2
1.50 moles O_2

0.34 mole H_2O
?　moles H_2
?　moles O_2

$$N_2O_4(g) \rightleftharpoons 2NO_2(g)$$

Moles　$0.100 - x$　$2x$

$V = 2.0$ liters

$$2HI(g) \rightleftharpoons H_2(g) \;+\; I_2(g)$$

Equil.
moles　$3.00 - 2x$　x　　$2.50 + x$

$V = 4.00$ liters

ITEM 2

Each mole of PCl_5 that dissociates produces _____ mole(s) of PCl_3 and _____ mole(s) of Cl_2.

ITEM 17

To perform the calculations in the preceding items, you had to know the _____ for the reaction.

ITEM 32

Once you know the equation for a reaction, the value of K (the symbol for the _____), and the initial concentrations of reagents, you can calculate the concentrations at equilibrium.

ITEM 47

The percentage of N_2O_4 that dissociates (in the system treated in the preceding items) is _____.

ITEM 62

Any component of a mixture of gases has a concentration and a pressure, known as its *partial pressure*. Since the concentration and partial pressure are simply related (assuming ideal gas behavior) by the expression $p = RT(n/V)$, where R is a constant, T is the absolute temperature, and n/V is the concentration in moles per unit volume, equilibrium calculations for gas reactions can be done either in terms of concentrations or of _____.

$PCl_5(g) \rightleftharpoons PCl_3(g) + Cl_2(g)$

	At equilibrium	
	$N_2O_4(g) \rightleftharpoons$	$2NO_2(g)$
Moles	0.084	0.032
Conc.,		
moles liter^{-1}	0.042	0.016

ANSWER 1   less

ANSWER 16

	Used up	Remaining
	0.34	1.16
	0.17	1.33

ANSWER 31

$$54 = \frac{(1.6 \times 10^{-2})^2}{[H_2](1.3 \times 10^{-3})}$$

$$[H_2] = 3.6 \times 10^{-3}$$

ANSWER 46   0.084   0.032
0.042   0.016

ANSWER 61   0.07
2.57
2.86

$$K = \frac{(0.07/4)(2.57/4)}{(2.86/4)^2} = 0.022$$

As the reaction proceeds, the number of moles of PCl_5 will _____crease, the number of moles of PCl_3 and Cl_2 will _____crease, and the total number of moles in the system will _____crease until a state of equilibrium is attained.

It is convenient to write the initial and later amounts beneath the symbols in the equation, as at the right. Complete the entries.

A 1.8-mole sample of PCl_5 was added to a 5.0-liter reaction chamber at 250°. To calculate the amount of each reagent that was present after equilibrium had been established, it is first necessary to write the expression for K. In this case $K = $ _____.

Equilibrium calculations of the types just treated can be made directly in terms of concentrations. As an example, let x = number of moles per liter of N_2O_4 that dissociate, and tabulate below the equilibrium concentrations from the data at the right.

Initial $[N_2O_4] = $ _____ $[NO_2] = $ _____

Equil. $[N_2O_4] = $ _____ $[NO_2] = $ _____

When partial pressures are used in equilibrium calculations, the equilibrium constant is written K_p. The equilibrium expression for the reaction $PCl_5(g) \rightleftharpoons PCl_3(g) + Cl_2(g)$ is

$$\underline{\hspace{2cm}} = \frac{(p_{PCl_3})(p_{Cl_2})}{\underline{\hspace{2cm}}}$$

$PCl_5(g) \rightleftharpoons PCl_3(g) + Cl_2(g)$

ANSWER 2   1
                                          1

$PCl_5(g)$	$\rightleftharpoons$	$PCl_3(g)$	$+$	$Cl_2(g)$
Initial				
moles 0.83		0.19		0
Later				
moles 0.71				

ANSWER 17   equation

$PCl_5(g) \rightleftharpoons PCl_3(g) + Cl_2(g)$

ANSWER 32   equilibrium constant

2.0 moles N_2O_4

$N_2O_4(g) \rightleftharpoons 2NO_2(g)$

V = 5.0 liters

T = 25°C

ANSWER 47 $\dfrac{(0.016)}{(0.100)} 100 = 16\%$

ANSWER 62   partial pressures

ITEM 4

A 1.00-mole sample of PCl_5 was introduced into a container as indicated at the right. If there is now only 0.75 mole of PCl_5, there must be _____ mole(s) of PCl_3 and _____ mole(s) of Cl_2.

ITEM 19

Complete the entries at the right.

ITEM 34

The second step is the expression of the equilibrium concentrations of the reagents in terms of some convenient unknown. Let x be the number of moles of PCl_5 that dissociate. Complete the table at the right.

ITEM 49

The next step in the calculation is, as usual, the substitution of the equilibrium concentrations, in terms of x, into the expression for K. Since $K = 0.0058$, the equation that permits the calculation of the number of _____ per _____ that dissociate is _____ .

ITEM 64

The expression for K_p for the reaction $2HI(g) \rightleftharpoons H_2(g) + I_2(g)$ is _____ .

1.00 mole PCl$_5$

0.75 mole PCl$_5$
? mole PCl$_3$
? mole Cl$_2$

$$2H_2O(g) \rightleftharpoons 2H_2(g) + O_2(g)$$

Initial			
moles	5.8	0	0
Later			
moles	2.0		

$$PCl_5(g) \rightleftharpoons PCl_3(g) + Cl_2(g)$$

Initial			
moles	1.8	0	0
Equil.			
moles	$1.8 - x$		
Equil.			
conc.			

$V = 5.0$ liters

$$N_2O_4(g) \rightleftharpoons 2NO_2(g)$$

Equil. conc.,
moles liter^{-1} $0.40 - x$ $2x$

$K = 0.0058$ at 25°C

ANSWER 3   de
in
in

ANSWER 18   PCl$_3$(g): $0.19 + 0.12 = 0.31$
Cl$_2$(g): $0 + 0.12 = 0.12$

ANSWER 33 $\dfrac{[PCl_3][Cl_2]}{[PCl_5]}$

ANSWER 48 $\dfrac{2.0}{5.0} = 0.40$ 0

$0.40 - x$ $2x$

ANSWER 63 K_p
(p_{PCl_5})

If 1.00 mole of PCl_5 were introduced and x moles now remain, the amount of PCl_3 present would be _____ mole(s).

Complete the entries at the right.

The third step is the substitution of the concentrations, in terms of x, and the value of K, 0.042, into the expression for the equilibrium constant. This gives the equation _____.

Solution of this equation yields $x = 0.023$ mole liter^{-1}. Tabulate below the concentrations and number of moles at equilibrium.

	$N_2O_4(g)$	$\rightleftharpoons$	$2NO_2(g)$
Equil. conc., moles liter^{-1}	_____		_____
Equil. moles	_____		_____

Note that K and K_p are equal for a reaction in which no change in the total number of molecules occurs as the reaction proceeds. For other reactions, K and K_p are different [but related by $K_p = K(RT)^{\Delta n}$, where Δn is the increase in the number of molecules in the reaction]. Write the expressions for K and K_p for the reaction $2SO_2 + O_2 \rightleftharpoons 2SO_3$. Is K_p equal to K?

1.00 mole PCl₅

x mole PCl₅

? mole PCl₃

$$2CO_2(g) \rightleftharpoons 2CO(g) + O_2(g)$$

Initial moles	0.0	0.8	0.6
Later moles	0.2		

$$PCl_5(g) \rightleftharpoons PCl_3(g) + Cl_2(g)$$

Equil. conc.	$\dfrac{1.8 - x}{5.0}$	$\dfrac{x}{5.0}$	$\dfrac{x}{5.0}$

$K = 0.042$ at 250°C

$$N_2O_4(g) \rightleftharpoons 2NO_2(g)$$

Equil. conc., moles liter⁻¹	$0.40 - x$	$2x$

$V = 5.0$ liters

ANSWER 4 0.25
0.25

ANSWER 19 $H_2(g)$: $5.8 - 2.0 = 3.8$
$O_2(g)$: $\frac{1}{2}(3.8) = 1.9$

ANSWER 34

$$PCl_5(g) \rightleftharpoons PCl_3(g) + Cl_2(g)$$

1.8	0	0
$1.8 - x$	x	x
$\dfrac{1.8 - x}{5.0}$	$\dfrac{x}{5.0}$	$\dfrac{x}{5.0}$

ANSWER 49 moles
liter

$$0.0058 = \frac{(2x)^2}{0.40 - x}$$

ANSWER 64 $$K_p = \frac{(p_{H_2})(p_{I_2})}{(p_{HI})^2}$$

ITEM 6

The *concentration* of a compound is the amount of that compound per unit volume, often expressed in terms of moles per liter. If a 1.00-mole sample of PCl_5 were introduced into a 5.0-liter vessel, the initial concentration (before any dissociation) would be _____ mole liter^{-1}. The concentration of PCl_5 will ____crease with time.

ITEM 21

The concentrations of the reagents in a reaction vessel can be calculated if one knows the number of _____ of the reagents and the _____ of the container.

ITEM 36

Solution of the quadratic equation (verify if you like) gives $x = 0.52$. Thus, the equilibrium amounts are

PCl_5:   _____ mole(s)
PCl_3:   _____ mole(s)
Cl_2:   _____ mole(s)

ITEM 51

For problems requiring calculation of equilibrium amounts of reagents when the equilibrium constant and the initial amounts of the dissociating species are known, it is necessary to have a balanced _____ for the reaction, to be able to write the expression for the _____ and to express, in terms of some convenient unknown, the _____.

ITEM 66

When initial partial pressures and K_p for a reaction are known and equilibrium pressures must be calculated, the procedure is exactly the same as for calculations using concentrations. The first step is to write the expression for the _____ for the balanced _____.

$$PCl_5(g) \rightleftharpoons PCl_3(g) + Cl_2(g)$$

| Equil. moles | $1.8 - x$ | x | x |

ANSWER 5 $1.00 - x$

ANSWER 20 $CO(g)$: $0.8 - 0.2 = 0.6$
                      $O_2(g)$: $0.6 - 0.1 = 0.5$

ANSWER 35 $0.042 = \dfrac{(x/5.0)(x/5.0)}{(1.8 - x)/5.0}$

$$= \dfrac{x^2}{5.0(1.8 - x)}$$

ANSWER 50   0.38   0.046
                         1.9   0.23

ANSWER 65

$$K = \dfrac{[SO_3]^2}{[SO_2]^2[O_2]}$$

$$K_p = \dfrac{(p_{SO_3})^2}{(p_{SO_2})^2(p_{O_2})}$$

No. $K_p = \dfrac{(RT)^2[SO_3]^2}{(RT)^2[SO_2]^2(RT)[O_2]}$

$$= \dfrac{1}{RT}\dfrac{[SO_3]^2}{[SO_2]^2[O_2]}$$

ITEM 7

A 1.00-mole sample of PCl_5 was put into a 10.0-liter container. Later, when 0.30 mole of PCl_5 remained, the number of moles of PCl_3 was _____ and the concentration of PCl_3 was _____ mole(s) liter^{-1}.

ITEM 22

Complete the entries at the right for hydrogen, nitrogen, and ammonia in a 5.0-liter container.

ITEM 37

The percentage dissociation is often useful information. In the example of Item 36, _____ mole(s) of the original 1.8 moles dissociated; therefore, the percent dissociation = $100($_____$/1.8) =$ _____ %.

ITEM 52

Then substitution of the _____ and the _____ into the expression for the equilibrium constant yields an equation that can be solved for x.

ITEM 67

HI is put in a vessel held at 490°C at an initial pressure of 1.50 atm. Letting x represent the decrease in pressure of HI because of dissociation, tabulate at the right the partial pressures of each reagent at equilibrium.

1.00 mole PCl₅

0.30 mole PCl₅
?   mole PCl₃

$V = 10.0$ liters

$$3H_2(g) + N_2(g) \rightleftharpoons 2NH_3(g)$$

Initial			
moles	0.6	0.4	0.0
Later			
moles	0.3	0.3	0.2
Later			
conc.			

$V = 5.0$ liters

At equilibrium

$PCl_5 = 1.3$ moles
$PCl_3 = 0.52$ mole
$Cl_2 = 0.52$ mole

$$2HI(g) \rightleftharpoons H_2(g) + I_2(g)$$

Initial p 1.50   0   0
Equil. p

ANSWER 6   0.20
de

ANSWER 21   moles
volume

ANSWER 36 $1.8 - 0.5 = 1.3$
0.52
0.52

ANSWER 51   equation
equilibrium constant
equilibrium concentrations
of the reagents

ANSWER 66   equilibrium constant
equation

A container of volume V originally contained n moles of PCl_5. If x moles of PCl_3 are formed, there remain _____ mole(s) of PCl_5. The concentrations are then

$PCl_5 = $ _____ moles liter^{-1}
$PCl_3 = $ _____ moles liter^{-1}
$Cl_2 \;\; = $ _____ moles liter^{-1}

Complete the table at the right.

In another experiment, a mixture of 1.00 mole of PCl_5 and 1.00 mole of PCl_3 was put into a 5.0-liter reaction vessel at 250°C. To calculate the amounts of the reagents present at equilibrium, it is first necessary to write the expression for the equilibrium constant: $K = $ _____.

The equation for the nitrogen–hydrogen–ammonia reaction is $N_2(g) + 3H_2(g) \rightleftharpoons 2NH_3(g)$. The equilibrium expression is _____.

At 490°C, K_p for the reaction $2HI(g) \rightleftharpoons H_2(g) + I_2(g)$ is 0.022. Write the expression for the equilibrium constant in terms of x, the decrease in pressure of HI.

n moles PCl_5

? moles PCl_5

x moles PCl_3

? moles Cl_2

volume = V liters

$$2HCl(g) \rightleftharpoons H_2(g) + Cl_2(g)$$

Initial moles	2.86	1.00	0
Later moles	1.30		
Later conc.			

V = 12.0 liters

1.00 mole PCl_5

1.00 mole PCl_3

$$PCl_5(g) \rightleftharpoons PCl_3(g) + Cl_2(g)$$

V = 5.0 liters

ANSWER 7   0.70
0.070

ANSWER 22 $H_2(g)$:   0.06
$N_2(g)$:   0.06
$NH_3(g)$:   0.04

ANSWER 37   0.52
$(100)(0.52/1.8) = 29$

ANSWER 52   equilibrium constant
concentrations, expressed
in terms of the unknown,

ANSWER 67 $1.50 - x$ $x/2$ $x/2$

ITEM 9

The concentration of a compound in moles per liter is often indicated by placing brackets around its formula. Thus, $[PCl_5] = 0.20$ means that the concentration of PCl_5 is _____.

ITEM 24

Complete the table at the right.

ITEM 39

The next step is to express the equilibrium concentrations in terms of a convenient unknown. Again, let x be the number of moles of PCl_5 that dissociate, and write expressions below for the number of moles and the concentrations at equilibrium in terms of x.

	$PCl_5(g)$	$\rightleftharpoons$ $PCl_3(g)$	+ $Cl_2(g)$
Initial moles	1.00	1.00	0
Later moles	_____	_____	_____
Later conc., moles liter^{-1}	_____	_____	_____

ITEM 54

At 500°C, 12.00 moles of NH_3 are sealed in a 2.00-liter reaction vessel. As a first step in the calculation of the equilibrium concentrations of NH_3, N_2, and H_2 in this system, let $x =$ number of *moles per liter* of NH_3 that dissociate. Then the expressions for the equilibrium concentrations of each reagent are

_____.

ITEM 69

Solution of the quadratic equation yields $x = 0.34$ atm. What are the partial pressures of HI, H_2, and I_2 at equilibrium?

Equil. p_{HI}: _____
Equil. p_{H_2}: _____
Equil. p_{I_2}: _____

$$3H_2(g) + N_2(g) \rightleftharpoons 2NH_3(g)$$

	3H₂(g)	N₂(g)	2NH₃(g)
Initial moles	0.00	0.35	0.92
Later moles			0.70
Later conc.			

$V = 4.0$ liters

1.00 mole PCl_5
1.00 mole PCl_3

$$PCl_5(g) \rightleftharpoons PCl_3(g) + Cl_2(g)$$

$V = 5.0$ liters

$$N_2(g) + 3H_2(g) \rightleftharpoons 2NH_3(g)$$

$$2HI(g) \rightleftharpoons H_2(g) + I_2(g)$$

Equil. p $1.50 - x$ $x/2$ $x/2$

ANSWER 8 $n - x$
$(n - x)/V$
x/V
x/V

ANSWER 23

2HCl(g) ⇌	H₂(g)	+	Cl₂(g)
2.86	1.00		0
1.30	$1.00 + 1.56/2 = 1.78$		0.78
0.108	0.148		0.065

ANSWER 38 $\dfrac{[PCl_3][Cl_2]}{[PCl_5]}$

ANSWER 53 $K = \dfrac{[NH_3]^2}{[N_2][H_2]^3}$

ANSWER 68 $K_p = \dfrac{(p_{H_2})(p_{I_2})}{(p_{HI})^2}$

$$0.022 = \dfrac{(x/2)(x/2)}{(1.50 - x)^2}$$

ITEM 10

In the system at the right, which resulted from the addition of PCl_5 to a 6.00-liter reaction chamber, $[PCl_5]$ is _____, $[PCl_3]$ is _____, and $[Cl_2]$ is _____.

ITEM 25

The concentration results from Item 24 can be indicated with the notation $[H_2] =$ _____, $[N_2] =$ _____, and $[NH_3] =$ _____.

ITEM 40

Using the expressions of Item 39 and the value of K at 250°C, 0.042, set up an equation that permits the calculation of x.

ITEM 55

For the reaction $N_2(g) + 3H_2(g) \rightleftharpoons 2NH_3(g)$, $K = 0.0579$ at 500°C. Write the equation from which x can be calculated.

ITEM 70

The expression for K_p for the reaction $PCl_5(g) \rightleftharpoons PCl_3(g) + Cl_2(g)$ is _____.

0.60 mole PCl_5

0.30 mole PCl_3

? mole Cl_2

$V = 6.00$ liters

ANSWER 9   0.20 mole liter^{-1}

ANSWER 24 $3H_2(g) + N_2(g) \rightleftharpoons 2NH_3(g)$

0.00	0.35	0.92
0.33	0.46	0.70
0.082	0.12	0.18

ANSWER 39 $1.00 - x$ $1.00 + x$ x

$\dfrac{1.00 - x}{5.0}$ $\dfrac{1.00 + x}{5.0}$ $\dfrac{x}{5.0}$

ANSWER 54

	$N_2(g)$	$+ 3H_2(g)$	$\rightleftharpoons 2NH_3(g)$
Initial conc.	0	0	6.00
Final conc.	$\frac{1}{2}x$	$\frac{3}{2}x$	$6.00 - x$

ANSWER 69   HI: 1.16 atm

H_2: 0.17 atm

I_2: 0.17 atm

If PCl_5 were introduced into a container at 250°, some PCl_3 and some Cl_2 would form. The dissociation equation _____ shows that the number of moles of PCl_3 will be _____ the number of moles of Cl_2.

ITEM 26

The brackets around a chemical symbol indicate that the _____ of the compound is being given and that the units are _____ per _____.

ITEM 41

Solution of the quadratic equation gives $x = 0.15$. Complete the tabulation of the equilibrium amounts below.

	Moles initially	Moles at equilibrium
PCl_5	1.00	
PCl_3	1.00	
Cl_2	0.0	

ITEM 56

Solution of the fourth-power equation yields $x = 3.07$ moles liter^{-1}. What are the equilibrium concentrations of N_2, H_2, and NH_3?

ITEM 71

For the reaction $PCl_5(g) \rightleftharpoons PCl_3(g) + Cl_2(g)$, K_p at 250°C is 1.78. If a reaction vessel initially contains 2.00 atm of PCl_5 and 0.50 atm of Cl_2 at 250°C, the expression for the equilibrium constant in terms of x, the decrease in the pressure of PCl_5, is _____.

ANSWER 10　　$\dfrac{0.60 \text{ mole}}{6.00 \text{ liters}} = 0.10$

$\dfrac{0.30 \text{ mole}}{6.00 \text{ liters}} = 0.050$

$\dfrac{0.30 \text{ mole}}{6.00 \text{ liters}} = 0.050$

ANSWER 25　　0.082
0.12
0.18

$$PCl_5(g) \ \rightleftharpoons PCl_3(g) \ + Cl_2(g)$$

Equil.
moles　　$1.00 - x$　　$1.00 + x$　　x

ANSWER 40　　$0.042 = \dfrac{x(1.00 + x)}{5.0(1.00 - x)}$

ANSWER 55　　$0.0579 = \dfrac{(6.00 - x)^2}{(0.500x)(1.50x)^3}$

$= \dfrac{(6.00 - x)^2}{1.69x^4}$

$$N_2(g) \ + \ 3H_2(g) \rightleftharpoons 2NH_3(g)$$

Equil.
conc.　　$0.5x$　　$1.5x$　　$6.00 - x$

ANSWER 70　　$K_p = \dfrac{(p_{PCl_3})(p_{Cl_2})}{p_{PCl_5}}$

According to the equation at the right, the dissociation of 1 mole of H_2O produces _____ mole(s) of H_2 and _____ mole(s) of O_2.

The expression for the equilibrium constant for the reaction

$$PCl_5(g) \rightleftharpoons PCl_3(g) + Cl_2(g)$$

has the form $K =$ _____.

Check the calculations of the preceding items by calculating the value of K from the results of Item 41. (Recall that $K = 0.042$ was used to obtain these values.)

What is the percentage dissociation of NH_3 in Item 56?

Solve the quadratic equation for x. Remember that for $ax^2 + bx + c = 0$

$$x = \frac{-b \pm \sqrt{b^2 - 4ac}}{2a}$$

$2H_2O(g) \rightleftharpoons 2H_2(g) + O_2(g)$

ANSWER 11 $PCl_5(g) \rightleftharpoons PCl_3(g) + Cl_2(g)$
equal to

ANSWER 26 concentration
moles
liter

At equilibrium

$[PCl_5] = \dfrac{0.85}{5.0} = 0.17$

$[PCl_3] = \dfrac{1.15}{5.0} = 0.23$

$[Cl_2] \quad = \dfrac{0.15}{5.0} = 0.030$

ANSWER 41 0.85
1.15
0.15

ANSWER 56 $[N_2] \quad = 1.54$
$[H_2] \quad = 4.60$
$[NH_3] = 2.93$

ANSWER 71 $1.78 = \dfrac{x(0.50 + x)}{2.00 - x}$

If n moles of H_2O are heated until x moles have dissociated, the amounts of the three reagents present will be $H_2O =$ _____ moles, $H_2 =$ _____ moles, and $O_2 =$ _____ moles.

In one experiment PCl_5 was heated at 250°C until its concentration remained constant. The equilibrium concentration of each reagent was that given at the right. Calculate the value of K at 250°C.

For the system $N_2O_4(g) \rightleftharpoons 2NO_2(g)$ the applicable equilibrium expression is _____.

The equation for the hydrogen–iodine–hydrogen iodide reaction is $2HI(g) \rightleftharpoons H_2(g) + I_2(g)$. The equilibrium expression for this reaction is _____.

Tabulate the equilibrium partial pressures.

$p_{PCl_5} =$ _____
$p_{PCl_3} =$ _____
$p_{Cl_2} =$ _____

What is the percentage decomposition of PCl_5?

$$2H_2O(g) \rightleftharpoons 2H_2(g) + O_2(g)$$

At equilibrium

$[PCl_5] = 0.015$
$[PCl_3] = 0.025$
$[Cl_2]\ = 0.025$

$V = 5.0$ liters

	$PCl_5(g)$	$\rightleftharpoons$	$PCl_3(g)$	$+$	$Cl_2(g)$
Equil. p	$2.00 - x$		x		$0.50 + x$

ANSWER 12 1
$\frac{1}{2}$

ANSWER 27 $\dfrac{[PCl_3][Cl_2]}{[PCl_5]}$

ANSWER 42 $K = \dfrac{(0.23)(0.030)}{0.17} = 0.041$

(0.042 is not obtained because the value of x was rounded off to two significant figures for Item 41.)

ANSWER 57 $\dfrac{3.07}{6.00} \times 100 = 51.2\%$

ANSWER 72 $x^2 + 2.28x - 3.56 = 0$

$x = \dfrac{-2.28 \pm \sqrt{5.20 + 14.24}}{2}$

$x = 1.06$

ITEM 14

If n moles of H_2O were heated until the system contained, as a result of dissociation, y moles of O_2, the amounts present would be y moles of O_2, _____ moles of H_2, and _____ moles of H_2O.

ITEM 29

If the cell had been filled originally with pure PCl_5, its concentration before dissociation must have been _____, and the total number of moles of PCl_5 before dissociation must have been _____.

ITEM 44

An amount of 0.100 mole of N_2O_4 is placed in a 2.0-liter vessel at 25°C and allowed to equilibrate. The expressions for the equilibrium concentrations of the reagents in terms of x, the number of moles of N_2O_4 that dissociate, are

	N_2O_4	NO_2
Initial moles	_____	_____
Equil. moles	_____	_____
Equil. conc.	_____	_____

ITEM 59

A mixture of 3.00 moles of HI and 2.50 moles of I_2 is heated at 490°C in a 4.00-liter reaction vessel. Letting x = number of moles of H_2 present at equilibrium, express the equilibrium concentration of each reagent in terms of x.

ITEM 74

Check the solution to Item 73 by substituting the calculated partial pressures into the equilibrium expression and solving for K_p.

$$2H_2O(g) \rightleftharpoons 2H_2(g) + O_2(g)$$

At equilibrium

$[PCl_5] = 0.015$
$[PCl_3] = 0.025$
$[Cl_2] \ = 0.025$

$V = 5.0$ liters

0.100 mole N_2O_4

$N_2O_4(g) \rightleftharpoons 2NO_2(g)$

$V = 2.0$ liters

$$2HI(g) \rightleftharpoons H_2(g) + I_2(g)$$

$$PCl_5(g) \rightleftharpoons PCl_3(g) + Cl_2(g)$$

$K_p = 1.78$ at 250°C

ANSWER 13 $n - x$
x
$x/2$

ANSWER 28 $\dfrac{(0.025)(0.025)}{0.015} = 0.042$

ANSWER 43 $K = \dfrac{[NO_2]^2}{[N_2O_4]}$

ANSWER 58 $K = \dfrac{[H_2][I_2]}{[HI]^2}$

ANSWER 73   0.94
1.06
1.56
% decomposition
$$= \dfrac{(100)(1.06)}{2.00} = 53$$

A reaction cell contained 0.52 mole of H_2 and 0.26 mole of O_2. After the cell was heated, it was found to contain 0.12 mole of H_2O. Fill in the following table.

	Initially	Used up	Remaining
Moles H_2	0.52		
Moles O_2	0.26		

Write the expression for the equilibrium constant K for the reaction $H_2(g) + I_2(g) \rightleftharpoons 2HI(g)$.

At 25°C, the value of K for the reaction $N_2O_4(g) \rightleftharpoons 2NO_2(g)$ is 0.0058. An equation from which x can be calculated is _____.

The equilibrium constant for the reaction $2HI(g) \rightleftharpoons H_2(g) + I_2(g)$ at 490° is 0.022. Write the equation from which a value of x can be obtained.

Items 75 through 78 are four problems to test your skill at doing equilibrium calculations. Set up each problem in an organized fashion and solve the quadratic equations. Remember that the forms of the concentration expressions in terms of x will vary with the definition of x, but that there is only one correct answer.

(*Turn to page 650.*)

0.26 mole O_2

0.52 mole H_2

0.12 mole H_2O

? mole O_2

? mole H_2

ANSWER 14 $2y$

$ n - 2y$

ANSWER 29

$[0.015] + [0.025] = 0.040$ mole liter^{-1}

$(0.040$ mole liter$^{-1})(5.0$ liters$) = 0.20$ mole

ANSWER 44

	N_2O_4	NO_2
Initial moles	0.100	0
Equil. moles	$0.100 - x$	$2x$
Equil. conc., moles liter^{-1}	$\dfrac{0.100 - x}{2.0}$	$\dfrac{2x}{2.0}$

ANSWER 59

$$2HI(g) \rightleftharpoons H_2(g) + I_2(g)$$

Initial moles	3.00	0	2.50
Equil. moles	$3.00 - 2x$	x	$2.50 + x$
Equil. conc.	$\dfrac{3.00 - 2x}{4.00}$	$\dfrac{x}{4.00}$	$\dfrac{2.50 + x}{4.00}$

ANSWER 74 $K_p = \dfrac{(1.06)(1.56)}{0.94} = 1.76$

For the reaction $3H_2(g) + N_2(g) \rightleftharpoons 2NH_3(g)$, the equilibrium constant K_p at 500°C is 1.43×10^{-5}. If the equilibrium partial pressure of H_2 is 3.00 atm and N_2 is 1.30 atm, what is the partial pressure of NH_3 at equilibrium?

ANSWER 15

	Used up	Remaining
	0.12	0.40
	0.06	0.20

(Item 16 is on page 620.)

ANSWER 30 $K = \dfrac{[HI]^2}{[H_2][I_2]}$

(Item 31 is on page 620.)

ANSWER 45 $0.0058 = \dfrac{(2x/2.0)^2}{(0.100 - x)/2.0}$

$$= \dfrac{2.0x^2}{0.100 - x}$$

(Item 46 is on page 620.)

ANSWER 60

$0.022 = \dfrac{(x/4.00)[(2.50 + x)/4.00]}{[(3.00 - 2x)/4.00]^2}$

$$= \dfrac{x(2.50 + x)}{(3.00 - 2x)^2}$$

(Item 61 is on page 620.)

For the reaction $2HI(g) \rightleftharpoons H_2(g) + I_2(g)$, the equilibrium constant, K, at 490°C is 0.022. If 2.7 moles of HI are allowed to dissociate in a 4.3-liter reaction vessel at 490°C, what *concentrations* of HI, H_2, and I_2 are present at equilibrium?

ANSWER 75

$$K_p = \frac{(p_{NH_3})^2}{(p_{H_2})^3(p_{N_2})}$$

$$1.43 \times 10^{-5} = \frac{(p_{NH_3})^2}{(3.00)^3(1.30)}$$

$$(p_{NH_3})^2 = 5.02 \times 10^{-4}$$

$$p_{NH_3} = 0.0224 \text{ atm}$$

The equilibrium constant, K, for the reaction $H_2(g) + CO_2(g) \rightleftharpoons H_2O(g) + CO(g)$ is 0.719 at 1000°K. If 3.00 moles of H_2O and 2.00 moles of CO are allowed to react in a 5.00-liter reaction vessel at 1000°K, what is the number of moles of each of the four reagents at equilibrium?

ANSWER 76

$$K = \frac{[H_2][I_2]}{[HI]^2}$$

If x = number of moles of HI that dissociate

$$2HI(g) \rightleftharpoons H_2(g) + I_2(g)$$

Initial moles	2.7	0	0
Equil. moles	$2.7 - x$	$x/2$	$x/2$
Equil. conc., moles liter^{-1}	$\left(\dfrac{2.7 - x}{4.3}\right)$	$\left(\dfrac{x/2}{4.3}\right)$	$\left(\dfrac{x/2}{4.3}\right)$

$$K = 0.022 = \frac{[(x/2)/(4.3)][(x/2)/(4.3)]}{[(2.7 - x)/4.3]^2}$$

$$= \frac{x^2/4}{(2.7 - x)^2}$$

$x = 0.62$ mole

Equil. $[HI] = 0.49$ $[H_2] = 0.072$ $[I_2] = 0.072$

Or if y = number of moles liter^{-1} of HI that dissociate

$$2HI(g) \rightleftharpoons H_2(g) + I_2(g)$$

Initial conc.	$\dfrac{2.7}{4.3} = 0.63$	0	0
Equil. conc.	$0.63 - y$	$y/2$	$y/2$

$$K = 0.022 = \frac{(y/2)(y/2)}{(0.63 - y)^2} = \frac{y^2/4}{(0.63 - y)^2}$$

$y = 0.144$ mole liter^{-1}

Equil. $[HI] = 0.49$ $[H_2] = 0.072$ $[I_2] = 0.072$

The equilibrium constant, K, for the reaction $PCl_5(g) \rightleftharpoons PCl_3(g) + Cl_2(g)$ is 0.042 at 250°C. In experiment A, 1.00 mole of PCl_5 is allowed to dissociate in a 5.0-liter reaction vessel at 250°C. In experiment B, a mixture of 1.00 mole of PCl_5 and 0.50 mole of Cl_2 is allowed to react in the 5.0-liter reaction vessel. For the two experiments, calculate and compare the percentage decomposition of PCl_5.

ANSWER 77

$$K = \frac{[H_2O][CO]}{[H_2][CO_2]}$$

Let x = number of moles of H_2O that react

	$H_2(g)$ +	$CO_2(g)$ ⇌	$H_2O(g)$	+	$CO(g)$
Initial moles	0	0	3.00		2.00
Equil. moles	x	x	$3.00 - x$		$2.00 - x$
Equil. conc.	$x/5$	$x/5$	$(3.00 - x)/5$		$(2.00 - x)/5$

$$K = 0.719 = \frac{[(3.00 - x)/5][(2.00 - x)/5]}{(x/5)(x/5)}$$

$$= \frac{(3.00 - x)(2.00 - x)}{x^2}$$

$$0.281x^2 - 5.00x + 6.00 = 0$$

$$x = 1.30 \text{ moles}$$

	$H_2(g)$ +	$CO_2(g)$ ⇌	$H_2O(g)$ +	$CO(g)$
Equil. moles	1.30	1.30	1.70	0.70

ANSWER 78

$$K = \frac{[PCl_3][Cl_2]}{[PCl_5]}$$

Let $x =$ number of moles of PCl_5 that dissociate

Experiment A

	$PCl_5(g)$	$\rightleftharpoons$	$PCl_3(g) + Cl_2(g)$	
Initial moles	1.00		0	0
Equil. moles	$1.00 - x$		x	x
Equil. conc.	$(1.00 - x)/5.0$		$x/5.0$	$x/5.0$

$$0.042 = \frac{(0.20x)(0.20x)}{0.20 - 0.20x}$$

$$0.040x^2 + 0.0084x - 0.0084 = 0$$

$$x = 0.37 \text{ mole}$$

$$\% \text{ decomposition} = 100 \times \frac{0.37}{1.00} = 37$$

Experiment B

	$PCl_5(g)$	$\rightleftharpoons$	$PCl_3(g)$	$+$	$Cl_2(g)$
Initial moles	1.00		0		0.50
Equil. moles	$1.00 - x$		x		$0.50 + x$
Equil. conc.	$(1.00 - x)/5.0$		$x/5.0$		$(0.50 + x)/5.0$

$$0.042 = \frac{(0.20x)(0.10 + 0.20x)}{0.20 - 0.20x}$$

$$0.040x^2 + 0.028x - 0.0084 = 0$$

$$x = 0.23 \text{ mole}$$

$$\% \text{ decomposition} = 100 \times \frac{0.23}{1.00} = 23$$

EQUILIBRIUM CALCULATIONS FOR THE
IONIZATION OF ACIDS AND BASES

When certain acids and bases are dissolved in water they undergo only partial dissociation or ionization. Thus a solution of acetic acid in water contains

$$CH_3COH$$
$$\parallel$$
$$O$$

molecules and

$$CH_3CO^-$$
$$\parallel$$
$$O$$

and H_3O^+ ions. Some inorganic acids and bases, too, are only partially ionized in water; hydrogen sulfide and ammonia are examples. Partially ionized acids and bases such as these are referred to collectively as weak acids and bases.

This review will help you with parts of Sections 16–1 through 16–5 of *Chemical Principles*. We will examine equilibria that exist between the various species in solutions of weak acids and bases and will present some simple types of concentration calculations. Items 81 through 85 are representative of the kinds of problems that you will learn to solve.

ITEM 1

According to the Brønsted definitions, an acid is a compound that donates a proton, and a base is a compound that _____.

ITEM 15

Substitution of the experimentally determined concentrations into the expression for the acidity constant gives the value

$$K_a = \frac{(\underline{\hphantom{xxxx}})(\underline{\hphantom{xxxx}})}{(\underline{\hphantom{xxxx}})} = \underline{\hphantom{xxxx}}$$

ITEM 29

Hydrochloric acid, HCl, is a strong acid and dissociates completely in dilute aqueous solution. The hydrogen ion concentration of a 0.0010-molar solution of HCl is _____. The pH is _____.

ITEM 43

The value of K_a for HCN at 25°C is 4.0×10^{-10}. The equation to be solved for x is then _____.

ITEM 57

Since K_b for NH_3 is 1.74×10^{-5} and the equilibrium expression is _____, the equation that must be solved for x to determine the equilibrium concentrations of the reagents is _____.

ITEM 71

The extent of dissociation of 0.020-molar HNO_2 in 0.10-molar HCl is 0.45%, and the dissociation of 0.020-molar HNO_2 in 0.00010-molar HCl is 14%. This is an example of the *common ion effect*: An increase in the concentration of the common ion, the ion _____, causes a(n) _____crease in the extent of dissociation of the weak acid.

ITEM 85

The acid HSO_4^- partially dissociates according to the equation $HSO_4^- \rightleftharpoons H^+ + SO_4^{2-}$. K_a for HSO_4^- is 1.2×10^{-2} at 25°C. What is the value of $[H^+]$ in a solution made by adding 0.0050 mole of $NaHSO_4$ to enough water to make 100 ml of solution?

$$CH_3COOH \rightleftharpoons H^+ + CH_3COO^-$$
$$0.019M \qquad 0.00058M \qquad 0.00058M$$

	HCN	$\rightleftharpoons$ H$^+$ +	CN$^-$
Equil. M	$0.020 - x$	x	x

$$NH_3 + H_2O \rightleftharpoons NH_4^+ + OH^-$$

ITEM 2

In an aqueous solution of an acid, the acid dissociates by donating a proton to _____.

ITEM 16

The weak base methyl amine, CH_3NH_2, reacts with water according to the equation $CH_3NH_2 + H_2O \rightleftharpoons CH_3NH_3^+ + OH^-$. The expression for K_b is

_____.

ITEM 30

In a 0.0028-molar solution of the strong acid nitric acid, HNO_3, $[H^+] =$ _____. The pH is _____.

ITEM 44

Solution of this equation yields $x = 2.8 \times 10^{-6}$. The concentration of H^+ at equilibrium is therefore _____. The concentration of undissociated HCN is essentially unchanged from the initial concentration.

ITEM 58

This equation may be simplified considerably by trying the assumption that x is small compared with both 0.0200 and 0.100. The simplified equation is

_____.

ITEM 72

A solution of 0.080-molar HNO_2 is prepared. It has $[H^+] =$ _____, $[NO_2^-] =$ _____, and $[HNO_2] =$ _____.

*Equilibrium
calculations
for the ionization
of acids
and bases*

664

$0.0028 = 2.8 \times 10^{-3}$
$\log 0.0028 = -3 + \log 2.8$
$\qquad = -3 + 0.5$
$\qquad = -2.5$

$HNO_2 \rightleftharpoons H^+ + NO_2^-$

$K_a = 4.5 \times 10^{-4}$

ANSWER 1 accepts a proton

ANSWER 15 $\dfrac{(5.8 \times 10^{-4})(5.8 \times 10^{-4})}{1.9 \times 10^{-2}}$

$\qquad = 1.8 \times 10^{-5}$

ANSWER 29 $1.0 \times 10^{-3} \ M$
3

ANSWER 43 $\dfrac{x^2}{0.020 - x} = 4.0 \times 10^{-10}$

ANSWER 57 $K_b = \dfrac{[NH_4^+][OH^-]}{[NH_3]}$

$1.74 \times 10^{-5} = \dfrac{x(x + 0.0200)}{0.100 - x}$

ANSWER 71 H^+
de

ANSWER 85 $K_a = \dfrac{[H^+][SO_4^{2-}]}{[HSO_4^-]}$

Let x = number of moles per liter of HSO_4^- that dissociate.

$1.2 \times 10^{-2} = \dfrac{x^2}{0.050 - x}$

K_a is large and no simplification is possible.
$x = 0.019$
Therefore, $[H^+] = 0.019$.

665

ITEM 3

For example, in an aqueous solution of the weak acid nitrous acid, HNO_2, the HNO_2 molecules donate protons to the water molecules to form NO_2^- and H_3O^+ ions. The equation for this ionization reaction is $HNO_2 + H_2O \rightleftharpoons$ _____.

ITEM 17

Since methyl amine is a relatively weak base, it has _____ tendency to accept a proton from an acid than does a strong base. The weaker a base is, the smaller is the extent of proton addition. This corresponds to a _____ value of K_b.

ITEM 31

The fact that $[H^+][OH^-] = 1.0 \times 10^{-14}$ in aqueous solution at 25°C allows us to calculate either $[H^+]$ or $[OH^-]$ whenever the other is known. In a 0.0010-molar solution of HCl, the concentration of OH^- is

_____.

ITEM 45

The extent of dissociation of HCN is so small that x is minute compared with 0.020, the molarity of HCN. We could simplify the equation of Item 43 by making the assumption that $0.020 - x \simeq 0.020$. The simplified equation is _____.

ITEM 59

Solution of the simplified equation gives a value for x of _____. The assumption that x is small compared with _____ is justified.

ITEM 73

The concentration of the H^+ ions in a dilute solution of HNO_2 will be decreased if more _____ ions are added because of the _____ ion effect.

$$CH_3NH_2 + H_2O \rightleftharpoons CH_3NH_3^+ + OH^-$$

$$4.0 \times 10^{-10} = \frac{x^2}{0.020 - x}$$

$$x = 2.8 \times 10^{-6}$$

$$HNO_2 \rightleftharpoons H^+ + NO_2^-$$

ANSWER 2   water

ANSWER 16 $\dfrac{[CH_3NH_3^+][OH^-]}{[CH_3NH_2]}$

ANSWER 30 2.8×10^{-3}
2.5

ANSWER 44 2.8×10^{-6} molar

ANSWER 58 $1.74 \times 10^{-5} = \dfrac{0.0200x}{0.100}$

ANSWER 72   Let $x =$ number of moles per liter of HNO_2 dissociated.

$$4.5 \times 10^{-4} = \frac{x^2}{0.080 - x}$$

$$\approx \frac{x^2}{0.080}$$

$$x = 6.0 \times 10^{-3}$$
$$= [H^+] = [NO_2^-]$$

$$[HNO_2] = 0.074$$

ITEM 4

The equilibrium constant expression for this reaction has the form

$$K_{eq} = \frac{[H_3O^+][NO_2^-]}{[HNO_2][H_2O]}$$

in which the brackets around the symbols denote _____.

ITEM 18

A 0.0100-molar solution of methyl amine in water is 22.4% ionized. The concentrations needed for the calculation of K_b are CH_3NH_2, _____; $CH_3NH_3^+$, _____; and OH^-, _____.

ITEM 32

Sodium hydroxide, NaOH, dissociates completely in water solution. In a solution of 1.3×10^{-4}-molar NaOH, the hydroxide ion concentration is _____ and the hydrogen ion concentration is _____.

ITEM 46

Such simplifications are usually satisfactory when the value of x calculated from the simplified equation is less than about 10% of the value to which it is added or from which it is _____.

ITEM 60

In the solution 0.0200 molar in NaOH and 0.100 molar in NH_3, $[NH_4^+] = $ _____, $[OH^-] = $ _____, $[NH_3] = $ _____, and $[Na^+] = $ _____.

ITEM 74

Suppose that you want a solution in which the hydrogen ion concentration in 0.080-molar HNO_2 is 1.0×10^{-3} mole liter^{-1}. The number of moles per liter of HNO_2 dissociated at equilibrium will be _____.

$$HNO_2 + H_2O \rightleftharpoons H_3O^+ + NO_2^-$$

$$CH_3NH_2 + H_2O \rightleftharpoons CH_3NH_3^+ + OH^-$$

At equilibrium
$[NH_4^+] = x$
$[OH^-] = 0.0200 + x$
$[NH_3] = 0.100 - x$

ANSWER 3 $H_3O^+ + NO_2^-$

ANSWER 17   less
low

ANSWER 31 $\dfrac{K_w}{[H^+]} = \dfrac{1.0 \times 10^{-14}}{1.0 \times 10^{-3}}$

$= 1.0 \times 10^{-11}$ molar

ANSWER 45 $4.0 \times 10^{-10} = \dfrac{x^2}{0.020}$

ANSWER 59 8.7×10^{-5}
0.0200 and 0.100

ANSWER 73 NO_2^-
common

However, because $[H_2O]$ remains essentially constant in dilute solutions of HNO_2 (those of concern to us here), we can write a new and simpler expression in which the constant terms are collected: $K_a = K_{eq}[H_2O] = $ _____ .

The value of K_b for CH_3NH_2 is

$$K_b = \frac{(\underline{\hspace{2cm}})(\underline{\hspace{2cm}})}{(\underline{\hspace{2cm}})} = \underline{\hspace{2cm}}$$

What is the value of $[H^+]$ for a solution prepared by adding enough water to 0.0070 mole of HNO_3 to make 350 ml of solution?

The expression in terms of x that will yield the concentration of H^+ in a 0.85-molar solution of acetic acid, CH_3COOH, is _____ .

In a solution 0.100 molar in NH_3, the concentration of NH_4^+ is 1.3×10^{-3} molar (Item 53) and the percentage ionization of NH_3 is _____ . In a solution 0.100 molar in NH_3 and 0.0200 molar in NaOH, the concentration of NH_4^+ is 8.7×10^{-5} molar and the percentage ionization is _____ .

Equilibrium
calculations
for the ionization
of acids
and bases
670

You can control the hydrogen ion concentration by adding the appropriate amount of $NaNO_2$ to furnish NO_2^- ions. To calculate the concentration of $NaNO_2$ needed to produce a $[H^+]$ of 1.0×10^{-3} in a 0.080-molar HNO_2 solution, let x equal the required $NaNO_2$ molarity and write the equilibrium concentrations of NO_2^- _____ , H^+ _____ , and HNO_2 _____ .

$$K_{eq} = \frac{[H_3O^+][NO_2^-]}{[HNO_2][H_2O]}$$

$$CH_3NH_2 + H_2O \rightleftharpoons CH_3NH_3^+ + OH^-$$

$$K_b = \frac{[CH_3NH_3^+][OH^-]}{[CH_3NH_2]}$$

$$CH_3COOH \rightleftharpoons H^+ + CH_3COO^-$$

$$K_a = 1.8 \times 10^{-5} \text{ at } 25°C$$

ANSWER 4   concentrations in moles per liter

ANSWER 18

CH_3NH_2:
$$0.0100 - (0.224 \times 0.0100) = 7.8 \times 10^{-3}M$$
$CH_3NH_3^+$:
$$0.224 \times 0.0100 = 2.24 \times 10^{-3}M$$
OH^-:
$$0.224 \times 0.0100 = 2.24 \times 10^{-3}M$$

ANSWER 32 1.3×10^{-4} molar

$$\frac{K_w}{[OH^-]} = \frac{1.0 \times 10^{-14}}{1.3 \times 10^{-4}}$$

$$= 7.7 \times 10^{-11} \text{ molar}$$

ANSWER 46   subtracted

ANSWER 60 8.7×10^{-5}
0.0201
0.100
0.0200

ANSWER 74 1.0×10^{-3}

An equilibrium constant expression of the same form can be found directly by omitting the solvent in the ionization equation. Thus, $HNO_2 \rightleftharpoons H^+ + NO_2^-$ leads to the equilibrium expression _____. $[H_3O^+]$ represents the same concentration of hydrogen ions as does $[H^+]$, so the expressions of Items 5 and 6 are the same.

ITEM 20

Water has the capacity to act as either an acid or a base and, in fact, pure water is ionized to a small extent according to the equation $H_2O + H_2O \rightleftharpoons H_3O^+ + OH^-$. The constant for the dissociation of water, in which $[H_2O]$ has been combined with the equilibrium constant, is known as the *ion product* for water, K_w. The expression for K_w is _____.

ITEM 34

The calculation of $[H^+]$ and $[OH^-]$ for solutions of strong acids and bases of given concentration requires only the value of K_w at the appropriate temperature. For solutions of weak acids and bases, it is also necessary to know the value of K_a, the _____ constant, or K_b, the _____ constant.

ITEM 48

To simplify the solution of the equation for x, the trial approximation $0.85 - x \approx 0.85$ can be made. When this is done a value for x of _____ is obtained. The approximation accordingly (is, is not) justified.

ITEM 62

The effect of the *common ion*, OH^-, on the ionization of NH_3 in H_2O is to _____crease the extent of ionization.

ITEM 76

Substitution of the expressions from Item 75 into the equilibrium expression for HNO_2 ($K_a = 4.5 \times 10^{-4}$) gives the equation _____.

ANSWER 5

$$\frac{[H_3O^+][NO_2^-]}{[HNO_2]}$$

(K_a will be used here for the acidity constant. Readers of *Chemical Principles* should note that this is not the equilibrium constant in terms of activities.)

ANSWER 19

$$\frac{(2.24 \times 10^{-3})(2.24 \times 10^{-3})}{7.8 \times 10^{-3}}$$

$$= 6.4 \times 10^{-4}$$

ANSWER 33

0.0070 mole in 350 ml equals 0.020 mole liter^{-1}. Therefore, $[H^+] = 0.020$.

ANSWER 47

$$1.8 \times 10^{-5} = \frac{x^2}{0.85 - x}$$

where x = number of moles per liter of acetic acid that dissociate

ANSWER 61

$$\frac{100(1.3 \times 10^{-3})}{1.00 \times 10^{-1}} = 1.3\%$$

$$\frac{100(8.7 \times 10^{-5})}{1.00 \times 10^{-1}} = 0.087\%$$

ANSWER 75

$[NO_2^-] = x + 1.0 \times 10^{-3}$
$[H^+] = 1.0 \times 10^{-3}$
$[HNO_2] = 0.080 - 1.0 \times 10^{-3}$
$\qquad = 0.079$

ITEM 7

Ammonia is a weak base in aqueous solution. It ionizes according to the equation $NH_3 + H_2O \rightleftharpoons NH_4^+ + OH^-$. Accordingly, the expression for its basicity constant, in which the constant term $[H_2O]$ is absorbed into the equilibrium constant, is $K_b =$ _____.

ITEM 21

At 25°C, the concentration of H^+ in pure water is 1.01×10^{-7} molar. The numerical value of K_w at 25°C is _____.

ITEM 35

Once K_a or K_b for a compound has been determined, the value can be used to calculate the concentrations of all species at equilibrium in solutions of various concentrations. Of course, you must also have a balanced _____ for the dissociation.

ITEM 49

Based on the result of Item 48, the percentage dissociation of 0.85-molar acetic acid at 25°C is calculated to be _____.

ITEM 63

A solution is prepared in which the total concentration of HNO_2 is 0.020 molar and the concentration of HCl is 0.10 molar. To calculate the percentage dissociation of HNO_2 in this solution, first write the concentration expressions in x for HNO_2, _____; H^+, _____; and NO_2^-, _____.

ITEM 77

Solution of the equation yields $x =$ _____. Therefore, if the equilibrium concentration of H^+ in the 0.080-molar HNO_2 solution is 1.0×10^{-3}, the concentration of $NaNO_2$ is _____ and the total NO_2^- concentration is _____.

*Equilibrium
calculations
for the ionization
of acids
and bases*
674

$$K_w = [H^+][OH^-]$$

$$CH_3COOH \rightleftharpoons H^+ + CH_2COO^-$$
$$0.85M \qquad 0.0039M \qquad 0.0039M$$

$$HNO_2 \rightleftharpoons H^+ + NO_2^-$$

ANSWER 6 $\dfrac{[H^+][NO_2^-]}{[HNO_2]}$

ANSWER 20 $K_w = [H^+][OH^-]$
(or $K_w = [H_3O^+][OH^-]$)

ANSWER 34 acidity
basicity

ANSWER 48 $1.8 \times 10^{-5} = x^2/0.85$
$x = 0.0039 = [H^+]$
is (0.0039 is less than 10% of 0.85.)

ANSWER 62 de

ANSWER 76

$$K_a = \frac{[H^+][NO_2^-]}{[HNO_2]}$$

$$4.5 \times 10^{-4} = \frac{(1.0 \times 10^{-3})(x + 1.0 \times 10^{-3})}{0.079}$$

ITEM 8

The numerical value of K_a or K_b indicates the degree of ionization and, therefore, the strength of the acid or base. A weak acid or base has _____ tendency to donate or accept a proton than does a strong acid or base.

ITEM 22

The product $[H^+][OH^-]$ for pure water equals 1.0×10^{-14} at $25\,°C$. Even when the concentrations of H^+ and OH^- are not equal, it is still true that, to a good approximation, the product $[H^+][OH^-]$ is equal to _____ in *any* dilute aqueous solution at $25\,°C$.

ITEM 36

Then it is necessary to express the _____ of the reagents at equilibrium in terms of some convenient unknown and to substitute these relations into the expression for the _____.

ITEM 50

Calculate the percentage dissociation of acetic acid at $25°C$ in a 0.0085-molar solution, which is more dilute than the solution of Item 49 by a factor of 100.

ITEM 64

K_a for HNO_2 at $25°C$ is 4.5×10^{-4}. The expression for K_a for HNO_2 is _____, and the equation in terms of x is _____.

ITEM 78

In solutions of HF, hydrofluoric acid ($K_a = 6.7 \times 10^{-4}$), the H^+ ion concentration can be adjusted by the addition of _____ ions and the F^- ion concentration can be adjusted by the addition of _____ ions.

$CH_3COOH \rightleftharpoons H^+ + CH_3COO^-$

$K_a = 1.8 \times 10^{-5}$ at 25°C

ANSWER 7 $\dfrac{[NH_4^+][OH^-]}{[NH_3]}$

ANSWER 21 $1.01 \times 10^{-7} \times 1.01 \times 10^{-7}$
$= 1.02 \times 10^{-14}$

ANSWER 35   equation

ANSWER 49 $100\left(\dfrac{0.0039}{0.85}\right) = 0.46\%$

ANSWER 63   Let x = number of moles per liter of HNO_2 that dissociate.
$[HNO_2] = 0.020 - x$
$[H^+] = 0.10 + x$
$[NO_2^-] = x$

ANSWER 77   0.035
0.035 mole liter^{-1}
$0.035 + 0.001$
$= 0.036$ mole liter^{-1}

ITEM 9

Therefore, the extent of dissociation and the value of K_a or K_b of a weak acid or base are _____ than those of a strong acid or base.

ITEM 23

A solution in which the concentrations of H^+ and OH^- are equal is called a *neutral* solution. At 25°C a neutral aqueous solution must have $[H^+] =$ _____ and $[OH^-] =$ _____.

ITEM 37

Dissociation of the weak acid nitrous acid occurs as follows: $HNO_2 \rightleftharpoons H^+ + NO_2^-$. The expression for K_a is _____.

ITEM 51

The preceding calculations illustrate a general principle: As the concentration of a weak acid or base is decreased, the degree of ionization _____, although the actual concentration of the H^+ or OH^-, respectively, _____.

ITEM 65

Solution of the equation by using the simplifications that can be justified later, _____ and _____, yields the equation _____.

ITEM 79

In a 0.012-molar HF solution to which NaF has been added, the concentration of H^+ is 1.0×10^{-4} molar. Set up the expression for the equilibrium constant in terms of x, the concentration of NaF.

$K_w = [H^+][OH^-]$
   $= 1.0 \times 10^{-14}$ at 25°C

$$\left[\begin{array}{c} O \\ \| \\ CH_3COH \end{array} \right]$$ [H$^+$]   % dissociation

$\left[CH_3\overset{\overset{\displaystyle O}{\displaystyle \|}}{C}OH \right]$	[H$^+$]	% dissociation
0.85	3.9×10^{-3}	0.46
0.0085	3.9×10^{-4}	4.6

$HF \rightleftharpoons H^+ + F^-$

$K_a = 6.7 \times 10^{-4}$

ANSWER 8   less

ANSWER 22 1.0×10^{-14}

ANSWER 36   concentrations
                acidity or basicity constant
                    (or equilibrium constant)

ANSWER 50

$$1.8 \times 10^{-5} = \frac{x^2}{0.0085 - x} \simeq \frac{x^2}{0.0085}$$

$$x = 3.9 \times 10^{-4} = [H^+]$$

$$\% \text{ dissociation} = \frac{(3.9 \times 10^{-4})100}{8.5 \times 10^{-3}}$$

$$= 4.6\%$$

ANSWER 64 $K_a = \dfrac{[H^+][NO_2^-]}{[HNO_2]}$

$$4.5 \times 10^{-4} = \frac{(0.10 + x)(x)}{0.020 - x}$$

ANSWER 78   F$^-$
                   H$^+$

ITEM 10

Acids and bases that are classified as *strong* are completely ionized in dilute solutions. Conversely, acids and bases that are classified as _____ are incompletely ionized in dilute solutions.

ITEM 24

A common measure of acidity is the pH, defined as $pH = -\log [H^+]$. For a neutral solution the pH = $-\log$ (_____) = _____.

ITEM 38

The equilibrium concentrations of species present in an aqueous nitrous acid solution can be expressed in terms of x, the number of moles per liter of HNO_2 that dissociate. Complete the entries at the right for a solution of HNO_2 made by adding 0.100 mole of HNO_2 to enough water to make 1.00 liter of solution.

ITEM 52

Ammonia, NH_3, ionizes in water according to the equation $NH_3 + H_2O \rightleftharpoons NH_4^+ + OH^-$. The expression for K_b for ammonia is _____.

ITEM 66

The value of x is _____. Was the simplification justified?

ITEM 80

Solution of the equation gives $x =$ _____. Therefore, the concentration of NaF in the HF–NaF solution must be _____.

The following five problems will be a review and a test of what you remember about acid–base ionization calculations. Set up the solution to each problem in a logical way and solve it completely.

$K_w = [H^+][OH^-]$
   $= 1.0 \times 10^{-14}$ at 25°C

$$\underset{\text{Equil. } M \rule{2cm}{0.4pt} \quad \rule{1.5cm}{0.4pt} \quad \rule{1.5cm}{0.4pt}}{\mathrm{HNO_2} \rightleftharpoons \mathrm{H^+} + \mathrm{NO_2^-}}$$

ANSWER 9   smaller

ANSWER 23 1.0×10^{-7}
1.0×10^{-7}

ANSWER 37 $K_a = \dfrac{[H^+][NO_2^-]}{[HNO_2]}$

ANSWER 51   increases
decreases

ANSWER 65 $0.10 + x \approx 0.10$
$0.020 - x \approx 0.020$

$4.5 \times 10^{-4} = \dfrac{0.10x}{0.020}$

ANSWER 79

$K_a = \dfrac{[H^+][F^-]}{[HF]}$

$6.7 \times 10^{-4} = \dfrac{(1.0 \times 10^{-4})(x + 1.0 \times 10^{-4})}{0.012 - 1.0 \times 10^{-4}}$

$$\overset{O}{\overset{\|}{}}$$

Acetic acid, CH_3COH, is an acid in aqueous solution because some of the molecules donate to water the hydrogen atom that is attached to an oxygen atom. The equation for the dissociation of acetic acid can be written $CH_3COOH + H_2O \rightleftharpoons CH_3COO^- +$ _____ or, more simply, $CH_3COOH \rightleftharpoons$ _____.

An *acidic* solution has a greater concentration of H^+ than of OH^-. Nevertheless, the product $[H^+][OH^-]$ must be equal to _____.

The value of K_a for nitrous acid at 25°C is 4.5×10^{-4}. The value of x can be calculated from the equation _____.

Let x be the number of moles per liter of NH_3 that are ionized at equilibrium, and calculate the concentrations of NH_3, NH_4^+, and OH^- in a 0.100-molar solution of NH_3 at 25°C.

The percentage dissociation of 0.020-molar HNO_2 in 0.10-molar HCl at 25°C is _____.

What is the concentration of NH_4Cl in an NH_3–NH_4Cl solution having an initial concentration of NH_3 of 0.0090 molar and a pH of 9.0? K_b for NH_3 is 1.8×10^{-5}.

$$K_a = \frac{[H^+][NO_2^-]}{[HNO_2]}$$

$$NH_3 + H_2O \rightleftharpoons NH_4^+ + OH^-$$

$K_b = 1.74 \times 10^{-5}$ at 25°C

ANSWER 24 1.0×10^{-7}
7

ANSWER 38 HNO_2: $0.100 - x$
H^+: x
NO_2^-: x

ANSWER 52 $K_b = \dfrac{[NH_4^+][OH^-]}{[NH_3]}$

ANSWER 66 9.0×10^{-5}
Yes.

ANSWER 80   0.080
0.080 mole liter^{-1}

The expression for the acidity constant of acetic acid is $K_a = $ _____.

ITEM 26

A solution in which the hydrogen ion concentration is 1.0×10^{-4} has a pH of _____.

ITEM 40

Solution of this equation gives $x = 0.0065$. The equilibrium concentrations are $[H^+] = $ _____, $[NO_2^-] = $ _____, and $[HNO_2] = $ _____. The percentage dissociation of HNO_2 in a 0.100-molar solution at 25°C is _____.

ITEM 54

The solutions considered thus far have contained only one acid or base in addition to water. Consider a solution that is 0.100 molar in NH_3 and 0.0200 molar in NaOH. The concentration of OH^- ions in 0.0200-molar NaOH, in which there is no NH_3, is _____. If ammonia is added, the OH^- concentration will ___crease.

ITEM 68

Consider a solution of 0.020-molar HNO_2 in 0.00010-molar HCl. Calculate the number of moles per liter of HNO_2 that dissociate. Try the simplifying assumptions.

ITEM 82

$$\overset{O}{\overset{\|}{}}$$

Formic acid, $H\overset{O}{\overset{\|}{C}}OH$, partially dissociates in water according to the equation $HCOOH \rightleftharpoons H^+ + HCOO^-$. At 25°C, a 0.025-molar solution of formic acid is 8.1% dissociated. Calculate the concentration of each of the ions and molecules, except H_2O, in the solution.

$CH_3COOH \rightleftharpoons H^+ + CH_3COO^-$

At equilibrium

$[H^+] \quad = x$
$[NO_2^-] \quad = x$
$[HNO_2] = 0.100 - x$

$NH_3 + H_2O \rightleftharpoons NH_4^+ + OH^-$

$HNO_2 \rightleftharpoons H^+ + NO_2^-$
$K_a = 4.5 \times 10^{-4}$

ANSWER 11 H_3O^+
$H^+ + CH_3COO^-$

ANSWER 25 1.0×10^{-14} (at $25°C$)

ANSWER 39 $4.5 \times 10^{-4} = \dfrac{(x)(x)}{0.100 - x}$

ANSWER 53

$1.74 \times 10^{-5} = \dfrac{x^2}{0.100 - x} \simeq \dfrac{x^2}{0.100}$

$x = 0.0013 = [NH_4^+] = [OH^-]$
$[NH_3] = 0.100 - 0.001 = 0.099$

ANSWER 67 $\dfrac{100(9.0 \times 10^{-5})}{2.0 \times 10^{-2}} = 0.45\%$

ANSWER 81

$[H^+] = 1.0 \times 10^{-9}$

$[OH^-] = \dfrac{1.0 \times 10^{-14}}{1.0 \times 10^{-9}} = 1.0 \times 10^{-5}$

$K_b = \dfrac{[NH_4^+][OH^-]}{[NH_3]}$

Let $x =$ necessary $[NH_4Cl]$.

$1.8 \times 10^{-5} = \dfrac{(x + 1.0 \times 10^{-5})(1.0 \times 10^{-5})}{9.0 \times 10^{-3} - 1.0 \times 10^{-5}}$

$x = 0.016 = [NH_4Cl]$.

ITEM 13

It is possible to calculate the equilibrium constant of a weak acid or base if the total concentration of the acid or base and its percentage ionization at the given concentration are known. If 100 ml of solution are prepared with 0.0020 mole of acetic acid, the total concentration of acetic acid is _____ .

ITEM 27

Since, in any acidic solution, the hydrogen ion concentration is greater than _____ mole liter^{-1}, the pH of an acidic solution is _____ than 7.

ITEM 41

The equation for the dissociation of hydrocyanic acid, HCN, in aqueous solution is HCN $\rightleftharpoons$ _____ . The expression for K_a is $K_a =$ _____ .

ITEM 55

No matter what the OH$^-$ concentration in the solution is, the value of _____ remains constant with constant temperature.

ITEM 69

Are the assumptions justified in Item 68?

ITEM 83

The value of [H$^+$] for a solution of HCN in water is 1.0×10^{-5}. Calculate [HCN] in this solution. (K_a for HCN at 25°C is 4.0×10^{-10}.)

ANSWER 12 $\dfrac{[H^+][CH_3COO^-]}{[CH_3COOH]}$

ANSWER 26   4

ANSWER 40 H^+:   0.0065 mole liter^{-1}
NO_2^-:   0.0065 mole liter^{-1}
HNO_2:   0.093 mole liter^{-1}

$$\left(\frac{0.0065}{0.100}\right)100 = 6.5\%$$

ANSWER 54   0.0200 molar
in

ANSWER 68   Let x = number of moles per liter of HNO_2 that dissociate.

$$4.5 \times 10^{-4} = \frac{(0.00010 + x)x}{0.020 - x}$$

$$4.5 \times 10^{-4} = \frac{0.00010x}{0.020}$$

$$x = 0.09$$

ANSWER 82

$$[H^+] = [H\overset{\overset{\displaystyle O}{\|}}{C}O^-] = 0.081 \times 0.025 = 0.0020$$

$$[H\overset{\overset{\displaystyle O}{\|}}{C}OH] = 0.025 - 0.002 = 0.023$$

$$K_w = [H^+][OH^-]$$

$$[OH^-] = \frac{1.0 \times 10^{-14}}{2.0 \times 10^{-3}} = 5.0 \times 10^{-12}$$

ITEM 14

When acetic acid of this concentration is at equilibrium at 25°C, 2.9% of the acid is dissociated. Since the total acetic acid concentration is 0.020 molar, concentrations of the individual species are

$[H^+]$ = _____
$[CH_3COO^-]$ = _____
$[CH_3COOH]$ = _____

ITEM 28

A *basic* solution is one in which the concentration of OH^- ions is greater than the concentration of _____ ions. Therefore, the pH of a basic solution is _____ than 7.

ITEM 42

When the molarity of a solution is specified, it is the total concentration of solute — dissociated plus undissociated — that is given. Thus, the total concentration of HCN in a 0.020-molar solution is _____.
If x is the moles per liter of HCN that dissociate, $[H^+]$ = _____, $[CN^-]$ = _____, and $[HCN]$ = _____.

ITEM 56

In a solution that is 0.100 molar in NH_3 and 0.0200 molar in NaOH, the concentrations of NH_4^+, NH_3, and OH^- in terms of x (the moles per liter of NH_3 ionizing) are $[NH_4^+]$ _____ and $[NH_3]$ _____. The $[OH^-]$ resulting from NH_3 reaction is _____, and the total $[OH^-]$ is _____.

ITEM 70

Using only the assumption $0.020 - x \simeq 0.020$ does not save any work; recalculate the value of x without simplification. What is the percentage dissociation?

ITEM 84

How many moles of sodium acetate, $CH_3\overset{\overset{\displaystyle O}{\|}}{C}ONa$, are present in 500 ml of a sodium acetate–0.075-molar acetic acid solution that has a hydrogen ion concentration of 0.00010 molar? K_a for acetic acid is 1.8×10^{-5} at 25°C.

*Equilibrium
calculations
for the ionization
of acids
and bases*
688

$$CH_3COOH \rightleftharpoons H^+ + CH_3COO^-$$

$$HCN \rightleftharpoons H^+ + CN^-$$

$$NH_3 + H_2O \rightleftharpoons NH_4^+ + OH^-$$

$$K_b = 1.74 \times 10^{-5} \text{ at } 25°C$$

$$x = \frac{-b \pm \sqrt{b^2 - 4ac}}{2a}$$

ANSWER 13 0.020 mole liter^{-1} (0.020M)

ANSWER 27 1.0×10^{-7}
less

ANSWER 41 $H^+ + CN^-$

$$\frac{[H^+][CN^-]}{[HCN]}$$

ANSWER 55 K_b for ammonia

ANSWER 69 No, 0.09 is greater
than 0.020 and 0.00010.

ANSWER 83 $K_a = \dfrac{[H^+][CN^-]}{[HCN]}$

$$[H^+] = [CN^-] = 1.0 \times 10^{-5}$$

$$4.0 \times 10^{-10} = \frac{(1.0 \times 10^{-5})^2}{[HCN]}$$

$$[HCN] = \frac{1.0 \times 10^{-10}}{4.0 \times 10^{-10}} = 0.25$$

Equilibrium
calculations
for the ionization
of acids
and bases
690

ANSWER 14

H^+: $0.029 \times 0.020M = 0.00058M$
CH_3COO^-: $0.029 \times 0.020M = 0.00058M$
CH_3COOH: $0.020M - 0.00058M = 0.019M$

(*Item 15 is on page 662.*)

ANSWER 28 H^+
greater

(*Item 29 is on page 662.*)

ANSWER 42 0.020 molar
x
x
$0.020 - x$

(*Item 43 is on page 662.*)

ANSWER 56 x
$0.100 - x$
x
$x + 0.0200$

(*Item 57 is on page 662.*)

ANSWER 70
$$4.5 \times 10^{-4} = \frac{(0.00010 + x)x}{0.020 - x}$$

$$x^2 + (5.5 \times 10^{-4})x$$
$$- 9.0 \times 10^{-6} = 0$$

$$x = 0.0027$$

$$\% = \frac{100 \times 0.0027}{0.020} = 14\%$$

(*Item 71 is on page 662.*)

ANSWER 84

$$K_a = \frac{[H^+][CH_3COO^-]}{[CH_3COOH]}$$

Let $x = [CH_3COO^-]$ from CH_3COONa.

$$1.8 \times 10^{-5} = \frac{(1.0 \times 10^{-4})(x + 1.0 \times 10^{-4})}{0.075 - 1.0 \times 10^{-4}}$$

$x = 1.3 \times 10^{-2} = 0.013$.
Number of moles $= VM = 0.50 \times 0.013$
$= 0.0065$ mole

(*Item 85 is on page 662.*)

REVIEW 15 HETEROGENEOUS EQUILIBRIUM AND SOLUBILITY PRODUCT CALCULATIONS

The process of solution of many simple ionic compounds in water can be viewed as a simple transfer of the ions from the solid to the aqueous phase that is accompanied by the simultaneous hydration of the ions. If, for a certain amount of the solid and water, all the solid dissolves, the concentrations of the ions in solution depend directly on the relative amounts of water and solid. However, if all of the solid does not dissolve, the solution becomes saturated and additional solid does not increase the concentration of the ions in solution. In such a case there is an equilibrium between the ions in solution and the ions of the solid.

This review examines the equilibria existing in saturated solutions of relatively insoluble salts. It will help you to understand Section 17–3 of *Chemical Principles*. (The simple treatment given here is not applicable to salts that dissolve to more than 0.01 mole liter^{-1} because of complications arising from interactions between the ions.) When temperatures are not specified, room temperature is assumed. When you have finished the review, you will be able to solve easily problems such as those in Items 57 through 60.

ITEM 1

The equation for the solution of AgCl in water can be written $AgCl(s) \rightleftharpoons Ag^+(aq) + Cl^-(aq)$. However, the notations (s) for solid and (aq) for aqueous are often omitted, with the understanding that AgCl represents the undissolved silver chloride, and Ag^+ and Cl^- are the hydrated silver and chloride ions. The simplified equation is _____.

ITEM 11

The equation for the solution of strontium chromate is $SrCrO_4(s) \rightleftharpoons Sr^{2+} + CrO_4^{2-}$, so $K_{sp} =$ _____.

ITEM 21

Solution of this equation yields $x = 3.5 \times 10^{-4}$. Thus, in a saturated calcium fluoride solution at 20°C, $[Ca^{2+}] =$ _____, and $[F^-] =$ _____ mole liter^{-1}.

ITEM 31

Because we can assume that NaF is completely dissociated in this solution, the $[F^-]$ contributed by the sodium fluoride is _____, and that contributed by the calcium fluoride is _____. The total $[F^-]$ is _____.

ITEM 41

Solution of the original equation in x, which is $7.7 \times 10^{-13} = (1.0 \times 10^{-6} + x)(x)$, gives $x =$ _____.

ITEM 51

If $[Pb^{2+}]$ is 1.0×10^{-5} in a solution containing Pb^{2+} and Cl^-, what is the maximum possible concentration of Cl^-?

$$x = \frac{-b \pm \sqrt{-b^2 - 4ac}}{2a}$$

$PbCl_2 \rightleftharpoons Pb^{2+} + 2Cl^-$

$K_{sp} = 1.7 \times 10^{-5}$

ITEM 2

The expression for the equilibrium constant for this reaction can be written $K_{sp} = [Ag^+][Cl^-]$. A term containing $[AgCl]$ does not appear in the expression because AgCl is a pure solid phase with essentially fixed concentration. The brackets indicate that _____.

ITEM 12

In a saturated solution of pure strontium chromate at 15°C, the concentration of CrO_4^{2-} is 0.006 molar. The numerical value of K_{sp} for strontium chromate at 15°C is _____.

ITEM 22

The solubility product constant for barium sulfate at 20°C is 9.9×10^{-11}. Calculate the solubility of barium sulfate in water at 20°C.

ITEM 32

The solubility product expression for calcium fluoride has the form _____. The value of K_{sp} is 1.7×10^{-10} at 20°C. The expression that must be solved to obtain x is _____.

ITEM 42

In Items 39 through 41, $[Ag^+] =$ _____, $[Br^-]$ = _____, and the solubility of AgBr in 1.0×10^{-6}-molar silver nitrate solution is _____.

ITEM 52

The solubility product constant for strontium sulfate is 2.8×10^{-7}. SrSO$_4$ is precipitated from a Sr^{2+} solution by adding enough H_2SO_4 to make the final $[SO_4^{2-}]$ equal to 0.0010 molar. Calculate the molarity of Sr^{2+} remaining in solution.

$BaSO_4 \rightleftharpoons Ba^{2+} + SO_4^{2-}$

$[Ca^{2+}] = x$

$[F^-] = 0.010 + 2x$

CaF_2

$[Ag^+] = 1.0 \times 10^{-6} + x$

$[Br^-] = x$

$AgBr$

$SrSO_4 \rightleftharpoons Sr^{2+} + SO_4^{2-}$

ANSWER 1 $AgCl \rightleftharpoons Ag^+ + Cl^-$

ANSWER 11 $[Sr^{2+}][CrO_4^{2-}]$

ANSWER 21 3.5×10^{-4}
7.0×10^{-4}

ANSWER 31 0.010
$2x$
$0.010 + 2x$

ANSWER 41 $x^2 + (1.0 \times 10^{-6})x$
$\quad - 7.7 \times 10^{-13} = 0$
$x = 5.1 \times 10^{-7}$

ANSWER 51 Let $x = [Cl^-]$.
$K_{sp} = [Pb^{2+}][Cl^-]^2$
$1.7 \times 10^{-5} = (1.0 \times 10^{-5})(x)^2$
$x = 1.3$ moles liter^{-1}

ITEM 3

The expression $K_{sp} = [Ag^+][Cl^-]$ states that the product of the concentrations of Ag^+ and Cl^- in a _____ solution of silver chloride is a constant. This constant is called the *solubility product constant.*

ITEM 13

The equation for the solution of strontium fluoride is $SrF_2 \rightleftharpoons Sr^{2+} + 2F^-$. Accordingly, $K_{sp} =$ _____. The solubility of strontium fluoride at $25\,°C$ is 0.0073 g in 100 ml of solution. At $25°$ the numerical value for K_{sp} for strontium fluoride is _____.

ITEM 23

The preceding calculations have been limited to solutions of a pure salt. Consider, however, the solubility of AgCl in a 0.010-molar sodium chloride solution. In a 0.010-molar salt solution containing no silver chloride, $[Cl^-] =$ _____.

ITEM 33

Solution of the equation in Answer 32 gives $x = 1.7 \times 10^{-6}$. Therefore, $[Ca^{2+}]$ is _____, $[F^-]$ is _____, and the solubility of CaF_2 in 0.010-molar sodium fluoride is _____.

ITEM 43

For a solution of lead iodate, $Pb(IO_3)_2(s) \rightleftharpoons Pb^{2+} + 2IO_3^-$, and $K_{sp} = 3.2 \times 10^{-13}$. Calculate the molarity of IO_3^- in 0.0030-molar $Pb(NO_3)_2$ saturated with lead iodate. (The lead nitrate is completely soluble and dissociated.)

ITEM 53

Calculate the maximum concentration of barium nitrate, $Ba(NO_3)_2$, possible in a 7.5×10^{-4}-molar solution of potassium chromate, K_2CrO_4. The solubility product constant of $BaCrO_4$ is 2.4×10^{-10}. Assume 100% dissociation of $Ba(NO_3)_2$ and K_2CrO_4, both of which are quite soluble compared with $BaCrO_4$.

ANSWER 2 the concentration is being specified in units of moles per liter

ANSWER 12
$$K_{sp} = [Sr^{2+}][CrO_4^{2-}]$$
$$= (0.006)(0.006)$$
$$= 4 \times 10^{-5}$$

ANSWER 22 Let $x =$ number of moles per liter of $BaSO_4$ that dissolve.
$$K_{sp} = [Ba^{2+}][SO_4^{2-}]$$
$$9.9 \times 10^{-11} = x^2$$
$$x = 1.0 \times 10^{-5} \text{ mole liter}^{-1}$$

ANSWER 32
$$K_{sp} = [Ca^{2+}][F^-]^2$$
$$1.7 \times 10^{-10} = x(0.010 + 2x)^2$$

ANSWER 42
1.5×10^{-6}
5.1×10^{-7}
5.1×10^{-7} mole liter^{-1}

ANSWER 52 Let $x = [Sr^{2+}]$ left.
$$K_{sp} = [Sr^{2+}][SO_4^{2-}]$$
$$2.8 \times 10^{-7} = x(0.0010)$$
$$x = 2.8 \times 10^{-4} \text{ molar}$$

AgCl

0.010 M
NaCl
solution

$[Ca^{2+}] = x$
$[F^-] = 0.010 + 2x$

CaF_2

ITEM 4   The value of K_{sp} for a salt can be calculated if the concentrations of its ions in a saturated solution are known. For example, the solubility of silver chloride in water at 25°C is 1.27×10^{-5} mole liter^{-1}. That is, the maximum amount of silver chloride that will dissolve in 1 liter of water is _____ mole.

ITEM 14   If K_{sp} for a salt at a given temperature is known, it is possible to reverse the calculation and to find the equilibrium concentrations of the ions and the solubility of the salt in water. To do this calculation, it is necessary to have the balanced _____ for the solution reaction and to have the expression for the _____.

ITEM 24   To find the equilibrium concentrations of Ag^+ and Cl^- in a 0.010-molar salt solution saturated with silver chloride, the solubility product expression is again used. So long as the Ag^+ and Cl^- ions are in equilibrium with the solid, no matter what their individual concentrations, the _____ of their concentrations is fixed.

ITEM 34   The solution to the last problem is summarized at the right. The equation, $x(0.010 + 2x)^2 = 1.7 \times 10^{-10}$, need not be solved in this form. The quantity $2x$ is so small compared with 0.010 that the quantity $0.010 + 2x$ can be satisfactorily approximated by 0.010. The simplified equation is _____.

ITEM 44   Let us look at another type of problem. A solution containing Cl^- ion is added drop by drop to a solution containing Ag^+. So long as the product $[Ag^+][Cl^-]$ has a value less than the solubility product of silver chloride, no _____ forms.

ITEM 54   To 0.025 mole of Cu^+, enough water and NaBr are added to bring the final solution volume to 100 ml and the final Br^- concentration to 0.0010 molar. What fraction of the original Cu^+ is in solution at equilibrium? The solubility product of CuBr is 5.3×10^{-9}.

ANSWER 3   saturated

ANSWER 13

$K_{sp} = [Sr^{2+}][F^-]^2$

$$\frac{7.3 \times 10^{-2} \text{ g liter}^{-1}}{126 \text{ g mole}^{-1}} = 5.8 \times 10^{-4} \text{ molar}$$

$K_{sp} = (5.8 \times 10^{-4})(2 \times 5.8 \times 10^{-4})^2$
     $= 7.8 \times 10^{-10}$

ANSWER 23   0.010

ANSWER 33 1.7×10^{-6}
     0.010
     1.7×10^{-6} mole liter^{-1}

$1.7 \times 10^{-10} = [Ca^{2+}][F^-]^2$
$1.7 \times 10^{-10} = x(0.010 + 2x)^2$
$1.7 \times 10^{-6} = x$

ANSWER 43   Let x = number of moles per
liter of $Pb(IO_3)_2$ that dissolve.
$K_{sp} = [Pb^{2+}][IO_3^-]^2$
3.2×10^{-13}
     $= (x + 0.0030)(2x)^2$
Assume that x is much smaller
than 0.0030.
$3.2 \times 10^{-13} = 0.0030(2x)^2$
$x = 5.2 \times 10^{-6}$
$[IO_3^-] = 1.0 \times 10^{-5}$

ANSWER 53   Let $x = [Ba^{2+}]$.
$K_{sp} = [Ba^{2+}][CrO_4^{2-}]$
$2.4 \times 10^{-10} = x(7.5 \times 10^{-4})$
$x = 3.2 \times 10^{-7}$
$Ba(NO_3)_2$ concentration:
     3.2×10^{-7} molar

701

ITEM 5

Accordingly, in a saturated solution of silver chloride at 25°C, there is _____ mole of Ag^+ in a liter of solution: $[Ag^+] =$ _____.

ITEM 15

The next step is to express the ion concentrations in terms of a convenient unknown. For a saturated solution at 25°, let x be the moles per liter of silver bromide that are dissolved in water; then $[Ag^+] =$ _____ and $[Br^-] =$ _____.

ITEM 25

If x is the number of moles of silver chloride dissolved per liter of 0.010-molar NaCl solution, then $[Ag^+]$ is also equal to x. The $[Cl^-]$ resulting from the dissolved silver chloride is _____, and the total $[Cl^-]$ is _____.

ITEM 35

A summary of the solution to the NaCl–AgCl problem (Items 23 through 27) is given at the right. Again, x is so small that it makes no significant contribution to the quantity $(0.010 + x)$. The equation, $1.6 \times 10^{-10} = x(0.010 + x)$, may be simplified to _____.

ITEM 45

However, once the product $[Ag^+][Cl^-]$ has reached the value of the solubility product for silver chloride, any attempt to increase the concentration of Cl^- or Ag^+ will lead to the formation, or *precipitation*, of AgCl. As Cl^- or Ag^+ is added, the product $[Ag^+][Cl^-]$ remains _____, but the amount of $AgCl(s)$ _____creases.

ITEM 55

K_{sp} for $BaSO_4$ is 9.9×10^{-11}, and K_{sp} for $CaSO_4$ is 2.4×10^{-5}. The maximum concentration of SO_4^{2-} possible in a solution that is 0.010 molar in Ca^{2+} is _____. The maximum concentration of SO_4^{2-} possible in a solution that is 0.00010 molar in Ba^{2+} is _____.

Solubility of AgCl is 1.27×10^{-5} mole liter^{-1} at 25°C

0.010 M
NaCl
solution

$1.6 \times 10^{-10} = [Ag^+][Cl^-]$
$1.6 \times 10^{-10} = x(0.010 + x)$
$x = 1.6 \times 10^{-8}$

ANSWER 4 1.27×10^{-5}

ANSWER 14   equation
solubility product constant
(K_{sp})

ANSWER 24   product

ANSWER 34 $1.7 \times 10^{-10} = x(0.010)^2$

ANSWER 44   solid AgCl

ANSWER 54   Let $x = $ final $[Cu^+]$.
$K_{sp} = [Cu^+][Br^-]$
$5.3 \times 10^{-9} = x(1.0 \times 10^{-3})$
$x = 5.3 \times 10^{-6}$
fraction Cu^+ in 100 ml

$$= \frac{5.3 \times 10^{-7} \text{ mole}}{0.025 \text{ mole}}$$

$$= 2.1 \times 10^{-5}$$

ITEM 6

What is $[Cl^-]$ in the saturated solution at the right?

ITEM 16

Substitution of x, and the known value of 7.7×10^{-13} for the K_{sp} at 25°C, into the solubility product constant expression gives _____. Therefore, $x =$ _____.

ITEM 26

Substitution of the concentration expressions in x and the value 1.6×10^{-10} for the K_{sp} of AgCl at 25°C into the solubility product expression gives the equation _____.

ITEM 36

In equilibrium calculations, such a simplification is often, though by no means always, possible. If solution of the equation shows that x is less than about 10% of the number to which it is added or from which it is _____, the simplification is all right.

ITEM 46

The maximum concentration of sodium chloride that can be present in a solution that is 1.0×10^{-4} molar in Ag^+ (from $AgNO_3$) is _____. The solubility product for AgCl is 1.6×10^{-10}.

ITEM 56

From the results of Item 55, it is apparent that when H_2SO_4 is added to a solution containing 0.010-molar Ca^{2+} and 0.00010-molar Ba^{2+}, _____ will precipitate before _____.

Heterogeneous equilibrium and solubility product calculations

704

Items 57 through 60 provide a review and test of your skill in solving solubility product problems. Set up the solution to each problem in an organized way and solve it completely. Use the periodic table in the inside front cover to obtain atomic weights.

$[Ag^+] = 1.27 \times 10^{-5}$
$[Cl^-] = ?$

AgCl

25°C

$[Ag^+] = x$
$[Br^-] = x$
$K_{sp} = [Ag^+][Br^-]$

AgBr

$[Ag^+] = x$
$[Cl^-] = 0.010 + x$

AgCl

$AgCl \rightleftarrows Ag^+ + Cl^-$

ANSWER 5 1.27×10^{-5}
1.27×10^{-5}

ANSWER 15 x
x

ANSWER 25 x
$0.010 + x$

ANSWER 35 $1.6 \times 10^{-10} = x(0.010)$

ANSWER 45   constant
in

ANSWER 55   Let $x = [SO_4^{2-}]$ for Ca^{2+}.
$K_{sp} = [Ca^{2+}][SO_4^{2-}]$
$2.4 \times 10^{-5} = (1.0 \times 10^{-2})x$
$x = 2.4 \times 10^{-3}$ molar
Let $x' = [SO_4^{2-}]$ for Ba^{2+}.
$K_{sp} = [Ba^{2+}][SO_4^{2-}]$
$9.9 \times 10^{-11} = (1.0 \times 10^{-4})x'$
$x' = 9.9 \times 10^{-7}$ molar

705

ITEM 7

The saturated solution at the right is at equilibrium; hence, we can calculate $K_{sp} = [Ag^+][Cl^-]$ to be _____.

ITEM 17

From the result of Item 16, it is apparent that $[Ag^+] = [Br^-] = $ _____, and the solubility of AgBr is _____ mole liter^{-1} at 25°C.

ITEM 27

Solution of the equation in Answer 26 yields $x = 1.6 \times 10^{-8}$; therefore, $[Ag^+] = $ _____, $[Cl^-] = $ _____, and the solubility of silver chloride in a 0.010-molar solution of salt is _____.

ITEM 37

Consider the calculation of the solubility of silver chloride in 1.0×10^{-7}-molar sodium chloride. If $[Ag^+]$ is x, the total $[Cl^-]$ is _____. The K_{sp} is 1.6×10^{-10}, so the equation to be solved for x is _____.

ITEM 47

For compounds that dissociate when dissolved in water, the maximum value that the product of the ionic molarities, each raised to a power equal to the number of such ions in the solution equation, can have is the value of _____.

ITEM 57

The solubility of silver carbonate, Ag_2CO_3, is approximately 0.032 g liter^{-1} of solution at 20°C. Calculate the solubility product constant for Ag_2CO_3 at 20°C.

$$[Ag^+] = 1.27 \times 10^{-5}$$
$$[Cl^-] = 1.27 \times 10^{-5}$$

AgCl

$$AgCl(s) \rightleftharpoons Ag^+ + Cl^-$$

$$[Ag^+] = x = ?$$
$$[Cl^-] = 0.010 + x = ?$$

AgCl

$$Ag_2CO_3(s) \rightleftharpoons 2Ag^+ + CO_3^{2-}$$

ANSWER 6 1.27×10^{-5}

ANSWER 16 $7.7 \times 10^{-13} = x^2$
8.8×10^{-7}

ANSWER 26 $K_{sp} = [Ag^+][Cl^-]$
$1.6 \times 10^{-10} = x(0.010 + x)$

ANSWER 36   subtracted

ANSWER 46 $K_{sp} = [Ag^+][Cl^-]$
Let $x = [Cl^-]$ at precipitation point.
$1.6 \times 10^{-10} = (1.0 \times 10^{-4})x$
$x = 1.6 \times 10^{-6}$ mole liter^{-1}

ANSWER 56 $BaSO_4$
$CaSO_4$

ITEM 8

The equation for the solution of PbF_2 in water is $PbF_2 \rightleftharpoons Pb^{2+} + 2F^-$. Therefore, $K_{sp} = $ _____.

ITEM 18

For every mole of calcium fluoride, CaF_2, dissolved in water, there are produced _____ mole(s) of Ca^{2+} and _____ mole(s) of F^-. The expression for the K_{sp} is _____.

ITEM 28

Calculate the solubility of silver chloride ($K_{sp} = 1.6 \times 10^{-10}$) in pure water.

ITEM 38

Solve the equation with the assumption that x is much smaller than 10^{-7}. Is this simplification justified?

ITEM 48

Enough water is added to 0.0010 mole of Ba^{2+} [as $Ba(NO_3)_2$] and 0.00010 mole of CrO_4^{2-} (as K_2CrO_4) to make 1 liter of solution. K_{sp} for $BaCrO_4$ is 2.4×10^{-10}. A precipitate of $BaCrO_4$ (will, will not) form.

ITEM 58

Compare the solubility of CuBr ($K_{sp} = 5.3 \times 10^{-9}$) (a) in pure water and (b) in 0.0010-molar $CuNO_3$.

ANSWER 7 $(1.27 \times 10^{-5})(1.27 \times 10^{-5})$
$= 1.61 \times 10^{-10}$

ANSWER 17 8.8×10^{-7}
8.8×10^{-7}

ANSWER 27 1.6×10^{-8}
0.010
(to two significant fig-
ures)
1.6×10^{-8} mole liter^{-1}

ANSWER 37 $x + 1.0 \times 10^{-7}$
$x(x + 1.0 \times 10^{-7})$
$= 1.6 \times 10^{-10}$

ANSWER 47   the solubility product constant

ANSWER 57

molarity of dissolved Ag_2CO_3
$$= \frac{3.2 \times 10^{-2} \text{ g liter}^{-1}}{276 \text{ g mole}^{-1}}$$

$= 1.16 \times 10^{-4}$ mole liter^{-1}

$K_{sp} = [Ag^+]^2[CO_3^{2-}]$
$= (2.32 \times 10^{-4})^2(1.16 \times 10^{-4})$
$= 6.2 \times 10^{-12}$

(If your method of solution was wrong, review
Items 4 through 13.)

The maximum amount of PbF_2 that will dissolve in water at 20°C is 1.9×10^{-3} mole liter^{-1} of solution. In a saturated solution of PbF_2, then, $[Pb^{2+}] =$ _____ and $[F^-] =$ _____.

If x represents the number of moles of calcium fluoride that are dissolved per liter of solution, the concentrations are $[Ca^{2+}] =$ _____ and $[F^-] =$ _____.

In 0.010-molar NaCl the solubility of AgCl is 1.6×10^{-8} mole liter^{-1}, and in pure water the solubility of AgCl is 1.3×10^{-5} mole liter^{-1}. It is apparent that the presence of Cl$^-$, a common ion, _____creases the solubility of the silver chloride.

Let x be the number of moles per liter of silver bromide ($K_{sp} = 7.7 \times 10^{-13}$) that are dissolved in 1.0×10^{-6}-molar silver nitrate solution saturated with silver bromide. Substitution of numerical values in the general expression for $K_{sp} =$ _____ yields the equation _____.

To 0.010 mole of lead nitrate and 0.010 mole of potassium chloride, enough water is added to make the volume of the solution 1.0 liter. Since K_{sp} for $PbCl_2$ is 1.7×10^{-5}, a precipitate of $PbCl_2$ (will, will not) form.

K_{sp} for BaF_2 is 1.7×10^{-6}. Enough water is added to 0.0010 mole of Ba^{2+} [as $Ba(NO_3)_2$] and 0.0050 mole of F$^-$ (as NaF) to make the final volume 1.00 liter. Is a precipitate of BaF_2 present at equilibrium?

$CaF_2 \rightleftharpoons Ca^{2+} + 2F^-$

ANSWER 8 $[Pb^{2+}][F^-]^2$

ANSWER 18 $\dfrac{1}{2}$

$K_{sp} = [Ca^{2+}][F^-]^2$

ANSWER 28   Let $x =$ number of moles per liter of AgCl that dissolve.
$K_{sp} = [Ag^+][Cl^-]$
$1.6 \times 10^{-10} = x^2$
$x = 1.3 \times 10^{-5}$
solubility
    $= 1.3 \times 10^{-5}$ mole liter^{-1}

ANSWER 38 1.6×10^{-10}
    $= x(x + 1.0 \times 10^{-7})$
$1.6 \times 10^{-10} = x(1.0 \times 10^{-7})$
$x = 1.6 \times 10^{-3}$
Simplification is *not* justified: 1.6×10^{-3} is not small compared with 1.0×10^{-7}.

ANSWER 48

$[Ba^{2+}][CrO_4^{2-}] = (1.0 \times 10^{-3})(1.0 \times 10^{-4})$
    $= 1.0 \times 10^{-7}$
1.0×10^{-7} is greater than 2.4×10^{-10}, the K_{sp}.
Therefore, a precipitate will be present.

ANSWER 58

$CuBr(s) \rightleftharpoons Cu^+ + Br^-$
$K_{sp} = [Cu^+][Br^-]$
Let $x =$ number of moles per liter of CuBr that dissolve.
(a) $5.3 \times 10^{-9} = (x)(x)$
    $x = 7.3 \times 10^{-5}$ mole liter^{-1}
(b) $5.3 \times 10^{-9} = (x + 0.0010)x$
    Assume that x is much smaller than 0.0010.
    Then $5.3 \times 10^{-9} = 0.0010\ x$.
    $x = 5.3 \times 10^{-6}$ mole liter^{-1}
(If your method of solution was wrong, review Items 14 through 43.)

ITEM 10　　From the concentrations of Pb^{2+} and F^- in a saturated solution, the numerical value of K_{sp} for lead difluoride at 20°C is _____.

ITEM 20　　The solubility product for calcium fluoride is 1.7×10^{-10} at 20° C. Substitution of this and the concentration expressions into the equilibrium expression gives the equation _____.

ITEM 30　　In 0.010-molar sodium fluoride solution saturated with calcium fluoride, the concentration of the dissolved calcium fluoride can be represented as x mole liter^{-1}. In this saturated solution $[Ca^{2+}]$ is _____.

ITEM 40　　Solution of the equation with the assumption that x is much smaller than 1.0×10^{-6} yields $x=$_____. Is the assumption justified?

ITEM 50　　In Item 49, $[Pb^{2+}]$ is 0.010. The maximum possible concentration of Cl^- in this solution is _____.

ITEM 60　　Sulfide ions are added to a solution containing Pb^{2+} [as $Pb(NO_3)_2$] until only 5×10^{-10} mole of Pb^{2+} remains. The final volume of the solution is 1.0 liter. What is the concentration of S^{2-}? The solubility product for PbS is 1.0×10^{-29}.

$$[Pb^{2+}] = 1.9 \times 10^{-3}$$
$$[F^-] = 3.8 \times 10^{-3}$$

$$PbF_2$$

$$PbF_2 \rightleftharpoons Pb^{2+} + 2F^-$$

$$[Ca^{2+}] = x$$
$$[F^-] = 2x$$

$$CaF_2$$

K_{sp} for $PbCl_2$ is 1.7×10^{-5}

ANSWER 9 1.9×10^{-3}
3.8×10^{-3}

ANSWER 19 x
$2x$

ANSWER 29   de

ANSWER 39 $K_{sp} = [Ag^+][Br^-]$
7.7×10^{-13}
$= (1.0 \times 10^{-6} + x)(x)$

ANSWER 49

$[Pb^{2+}][Cl^-]^2 = (0.010)(0.010)^2 = 1.0 \times 10^{-6}$
1.0×10^{-6} is less than 1.7×10^{-5}
Therefore, $PbCl_2(s)$ will not form.

ANSWER 59

$[Ba^{2+}][F^-]^2 = (0.0010)(0.0050)^2$
$= 2.5 \times 10^{-8}$
$K_{sp} = 1.7 \times 10^{-6}$
Since the product of $[Ba^{2+}][F^-]^2$ is less than K_{sp}, no precipitation will occur. (If your method of solution was wrong, review Items 44 through 49.)

ANSWER 10 $(1.9 \times 10^{-3})(3.8 \times 10^{-3})^2$
$= 2.7 \times 10^{-8}$

(*Item 11 is on page 694.*)

ANSWER 20 $1.7 \times 10^{-10} = x(2x)^2$
(or $1.7 \times 10^{-10} = 4x^3$)

(*Item 21 is on page 694.*)

ANSWER 30 x

ANSWER 40 $x(1.0 \times 10^{-6}) = 7.7 \times 10^{-13}$
$x = 7.7 \times 10^{-7} = 0.77 \times 10^{-6}$
Not justified: 0.77×10^{-6} is not small compared with 1.0×10^{-6}.

(*Item 41 is on page 694.*)

ANSWER 50   Let $x = [Cl^-]$.
$K_{sp} = [Pb^{2+}][Cl^-]^2$
$1.7 \times 10^{-5} = (0.010)(x)^2$
$x = 4.1 \times 10^{-2} = 0.041$ molar

(*Item 51 is on page 694.*)

ANSWER 60   Let $x =$ final $[S^{2-}]$.
$K_{sp} = [Pb^{2+}][S^{2-}]$
$1.0 \times 10^{-29} = (5 \times 10^{-10})x$
$x = 2 \times 10^{-20}$ molar
(If your method of solution was wrong, review Items 44 through 55.)

REVIEW 16   RATES OF CHEMICAL REACTIONS

Many of the chemical reactions that you first do in the laboratory go from reactants to products so quickly that they appear to be instantaneous. Further study will show, however, that many reactions require an appreciable time to reach their final state. Study of the rates of such slow reactions is of obvious importance if you are depending on the reactions to yield the desired products. Furthermore, study of the rates of reactions provides remarkable insight into the way the reacting molecules, or ions, come together and rearrange to form the product molecules or ions.

The speed with which a reaction occurs depends on the concentration of the reactants and on the temperature of the system. In this review of Section 19–2 of *Chemical Principles*, only the effect of concentration will be considered.

The quantitative expression of the way in which the rate of a reaction depends on the concentrations of the reactants is the *rate equation* for the reaction. In this review you will learn how the rate equation is deduced from the observed effect of concentration on rate.

ITEM 1

When we say that a chemical reaction occurs, we mean that reactants are, to some extent, transformed into _____ in some reasonable length of time.

ITEM 11

If the rate of the reaction at the right is directly proportional to both $[A]$ and $[B]$, the equation defining the rate would take the form: rate $= k[A][B]$. If the rate is proportional to $[A]$ and to $[B]^2$, the rate equation would take the form: _____.

ITEM 21

The rate equation for the reaction of Items 18 through 20 is, therefore, _____. The order of the reaction is _____.

ITEM 31

So far you have deduced the order of a reaction by finding the relation between the rate of reaction and the _____ of reactants. Rates sometimes can be determined experimentally by measuring the change in concentrations of reactants with time.

ITEM 41

The slope of the curve at three distinct times is given at the right. The rate of reaction _____creases as the reaction proceeds.

A + B → Products

A + B → C

	[A]	[B]	Rate[a]
1	1.0	1.0	0.15
2	2.0	1.0	0.30
3	3.0	1.0	0.45
4	1.0	2.0	0.15
5	1.0	3.0	0.15

[a]Moles of product per liter per minute.

ITEM 2

When aqueous NaCl and $AgNO_3$ solutions are mixed, the AgCl is produced so rapidly that the reaction cannot be followed easily as a function of _____.

ITEM 12

The term "order of reaction" expresses the sum of the exponents to which the concentrations of the reactants are raised in the rate equation. Thus, rate $=k[A]$ represents a first-order reaction, whereas rate $=k[A]^2$ and rate $=k[A][B]$ both indicate _____ -order reactions.

ITEM 22

For this reaction, rate $=k[A]$ or $k=$ _____. Use the data in entry 3 to determine the value and units of k.

ITEM 32

Or, consider the decomposition of N_2O_5 in carbon tetrachloride. The reaction is $N_2O_5 \rightarrow N_2O_4 + \frac{1}{2}O_2$. The N_2O_4 is soluble in CCl_4 but the O_2 is not, so it escapes from the solution as the reaction proceeds. By measuring the amount of product (O_2) formed, you can calculate how much of the _____ decomposed.

ITEM 42

The rate of the reaction at three times is listed in the table at the right. Complete the last column.

$Ag^+ + Cl^- \rightarrow AgCl$

$$A + B \rightarrow C$$

	[A]	[B]	Rate^a
1	1.0	1.0	0.15
2	2.0	1.0	0.30
3	3.0	1.0	0.45
4	1.0	2.0	0.15
5	1.0	3.0	0.15

^{a}Moles of product per liter per minute.

sec	[N$_2$O$_5$]	Rate, moles liter^{-1} sec^{-1}	Rate/[N$_2$O$_5$] sec
00	1.88	11.6×10^{-4}	
00	1.37	8.5×10^{-4}	6.2×10^{-4}
00	0.955	5.9×10^{-4}	

ANSWER 1   products

ANSWER 11   rate $= k[A][B]^2$

ANSWER 21   rate $= k[A]$
first

ANSWER 31   concentrations

ANSWER 41   de

ITEM 3

Other reactions, such as the one at the right, take hours to reach their final state at room temperature. Thus, the extent of reaction that has occurred during successive intervals of _____ can be measured.

ITEM 13

A reaction that proceeds according to the rate equation rate = $k[A][B]^2$ is called first order in A and second order in B. But the order of the overall reaction corresponds to the sum of the exponents of $[A]$ and $[B]$ and is _____.

ITEM 23

Once the value of k is known, it is a simple matter to calculate the rate at any concentration of A. What is the rate of the reaction when $[A] = 0.020$?

ITEM 33

From a knowledge of how much of the N_2O_5 has decomposed at any time, the concentration of N_2O_5 can be calculated. The table on the right shows data obtained for the reaction $N_2O_5 \rightarrow N_2O_4 + \frac{1}{2}O_2$. From such data the equation for the _____ of a reaction can be deduced.

ITEM 43

Although the rate is not constant, the quantity _____ does remain constant.

$$\text{CH}_3\overset{\overset{\text{O}}{\|}}{\text{C}}\text{OC}_2\text{H}_5 + \text{H}_2\text{O} \rightarrow$$
$$\text{CH}_3\overset{}{\text{C}}\text{OH} + \text{C}_2\text{H}_5\text{OH}$$
$$\overset{}{\underset{\|}{\text{O}}}$$

ANSWER 2   time

ANSWER 12   second

$$\text{A} + \text{B} \rightarrow \text{C}$$

$$\text{rate} = 0.15\,[\text{A}]$$

ANSWER 22 $\dfrac{\text{rate}}{[\text{A}]}$

$$k = \dfrac{0.45 \text{ mole liter}^{-1}\text{ min}^{-1}}{3.0 \text{ moles liter}^{-1}}$$

$$= 0.15 \text{ min}^{-1}$$

t, sec	$[\text{N}_2\text{O}_5]$
0	2.00
100	1.88
200	1.77
400	1.56
800	1.21
1200	0.955
1800	0.654
2400	0.450
3000	0.310

ANSWER 32   reactant (N_2O_5)

ANSWER 42 6.2×10^{-4}
6.2×10^{-4}

Reactions generally become more rapid as the concentrations of some of the reactants are increased. The rate of reaction is then a function of the _____ of the reactants.

Write the rate equation for the reaction $A + B \rightarrow C$, which is first order in A and zeroth order in B.

The data at the right refer to the reaction symbolized by $D + E \rightarrow F$. Compare entries 2 and 3. Doubling [D] (with [E] constant) _____creases the rate by a factor of _____. Thus, the rate is _____ to [D].

Information about a reaction rate can be obtained by showing graphically the relationship between concentration and time. The $[N_2O_5]$ versus time curve, plotted from the data in the preceding item, is shown at the right. The tangent to this curve at $t = 600$ sec has the intercepts shown. Calculate the slope of the curve at $t = 600$ sec.

Since the quantity $(\text{rate}/[N_2O_5])$ is constant, we can write rate $= k$ _____; that is, the rate is _____ to $[N_2O_5]$.

	D + E → F		
	[D]	[E]	Rate[a]
1	0.37	1.26	0.036
2	0.37	0.63	0.009
3	0.74	0.63	0.018

[a]Moles of F per liter per second.

ANSWER 3   time

ANSWER 13   third

ANSWER 23

rate $= (0.15 \text{ min}^{-1})(0.020 \text{ mole liter}^{-1})$
    $= 0.0030 \text{ mole liter}^{-1} \text{ min}^{-1}$

ANSWER 33   rate

ANSWER 43 $\dfrac{\text{rate}}{[N_2O_5]}$

ITEM 5

By the *rate* of a reaction is meant the decrease in the amount of reactants, or the increase in the amount of _____, per unit interval of _____.

ITEM 15

The rate equation for the reaction $H_2 + I_2 \rightarrow 2HI$, which is first order in H_2 and first order in I_2, is _____.

ITEM 25

Compare entries 1 and 2. Halving [E] (with [D] constant) _____creases the rate by a factor of _____.

ITEM 35

As the diagram at the right suggests, the slope of the curve at any point is related to the change in the concentration of N_2O_5 with time as slope = _____.

ITEM 45

The rate of this reaction at any time is given by rate $= k[N_2O_5]$. This is a _____ -order reaction.

	D + E → F		
	[D]	[E]	Rate[a]
1	0.37	1.26	0.036
2	0.37	0.63	0.009
3	0.74	0.63	0.018

[a]Moles of F per liter per second.

$N_2O_5 \rightarrow N_2O_4 + \frac{1}{2}O_2$

ANSWER 4   concentrations

ANSWER 14   rate $= k[A]$

ANSWER 24   in
2
proportional
(or first order with respect)

ANSWER 34

$$\text{slope} = \frac{-1.88 \text{ mole liter}^{-1}}{2210 \text{ sec}}$$

$$= -8.51 \times 10^{-4} \text{ mole liter}^{-1} \text{ sec}^{-1}$$

ANSWER 44 $[N_2O_5]$
proportional

ITEM 6

For reactions occurring in solution, the rate can be measured in terms of the change per unit time of the amount of reagent in a given volume of solution, that is, the change in the _____ of the reactants or products. Similarly, the rates of reactions of gases can be expressed as the changes per unit time in the amounts of reagents per unit volume of the system.

ITEM 16

The rate equation for the reaction $2NO + 2H_2 \rightarrow N_2 + 2H_2O$, which is second order in NO and first order in H_2, is _____.

ITEM 26

Since halving $[E]$ changes the rate by a factor of 4, the rate is not proportional to $[E]$ but to _____.

ITEM 36

A small change in concentration during a small change in time is expressed as $d[N_2O_5]/dt$. Thus, the slope of the curve at any point is related to small changes in the concentration of N_2O_5 during short time intervals as slope = _____.

ITEM 46

The constant, k, is known as the _____. Since the value of rate/$[N_2O_5]$ is 6.2×10^{-4}, k in the equation, rate = $k[N_2O_5]$, has the value _____.

	D +	E →	F
	[D]	[E]	Rate^a
1	0.37	1.26	0.036
2	0.37	0.63	0.009
3	0.74	0.63	0.018

^{a}Moles of F per liter per second.

ANSWER 5   products
time

ANSWER 15   rate $= k[H_2][I_2]$

ANSWER 25   de
4

ANSWER 35 $\dfrac{\Delta[N_2O_5]}{\Delta t}$

ANSWER 45   first

ITEM 7

For any reaction A + B → Products, the concentrations of A and B in moles per liter are represented, as usual, by [A] and [B]. If the rate of the reaction A + B → Products is doubled when the concentration of A is doubled, the rate must be directly proportional to _____.

ITEM 17

The order of a reaction usually is determined from measurements of the dependence of the _____ of the reaction on the _____ of the reactants.

ITEM 27

The rate is proportional to [D] and to $[E]^2$. The rate equation for the reaction is rate = _____. The overall order of the reaction is _____; it is _____ order in D and _____ order in E.

ITEM 37

The rate of a reaction is always expressed as a positive quantity, but it may be defined in terms of either the disappearance of a reactant or in terms of the increase in concentration of a product. Since the change in concentration with time of a reactant is a negative quantity, the rate of the N_2O_5 decomposition reaction is written as $-d[N_2O_5]/dt$, where the minus sign indicates that $[N_2O_5]$ _____ with time.

ITEM 47

The rate of the N_2O_5 decomposition is equal to $-d[N_2O_5]/dt$. Since t was measured in seconds, the rate of the reaction has the units of _____.

	D + E → F		
	[D]	[E]	Rate^a
1	0.37	1.26	0.036
2	0.37	0.63	0.009
3	0.74	0.63	0.018

^{a}Moles of F per liter per second.

$N_2O_5 \rightarrow N_2O_4 + \frac{1}{2}O_2$

ANSWER 6   concentration

ANSWER 16   rate $= k[NO]^2[H_2]$

ANSWER 26 $[E]^2$

ANSWER 36 $\dfrac{d[N_2O_5]}{dt}$

ANSWER 46   (specific reaction) rate
constant
6.2×10^{-4}

If, in the same reaction, the rate does not depend on the concentration of B, we can write the proportionality as rate $\propto$ [A]. If the proportionality constant, k, is introduced, we can write the simple equation: rate = _____.

ITEM 18

The way in which the order is determined for simple reactions is as follows: The data at the right were obtained for the reaction A + B → C. Entries 1 and 2 show that doubling [A], while holding [B] constant, _____ the rate.

ITEM 28

The rate of the reaction is equal to $k[D][E]^2$. Using data from entry 1, evaluate k, the rate constant.

ITEM 38

You have seen that the rate $= -d[N_2O_5]/dt$ and the slope $= d[N_2O_5]/dt$. Therefore, the rate is related to the slope of the concentration–time curve for N_2O_5 as rate = _____.

ITEM 48

What are the units of k for the N_2O_5 decomposition reaction?

A + B → Products

A + B → C

	[A]	[B]	Rate[a]
1	1.0	1.0	0.15
2	2.0	1.0	0.30
3	3.0	1.0	0.45
4	1.0	2.0	0.15
5	1.0	3.0	0.15

[a]Moles of product per liter per minute.

D + E → F

	[D]	[E]	Rate[a]
1	0.37	1.26	0.036
2	0.37	0.63	0.009
3	0.74	0.63	0.018

[a]Moles of F per liter per second.

$N_2O_5 \rightarrow N_2O_4 + \frac{1}{2}O_2$

ANSWER 7   the concentration of A
            (or [A])

ANSWER 17   rate
            concentration

ANSWER 27 $k[D][E]^2$
            third
            first
            second

ANSWER 37   decreases

ANSWER 47   moles liter^{-1} sec^{-1}

733

Suppose that doubling the concentration of a reactant increases the rate by a factor of 4, and that tripling the concentration of the reactant increases the rate by a factor of 9. Then the rate is proportional to the concentration of the reactant raised to the _____ power.

ITEM 19

Since doubling [A] (holding [B] constant) doubles the rate, the rate is proportional to _____.

ITEM 29

For the reaction of the preceding items, you deduced that the rate was equal to $0.061[D][E]^2$. Calculate the rate at which D would be consumed in a solution that is 1.0 molar in D and 0.020 molar in E.

ITEM 39

If, then, we plot the concentration of a reactant versus time, the rate at any time t can be determined as the negative of the _____ of the curve.

ITEM 49

At what rate does N_2O_5 decompose in a solution when the concentration of N_2O_5 is 0.600 molar?

$$A + B \rightarrow C$$

	[A]	[B]	Rate[a]
1	1.0	1.0	0.15
2	2.0	1.0	0.30
3	3.0	1.0	0.45
4	1.0	2.0	0.15
5	1.0	3.0	0.15

[a]Moles of product per liter per minute.

$$D + E \rightarrow F$$

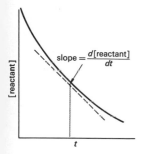

$k = 6.2 \times 10^{-4}$ sec^{-1}

ANSWER 8 $k[A]$

ANSWER 18   doubles

ANSWER 28

$$k = \frac{\text{rate}}{[D][E]^2}$$

$$= \frac{0.036 \text{ mole liter}^{-1} \text{ sec}^{-1}}{(0.37 \text{ mole liter}^{-1})(1.26 \text{ moles liter}^{-1})^2}$$

$$= 0.061 \text{ mole}^{-2} \text{ liter}^{-2} \text{ sec}^{-1}$$

ANSWER 38 $-$ slope

ANSWER 48 $k = \dfrac{\text{rate}}{[N_2O_5]}$

k has units of

$$\frac{\text{moles liter}^{-1} \text{ sec}^{-1}}{\text{moles liter}^{-1}} = \text{sec}^{-1}$$

If the rate of a reaction is proportional to the square of the concentration of A and independent of the concentrations of other reagents, the rate equation would have the form: rate $= k$ _____.

Entries 4 and 5 in the table at the right show the dependence of the rate of the reaction on the concentration of B. Changing [B] while holding [A] constant (does, does not) affect the rate.

The rate of a reaction is defined as _____.

In Item 34 the slope of the curve at $t = 600$ sec was -8.51×10^{-4} mole liter^{-1} sec^{-1}, so the rate of reaction at the instant $t = 600$ sec is $-d[N_2O_5]/dt =$

_____.

For any first-order reaction, where A $\rightarrow$ Products, the rate at any time is _____ to [A]. The proportionality constant is known as the _____.

Now you know that the rate equation for a reaction and the rate constant that appears in this equation can be deduced from measurements of the amount of reactant or product present at various reaction times. This will serve as an introduction to your further study of chemical reaction rates.

| | A + B → C | | |
	[A]	[B]	Rate^a
1	1.0	1.0	0.15
2	2.0	1.0	0.30
3	3.0	1.0	0.45
4	1.0	2.0	0.15
5	1.0	3.0	0.15

^{a}Moles of product per liter per minute.

ANSWER 9   second

ANSWER 19   [A]

ANSWER 29

rate = 0.061(1.0)(0.020)^2
    = 2.4 × 10^{-5} mole liter^{-1} sec^{-1}
(The rate of consuming D equals the rate of formation of F.)

ANSWER 39   slope

ANSWER 49

rate = $k[N_2O_5]$
    = (6.2 × 10^{-4} sec^{-1})(0.600 mole liter^{-1})
    = 3.7 × 10^{-4} mole liter^{-1} sec^{-1}

ANSWER 10 $[A]^2$

(Item 11 is on page 718.)

ANSWER 20   does not

(Item 21 is on page 718.)

ANSWER 30   the decrease in the amount of reactants, or the increase in the amount of products, per unit interval of time

(Item 31 is on page 718.)

ANSWER 40 8.51×10^{-4} mole liter^{-1} sec^{-1}

(Item 41 is on page 718.)

ANSWER 50   proportional
(specific reaction) rate
constant